Perspectives
on Human Evolution

Perspectives on Human Evolution 1

EDITORS

S. L. WASHBURN

PHYLLIS C. JAY

University of California, Berkeley

Perspectives on Human Evolution is the publication
of the Society for the Study of Human Evolution, Berkeley, California

HOLT, RINEHART AND WINSTON

New York   Chicago   San Francisco   Atlanta   Dallas
Montreal   Toronto   London

THE SOCIETY FOR THE STUDY OF HUMAN EVOLUTION

Dedicated to

ADOLPH HANS SCHULTZ

honoring his more than fifty years
of contributions to the study of the primates

Preface

Evolutionary biology has become increasingly complex. This is both because of technical advances in chemistry and in many other sciences and because of advances in evolutionary theory. The guiding principle in evolution is selection, and selection is for those behaviors that lead to reproductive success. This emphasis on behavior makes any single or simple approach to evolutionary problems obsolete; behaviors are the result of the genetic potential of populations as expressed in the phenotypes of individuals, and the individual lives in a complex ecological setting. It is by emphasizing the historical dimension that evolutionary biology seeks to integrate biological knowledge.

The variety of techniques and problems now current means that no one individual can be a master of evolutionary theory in the sense that used to seem reasonable and possible. The study of evolution must be a cooperative enterprise, and emphasis on this cooperative aspect should permeate the educational system. The ·synthetic theory of evolution brought together genetics, paleontology, and evolutionary thinking into a powerful theoretical system. Molecular biology has given a new unity to the life sciences by elucidating the precise nature of the genetic process.

It is our hope that the series of volumes *Perspectives on Human Evolution* will help to make new developments and old understandings available to students and teachers. We have no expectation that any one volume can begin to do justice to the subject, but we hope that a continuing effort will prove useful and that each successive volume will contribute toward a more adequate understanding.

In selecting papers for the first volume, we looked first for a general statement on human evolution, and we think that Simpson's "The Biological Nature of Man" serves as an admirable starting point. It summarizes recent developments in a few pages and succeeds in stressing not only man's relations with the apes (Pongidae) but also the uniqueness of man. Elsewhere, Simpson (1945:181) has described primate classification as "taxonomy in turmoil." No one has done more to reduce the confusion with regard to the fossil apes than has Elwyn L. Simons, and two of his papers have been included. These papers present Simons' point of view, and the bibliography includes the technical references on which the conclusions are based. Leakey's paper on early Miocene Hominidae presents data that were not available to Simons and raises the question of how far back the Hominidae existed as a lineage separate from that of the apes. Napier's paper on the classification of locomotor behavior is included in part because of the importance of locomotion in any analysis of behavior and in part for contrast with the papers by Simons and Leakey, which rely very heavily on the evidence of the dentition. There is a question how far reliance can be placed on dentition, particularly when the fossil record forces us to deal with fragments.

Many lines of evidence cited by Simpson (Chapter 1) suggest that man's closest living relatives are the chimpanzee and the gorilla. But, as shown in Chapters 2 and 4, there is not agreement on this conclusion, and there is the widest possible range of opinions as to how long man's lineage has been distinct from the Pongidae. Immunochemistry may provide the answer to these and many other similar problems, and in Chapter 6 Sarich presents data which allow quantitative comparisons of the different kinds of primates. He suggests further that since the molecules appear to have evolved at relatively constant rates, it is possible to estimate the time the different groups separated. The notion that it is possible to estimate the time man's lineage became distinct from that of the apes more accurately from the variability of living forms than from the fossil record will disturb many of those who have studied this problem. The traditional view has been that events in past time could be determined only from the geological and paleontological record. However, this is an unnecessary limitation; it is our belief that biochemical taxonomy will settle many of the problems which the traditional methods have left unsolved and that the biochemical clocks will afford a series of guidelines of time within which the anatomist and paleontologist will be able to work more effectively. Obviously, there is no agreement at the moment between the conclusions in Chapter 4 and those of Chapter 6, and reconciliation of the different lines of evidence is a major problem for the future. The issue can be briefly stated: if the immunochemical conclusions are accurate, then many of the conclusions based on the fossils are incorrect. This is not surprising because the fossil record is very scanty and the interpretations have had to be based largely on teeth. It may well be that with a richer fossil record, including especially more skulls and postcranial material, the apparent contradictions should disappear.

In assessing the differences among the fossils it is necessary to have an appreciation of the normal variation of primates. The chief contributor to this subject has been Adolph Schultz, and in Chapter 7 Schultz has summarized many of his findings. In addition he has presented data on other topics, such as the increase in length of the juvenile period, which are of great importance in interpreting the evolution of behavior. Comparison of Chapters 2, 6, and 7 shows how the study of the fossils, of immunochemistry, and of the structure of the contemporary primates supplement each other.

A further kind of evidence necessary for the understanding of human evolution is the behavior of the living nonhuman primates, and a brief survey of the field studies is given in Chapter 8. In view of the long-continued interest in the behavior of the monkeys and apes, it is remarkable how late it was before substantial field studies were undertaken. One hundred years elapsed between the publication of Huxley's *Man's Place in Nature* (1863) and Schaller's *The Mountain Gorilla* (1963), and it is particularly important for social scientists to realize that *all* the traditional evolutionary sequences were proposed prior to any substantial study of the behavior of any monkey or ape. The recent field studies are beginning to provide some of the needed information, but this is only a beginning, as Altmann has indicated (1967). A further point of great practical and theoretical interest is that analysis of primate behavior is proceeding in both field and laboratory, and these two kinds of efforts supplement each other. There is no doubt that the combination of field and laboratory experiences will provide a behavioral science of primate behavior far more useful than anything that has been available.

For at least the duration of the genus *Homo*, and possibly much longer, man has been a hunter. Probably it would be more accurate to say that our ancestors were gatherers with various kinds of hunting supplementing the main sources of their food. Some 99 percent of the evolution of our genus was before agriculture, and understanding the conditions and consequences of those times is the major task in the analysis of the transition of the earliest *Homo erectus* to the human populations of today. Chapter 9 offers a few speculations on the events of the Pleistocene. Obviously, this is an immense subject, and we are seeking a comprehensive statement on the archeology of this period for the second volume of *Perspectives*.

Anthropologists have tended to stress the differences between cultures, but from an evolutionary point of view it is the common features that are the most important. For example, probably by far the greatest difference between man and the nonhuman primates is language, with all the behaviors language makes possible. From an evolutionary point of view it is the origin of the uniquely human communication system that is important, not the differences between languages. There are a great many fundamental features shared by all known cultures, and Murdock's classic paper on "The Common Denominator of Cultures" is included as Chapter 10. Viewed historically, the common denominators may be regarded as the result of the gathering and hunting way of life having dominated 99 percent of human history.

The structure and physiology of our species evolved in a feedback relation with the human way of life, and the attempt to understand the interrelations of biological evolution and the changing ways of life presents a wide range of problems that will not be settled for many years to come. In his paper on human emotions Hamburg shows that the evolutionary perspective may help in understanding the human condition. The biology of our species was formed through selection for conditions of life that are rapidly ceasing to exist, and some of the problems of individuals in modern society may be seen as conflicts between new ways and old biology.

In the last chapter Freedman considers the development of personality as a biosocial problem. This comprehensive survey gives an indication of the kind of understanding that may come from a synthesis of an eclectic ethology with the detailed study of man. No one contends that definitive analyses can be made at the present time, but we are convinced that the understanding of human behavior can be advanced by studies of this kind.

Our aim in future numbers of *Perspectives* will be to continue to bring together papers that will enrich our understanding of human evolution. We hope to obtain more that are specially written, or revised, for *Perspectives*. We hope that this series will be useful to those interested in human evolution and the nature of man.

S.L.W.

P.C.J.

Berkeley, California
February 1968

Contents

*Perspectives
on Human Evolution*
1

1·The Biological Nature
of Man

George Gaylord Simpson
Harvard University
and the University of Arizona

It has often and confidently been asserted, that man's origin can never be known: but ignorance more frequently begets confidence than does knowledge: it is those who know little, and not those who know much, who so positively assert that this or that problem will never be solved by science. (1)

Those words were written by Charles Darwin nearly 100 years ago and were published in 1871 in the introduction to his book on *The Descent of Man.* In his even better known work on *The Origin of Species* (2), which had appeared 12 years earlier, he had been content to say (somewhat coyly) that by that work "light would be thrown on the origin of man and his history." Others soon indicated the nature of that light. Thomas Henry Huxley's classic *Man's Place in Nature* (3) was published in 1863, and by 1871 numerous other naturalists of the first rank had already accepted the evolutionary origin of the human species. Darwin's own contribution to the problem of man's origin firmly established two points: first, *Homo sapiens,* like all other organisms, has evolved from prior, extremely different species by natural means and under the directive influence of natural selection; and second, man is the descendant of apes or monkeys of the Old World.

Darwin's first point, that man is the product of evolution involving natural selection, has been attacked on emotional grounds, but it was not and is not now honestly questionable on strictly scientific grounds and by anyone

Reprinted from *Science*, April 22, 1966, Vol. 152, No. 3721, pp. 472–478. Copyright © 1966 by the American Association for the Advancement of Science. By permission of the author and the publisher.

really familiar with the facts. The second point, of man's descent from an Old World ape or monkey, was for some time more open to scientific dispute. However, here, too, the debate was often more emotional than objective. In some pedagogic circles it became usual to maintain that man is not descended from an ape but from a common ancestor neither man nor ape nor, if one cared to go still further afield, monkey. Some went so far as to attempt to enlist Darwin posthumously in their own pussyfooting ranks by saying that he never maintained that man arose from an ape but only from a common ancestor . . . and so forth. In fact, although Darwin was slow to enter the dispute, when he did so he was more honest than those supposed defenders. He flatly said, "We must conclude, however much the conclusion may revolt our pride, that our early progenitors would have been properly . . . designated [as apes or monkeys]." The unscientific and really uncalled-for remark on pride does little to modify the forthrightness of the conclusion.

Darwin's conclusions in 1871 already covered what is most vital for consideration of man's biological status. Subsequent discovery and study have fully corroborated Darwin and have added an enormous amount of detail. That is interesting and important, and most of what I have to say here concerns it. At this point, however, the essential thing is that Darwin put the whole subject of the nature of man on a new and sound footing. To be sure, in the introduction of *The Descent of Man,* from which I have already quoted, Darwin went on to say that "the conclusion that man is the codescendant with other species of some ancient, lower, and extinct form, is not in any degree new." He then cited Lamarck, Wallace, Huxley, Lyell, Vogt, Lubbock, Büchner, Rolle, Haeckel, Canestrini, and Barrago as "having taken the same side of the question." In fact, as regards this particular point, Darwin was doing too much honor to those worthies, some still famous and some now forgotten. It is true that they had all discussed the descent of man before Darwin himself did so in an explicit way, but with the sole exception of Lamarck they had done so after publication of *The Origin of Species* and on the basis of that work by Darwin. As for the few who really had postulated an evolutionary origin for man before *The Origin of Species,* their views were largely philosophical speculations inadequately or not at all supported by objective evidence and sometimes, as in the case of Lamarck, reaching a conclusion only approximately correct on grounds that were flatly wrong (4).

WHAT IS MAN

The question "What is man?" is probably the most profound that can be asked by man. It has always been central to any system of philosophy or of theology. We know that it was being asked by the most learned humans 2000 years ago, and it is just possible that it was being asked by the most brilliant australopithecines 2 million years ago. The point I want to make now is that all attempts to answer that question before 1859 are worthless and that we will be better off if we ignore them completely. The reason is that no answer had a solid, objective base until it was recognized that man is the product of evolution from primeval apes and before that through billions of years of gradual but protean change from some spontaneously, that is, naturally, generated primordial monad.

It is the biological nature of man, both in his evolutionary history and in his present condition, that presents us with our only fixed point of departure. These are the facts we can find out for ourselves, in great, ever-increasing detail and soundness, open to all of us in irrefutable observations. Their interpretation is in some respects ambiguous and disputable, but interpretation at a given point becomes increasingly clear and undisputed as time goes on. Doubtfulness moves outward with the expanding frontier of knowledge.

I do not mean to say that the biological study of man or even that the scientific study of man in terms broader than biological can here and now—if ever—provide a satisfactorily complete answer to the question "What is man?" The other, older approaches through metaphysics, theology, art, and other nonbiological, nonscientific fields can still contribute, or can now contribute anew. But unless they accept, by specification or by implication, the nature of man as a biological organism, they are merely fictional fancies or falsities, however interesting they may be in those nonfactual categories. I am here concerned with man's biological nature in a rather broad sense, on the grounds that this is a necessary, even though it is not a completely sufficient, approach to comprehension of man's nature.

Already in Darwin's day it was clearly established that among living animals the great apes are anatomically most similar to man. Some anatomists, reluctant to acknowledge their poor relatives, stressed differences between man and any apes: the larger human brain, obviously; the longer and less divergent first toe of man; the absence or, more commonly, the only-sporadic presence in us of certain apish muscles and other structures. Such discussions completely missed the point. Of course men and apes differ. In itself, that means only that we belong to different species. The point at issue is not whether we differ, but in what way and how closely the different species are related.

All later study has corroborated the special relationship between men and apes and has made knowledge of it more precise. The evidence has lately been greatly increased in extent, in detail, and in its basic character. It now includes such fundamental points as the numbers and shapes of chromosomes, the exact molecular structure of hemoglobins, the resemblances and differences of serum proteins, and many others (5). All the evidence agrees and the conclusion is unequivocal. Man is not identical with apes in these or other respects. However, he is clearly related to the apes, and among the apes he is most particularly related to chimpanzees and gorillas, which are closely related between themselves. A necessary inference from this evidence is that the common ancestor of apes and men was itself a member of the ape family. Not only that; we had a common ancestor with gorilla and chimpanzee after their ancestry had become distinct from that of the other living apes (orangutan and gibbons). Our relationships to gorilla and to chimpanzee are about equal, although gorillas may have become somewhat more specialized with respect to the common ancestry.

EVIDENCE FROM FOSSILS

More precise evidence as to relationships and as to the course of anatomical change in the human ancestry must come from fossils. There are special reasons why pertinent fossils are comparatively uncommon: Crucial stages apparently occurred in the tropics, where preservation and discovery of fossils are difficult and where exploration has generally lagged; populations of apes and of prehumans were always small, not at all comparable with the great herds of grazing animals, for example, common as fossils; and the habits and abilities of apes and prehumans were such as to reduce chances of natural burial and preservation as fossils.

Nevertheless, a great many fossils have been recovered and discovery is active at present. We are far from having the whole story, but parts of it are increasingly clear.

In Darwin's time only one really distinctive kind of fossil ape (*Dryopithecus*) and only one really distinctive kind of fossil man (Neandertal) were known. From the former, Darwin correctly inferred that by late Miocene, at least, the lineages of apes and monkeys had separated. He was not clear as to the possible implications for separation of the strictly human lineage, which he thought might have occurred much earlier. As regards Neandertal man Darwin could only express surprise that in spite of their antiquity the Neandertals had brain capacities probably greater than the average for modern man.

Now it is known that apes more or less similar to *Dryopithecus* were widespread and, as apes go, numerous through the Miocene and Pliocene of Europe, Asia, and Africa (6). Present estimates place the beginning of the Miocene at approximately 25 million years ago (7). The divergence of apes and Old World monkeys is thus at least that old. There is, in fact, some evidence that this divergence occurred in the Oligocene, which preceded the Miocene and began some 10 million years earlier. Divergence of apes and monkeys was identical with divergence of the human ancestry and monkeys, because the earliest apes were also ancestral to man. The time of the final split of the specifically prehuman lineage from that leading to gorilla and chimpanzee has not yet been closely determined. On present evidence it seems most likely to have occurred during the Miocene, that is, quite roughly between 10 and 25 million years ago. The earliest known forms that may be definitely on a prehuman line as distinct from a pre-gorilla-chimpanzee line are *Ramapithecus* from India and the closely similar, indeed probably identical supposed genus *Kenyapithecus* from Africa (8). Unfortunately those animals are known only from teeth and fragments of jaws, so that their affinities are somewhat uncertain and the anatomy of their skulls and skeletons is entirely unknown. The known specimens are approximatley 10 million years old, give or take a few million.

The next significant group of fossils is that of the australopithecines, literally "southern monkeys" although they almost certainly were not exclusively southern and with complete certainty were not monkeys. They are surely and comparatively well known from East and South Africa, doubtfully and, at best, poorly known from elsewhere in Africa and from Eurasia. In Africa they are clearly divisible into two distinct groups. There is dispute as to whether those groups should not be subdivided still further and whether they should be called species or genera. Although the specialists can become enraged over those questions, they have no real importance for others, the important fact being simply that the two separate groups did exist, a point on which even the specialists now agree. Both groups resemble apes much more than we do now, but both are more nearly related to us than to the apes—another point on which the specialists have finally agreed after years of wrangling. They definitely belong to the human family, Hominidae.

One group, typified by *Australopithecus robustus* or, as it is also often called, *Paranthropus robustus*, retained some particularly primitive (more or less apelike) features and yet became somewhat aberrantly specialized. It cannot have been directly ancestral to modern man. The other group, typified by *Australopithecus africanus*, although also primitive within the human family, more closely resembles our own genus, *Homo*. Both groups are now believed to have appeared at least 2 million years ago. For a long time, perhaps $1^1/2$ million years, there were at least two distinct lineages of the human family living in Africa and probably throughout the warmer parts of the Old World. One, more primitive and aberrant, showed little progress and finally became extinct. The other, more progressive, evolved into *Homo*. A matter still under sharp dispute is whether the latter lineage included *Australopithecus africanus* as our direct ancestor, or whether for a time there were not actually three distinct lines: the two kinds of australopithecines and still another more directly related to *Homo*. The latter suggestion arises from Leakey's discovery of what he calls *Homo habilis* (9). However, some authorities believe that supposed species not to be on a distinct lineage but to belong to the line leading from *Australopithecus africanus* eventually to *Homo sapiens*.

That dispute is interesting and we hope it may soon be settled, but it is far less important than the fact that our ancestry passed through a stage closely similar to *Australopithecus africanus* if it was not that group itself. Our ancestors were then fully bipedal, ground-living animals, using their hands for manipulation as we do but perhaps not quite so skillfully. Their teeth were so like ours as to be hard to distinguish, but their brains were little larger than those of apes, and if we could see them alive their physiognomy, while distinctive, would probably strike us as more apelike than manlike.

By a time probably not later than 500,000 years ago and perhaps earlier, gradual evolution from australopithecines had reached a stage that was human in a more restricted sense, belonging not only to the human family, Hominidae, but also to the same genus as ourselves, *Homo*. Doting and ambitious discoverers have given many different names to such early fossil men, including *Pithecanthropus* and *Sinanthropus*, but most of them are now usually placed in a single species, *Homo erectus*. Bodily anatomy and even physiognomy were now almost fully human, but to our eyes there was still a coarse or brutish cast of countenance because of heavy brow ridges over the eyes and a low, small brain case. The brain size was neatly intermediate between australopithecines (or modern apes) and modern man.

Finally, and still gradually, our own species, *Homo sapiens*, emerged. Although not entirely certain, it is now the usual opinion that the quite varied fossils known collectively as Neandertal men belonged to *Homo sapiens* and only represent ancient races that were at first primitive (not so far removed from *Homo erectus*) and later somewhat aberrant. The more aberrant late Neandertals became extinct as such, although it is probable that some of their genes survive.

So much for more or less direct knowledge of man's physical, anatomical origin. The main points are these:

1) Man evolved from apes also ancestral to chimpanzees and gorillas, but less specialized than the latter.

2) The divergence of man's ancestry from the apes was early marked by bipedalism and upright posture, with extensive correlations and implications in anatomy, habits, and capabilities.

3) Also early was divergent dental evolution, again with other implications, for example as to diet and means of defense. It is not known whether posture and dentition diverged from the apes simultaneously or in which order.

4) Only after evolution of human posture and dentition was essentially complete did man's brain begin to enlarge beyond that of the apes. (Intelligence depends not only on size of the brain but also on its internal anatomy, and we do not know the internal anatomy of our fossil ancestors' brains. However, it is fairly certain that a species with average brain size as in apes could not be as intelligent as *Homo sapiens*.)

Systematics of Modern Man

Now let us briefly consider the taxonomic, biological systematic nature of mankind as it exists today. First and most important is the fact that mankind *is* a kind, a definite and single species. A biological species is an evolutionary unit composed of continuing populations that regularly interchange genes by inter-breeding and that do not or cannot have such regular interchange with other species (10). The definition clearly applies to mankind: all human populations can and, as opportunity occurs, do interbreed, producing fertile offspring and thus continuing the species and keeping it bound together as a unit. It is un-likely that, for example, a Greenland Eskimo has ever interbred with a South African Bushman, but since all intervening populations can and do interbreed they are nevertheless members of the same species. That species, *Homo sapiens*, is not connected with any other species by interbreeding.

Comparison of Eskimo and Bushman brings up the obvious (although oc-casionally denied) fact that the human species includes quite diverse races. A race is simply a population (or group of populations) that is genetically distin-guished from others. The distinction is not absolute. It is unlikely that Negroes, for example, have any genes that do not occur in some white populations, or that whites have any genes absent in all Negro populations. The usual situa-tion is that a race has certain genes and gene combinations that are more frequent in it than elsewhere, and therefore typical in that sense, but not con-fined to the race. Races always grade into each other without definite bounda-ries. There is not now and never has been such a thing as a pure race, biologi-cally speaking. Any two human populations, no matter how small or how large, differ in some respects, so that there is no fixed number of races. One could count thousands or two, and no matter how many are counted, there will be some populations and many individuals that do not clearly fit into one or another. Moreover, races are evanescent in the course of evolution. A given race may change, disappear by fusion with others, or die out altogether while the species as a whole simply continues its evolutionary course (11).

Races of man have, or perhaps one should say "had," exactly the same biological significance as the subspecies of other species of mammals. Widespread animals have local populations that live under diverse conditions and that may become temporarily and in part isolated from each other. They may then more or less accidentally have different proportions of genes (in stricter technical language, of alleles) from other such populations, and if the situation continues long enough, they will almost inevitably evolve somewhat different adaptations to local conditions. Primitive men were relatively few in number and relatively immobile, but they spread over enormous areas—the whole land area of the earth except for Antarctica and a few small islands. They evolved into races or, in better biological terms, into subspecies exactly as any other animal would have under those circumstances. Racial differentiation in man was originally geographic and, for the most part, adaptive.

That was the original biological significance of race. One must say that Negroes were biologically superior to whites, if reference is to prehistoric times, when the races were originating, and to African conditions, to which Negroes were biologically adapted and whites were not. At the present time race has virtually no strictly biological significance because of two crucial changes. First, human adaptation to different environments is now mostly cultural and is directly biological only in lesser part, so that the prehistoric biological adaptations have lost much of their importance. Second, tremendous increases in population size, in mobility, and in environmental changes brought about by man himself have the result that extremely few men are now living under the conditions to which their ancestors were racially adapted.

Evolution does not necessarily proceed at the same rate in different populations, so that among many groups of animals it is possible to find some species that have evolved more slowly, hence are now more primitive, as regards some particular trait or even over-all. It is natural to ask—as many have asked—whether among human races there may not similarly be some that are more primitive in one way or another or in general. It is indeed possible to find single characteristics that are probably more advanced or more primitive in one race than in another. For example, the full lips and kinky hair of some Negroes are almost certainly progressive traits in comparison with the more primitive, decidedly apelike thin lips and straight hair of most whites. However, that does not mean that whites in general are more primitive than Negroes or otherwise inferior to them. Overall primitiveness and progressiveness in comparison of different groups of animals is practically confined to cases in which the groups are of different species, so that genes of the more rapidly evolving species cannot be transferred to the lagging species. Human races all belong to the same species and have generally had enough interbreeding so that genetic progress, as distinct from local adaptation, could and evidently did spread through the entire species. Only if some race entirely ceased to interbreed with any other would it be likely for it to fall behind and become definitely inferior. Let us hope that will not happen.

Resemblances, Anatomical
and Psychological

Regardless of the diversity of races, it is obvious that all men resemble one another much more than any of them differ from each other. They all share the basic qualities, anatomical, physiological and psychological, that make us human, *Homo sapiens*, and no other species that is or ever was. Something has already been said of anatomical peculiarities of *Homo sapiens* with respect to living apes and human ancestors. Here are some of the most striking human anatomical traits:

Normal posture is upright.

Legs are longer than arms.

Toes are short, the first toe frequently longest and not divergent.

The vertebral column has an *S* curve.

The hands are prehensile, with a large and strongly opposable thumb.

Most of the body is bare or has only short, sparse, inconspicuous hair.

The joint for the neck is in the middle of the base of the skull.

The brain is uniquely large in proportion to the body and has a particularly large and complex cerebrum.

The face is short, almost vertical under the front of the brain.

The jaws are short, with a rounded dental arch.

The canine teeth are usually no larger than the premolars, and there are normally no gaps in front of or behind the canines.

The first lower premolar is like the second, and the structure of the teeth in general is somewhat distinctive.

Given those characteristics, a museum curator could readily identify any specimen of *Homo sapiens* that was added to the collections, or that happened to walk into his office. However, we who are pondering the question "What is man?" must feel that these anatomical features, fully diagnostic as they are, yet do not amount to an answer adequate for our purposes. Even if we were defining, say, a species of mouse, the anatomical definition would not take us far toward understanding "What is mouse?" or, better, "What is mouseness?" unless we related the bodily mouse to the behaving mouse and the thinking mouse. Even thus, human anatomy reflects truly essential man-ness or human nature only to the extent that it is related to human activities and psychology. Already in *The Descent of Man* (1) Darwin discussed such traits in which man appears to be most distinctive. His points, here greatly abbreviated and paraphrased, were as follows:

In proportion with his higher intelligence, man's behavior is more flexible, less reflex or instinctive.

Man shares such complex factors as curiosity, imitation, attention, memory, and imagination with other relatively advanced animals, but has them in higher degree and applies them in more intricate ways.

More, at least, than other animals, man reasons and improves the adaptive nature of his behavior in rational ways.

Man regularly both uses and makes tools in great variety.

Man is self-conscious; he reflects on his past, future, life, death, and so forth.

Man makes mental abstractions and develops a related symbolism; the most essential and complexly developed outcome of these capacities is language.

Some men have a sense of beauty.

Most men have a religious sense, taking that term broadly to include awe, superstition, belief in the animistic, supernatural, or spiritual.

Normal men have a moral sense; in later terms, man ethicizes.

Man is a cultural and social animal and has developed cultures and societies unique in kind and in complexity.

The last point, which some students now consider the most important of all, was least emphasized by Darwin, who was here mainly concerned with the relationship of social evolution to the origin of the moral sense. Darwin's general purpose was not to characterize *Homo sapiens* as the unique species that he is. The purpose was to show that the characteristics that make him unique are nevertheless foreshadowed in other animals, and that the evolution of man from other, earlier, quite distinct species is therefore plausible. We are no longer concerned with *whether* man evolved, because we know that he did. We are still very much concerned with *how* he evolved, with what is most characteristically human about him and how those characteristics arose. The list of traits discussed by Darwin is still valid from this somewhat different point of view.

That list should not be taken as involving so many separate and distinct things. These are aspects of the behavior, capacities, and accomplishments of a species that is characterized by all of them together and not by each or any one separately. They interact and interlock not only with each other but also with the previously mentioned physical or anatomical characteristics of man. For example, complex human societies, especially the modern industrial civilization rapidly spreading to the whole world, require specialization of activities by different members of society further involving manipulation of complex machines. Such specialization, which is nongenetic, requires individual flexibility and could not occur in a mainly instinctive animal. The machines are tools and could only have been devised by a reasoning, toolmaking animal. Invention also required manual deftness, which was provided by (and which also gave selective value to) the structure of the human hand, which required upright posture and could not have been acquired by a quadruped. Further evolution of the early cultural adaptations that led eventually to modern industry also had increased intelligence as a necessary concomitant, and that eventually required larger brains, which in turn involved change in skull structure and in stance— and so on. Even the changing pattern of the teeth can be related to this unitary complex.

The Major Evolutionary Changes

Because all the specifically human traits are integrated within the whole that is human, and because each of the traits as well as their integration must have arisen gradually, it is somewhat questionable to speak of definite milestones or even of particular critical phases in the evolution of man. Yet there are three among these slow and coordinated changes that seem particularly basic for the concept of human-ness. The most crucial single anatomical point is acquisition of upright posture and strictly bipedal locomotion. Most of the other main peculiarities of human anatomy either follow from that or are coadapted with it. The other two major factors are cultural, but are no less biological since both represent attainment and maintenance of biological adaptation by cultural means. They are tool making and language.

Extremely crude but unmistakable stone tools are found in the oldest rock strata containing indisputable members of the human family, nearly, if not quite, 2 million years old. It will be difficult to authenticate still older and more primitive stone tools, because they must have consisted of natural pebbles or rock fragments picked up and used with little or no modification. It has long been maintained that deliberate manufacture of a tool is the distinctive human trait, since many other animals, even including some insects, use natural objects as tools but do not make tools. Now it has been found that chimpanzees may trim and shorten twigs or straws for use as tools (12), and although that simple behavior is almost too primitive to be called tool making, it sufficiently demonstrates that the capacity for tool making is biologically ancient and prehuman. If one wants a more diagnostic statement, it probably is true that man is the only living animal that uses tools to make tools. However, that trait would follow soon and inevitably once tool making really got under way. A stone used to knock flakes off an incipient stone ax is already a machine tool.

Ancient tools more perishable than stone are rarely preserved. Nevertheless, the course of increasing diversity and complication of tools can be followed well enough to demonstrate the gradual and inconstant but generally continual progress through prehistory. The tremendously accelerated progress in historic times is very well documented and is familiar to all of us in general outline, at least. The whole sweep from stone axes to electronic computers is a natural and comprehensible extension of the biological capacities of an unusual species. It is uniquely wonderful, and yet, lest we stand too much in awe of our own products, let us remember that a digital computer is merely a rapid and automated tool for what amounts to counting on fingers.

As posture is focal for consideration of man's anatomical nature and tools are for consideration of his material culture, so is language focal for his mental nature and his non-material culture (13). Language is also the most diagnostic single trait of man: all normal men have language; no other now living organisms do. That real, incomparably important, and absolute distinction has been blurred by imprecise use of the word "language" not only in popular speech but also by some scientists who should know better, speaking, for example, of the "language of the bees" (14).

In any animal societies, and indeed in still simpler forms of aggregation among animals, there must be some kind of communication in the very broadest sense. One animal must receive some kind of information about another animal. That information may be conveyed by specific signals, which may be of extremely diverse kinds both as to form and as to modality, that is, the sensory mode by which it is received. The odor of an ant, the movements of a bee, the color pattern of a bird, the howl of a wolf, and many thousands of others are all signals that convey information to other animals and that, in these and many other examples, are essential adaptations for behavioral integration in the species involved.

Human language is also a system of interpersonal communication and a behavioral adaptation essential for the human form of socialization. Yet human language is absolutely distinct from any system of communication in other animals. That is made most clear by comparison with other animal utterances, which most nearly resemble human speech and are most often called "speech." Nonhuman vocables are, in effect, interjections. They reflect the individual's physical or, more frequently, emotional state. They do not, as true language does, name, discuss, abstract, or symbolize. They are what the psychologists call affective; such purely affective so-called languages are systems of emotional signals and not discourse. The difference between animal interjection and human language is the difference between saying "Ouch!" and saying "Fire is hot."

That example shows that the nonlanguage of animal interjection is still present in man. In us it is in effect not a part of language, but the negative of language, something we use in place of speech. In part we even use the same signals as do the apes, a fact already explored to some depth by Darwin in another of his basic works, *The Expression of the Emotions in Man and Animals* (15). Much more is now known about such expressions in animals, and particularly in our closer relatives the apes and monkeys, and it is not surprising to find that the non-linguistic, affective system is particularly complicated in them and has not progressed but may even have retrogressed in man. Still we do retain that older system along with our wholly new and wholly distinct system of true language. It is amusing that the human affective interjectional reaction to a bad smell is practically the same as in all other primates, down even to the most primitive.

Attempts to Trace Language

Darwin's study and many later studies sought to trace the evolutionary origin of language from a prehuman source. They have not been successful. As a recent expert in the field (16) has said, "The more that is known about it [that is, communication in monkeys and apes], the less these systems seem to help in the understanding of human language."

Many other attempts have been made to determine the evolutionary origin of language, and all have failed. Because language is so important for any concept of man and because this is an interesting example of methodology and limitations, it is worthwhile to consider some of these futile attempts. One, fairly obvious once the idea of linguistic evolution had arisen, was by comparison of living languages. One result was a supposed genetic sequence: (i) isolating languages, like Chinese, which string together invariable word roots; (ii) agglutinating languages, like Mongolian, which modify roots by tacking on prefixes and suffixes; and (iii) flexional languages, like Latin, which modify by (partly) internal changes in words. The trouble is that these categories are not really distinct and, especially, that they did not historically occur in this sequence. For example, Chinese was probably flexional at one time and is now becoming agglutinating with a possibility of becoming flexional again. English was flexional until quite recently and is now mostly isolating with a strong dash of agglutination. Moreover at the present time no languages are primitive in the sense of being significantly close to the origin of language. Even the peoples with least complex cultures have highly sophisticated languages, with complex grammar and large vocabularies, capable of naming and discussing anything that occurs in the sphere occupied by their speakers. Tales of tribal natives who cannot count beyond 4 and who have vocabularies of only two or three hundred words betray the shortcomings of gullible travelers, not of the natives (17).

Another approach is to follow back directly historical records, which cover several thousand years for some European, Asiatic, and North African languages. It is then possible to project still further and to reconstruct, for example, a proto-Indo-European anterior to Sanskrit. But this still leaves us tens or hundreds of thousands of years—perhaps even more—from the origin of language. The oldest language that can reasonably be reconstructed is already modern, sophisticated, complete from an evolutionary point of view.

Still another attempt, which now seems very naive, is through the ontogeny of language, that is, the acquisition of language by children. This relies on the famous but, as it happens, quite erroneous saying that ontogeny repeats phylogeny. In fact the child is not evolving or inventing primitive language but is learning a particular modern language, already complete and unrecognizably different from any possible primitive language. Moreover, the child is doing this with a modern brain already genetically constructed (through the long, long action of natural selection) for the use of complete, wholly nonprimitive language.

It is a tempting hypothesis that the time, at least, of the origin of language might be determined by structural characteristics in fossils. One rather elaborate attempt departed from the fact that all linguistic phonetic systems, varied as they are, depend in part on the shape of the lower jaw and the hard palate, anatomically quite different in typical members of the human and the ape families. It was postulated that speech began when these anatomical parts reached human form, which was in the australopithecines or somewhat earlier. But the postulate is clearly wrong. Audible signals capable of expressing language do not require any particular phonetic apparatus, but only the ability to produce sound, any sound at all. Almost all mammals and a great number of other animals can do that. Moreover, a number of animals, not only birds but also some mammals, can produce sounds recognizably similar to those of human language, and yet their jaws and palates are radically nonhuman. A parrot is capable of articulating a human word but is completely incapable of understanding what the word means.

Given any method of sound production, the capacity for language depends not on characteristics of the sound apparatus but on the central nervous system. Speech is particularly connected with the left temporal lobe of the human brain, as shown, for example, by the fact that ability to speak is generally lost if that lobe is severely damaged. The gross development of the lobe can be seen in plaster casts of the insides of fossil skulls, and that, too, has been proposed as a means of determining whether or not a given fossil individual could speak. But all mammals have left temporal lobes, some smaller and some larger. Those with smaller lobes do not speak just a little and those with larger lobes more. There is no graded sequence: normal men speak completely; other animals, whatever the relative size of their temporal lobes, do not speak at all.

The essential anatomical and physiological basis of speech is nevertheless in the structure and function of the brain (18). That basis is not fully known, but it evidently involves not just a language center, such as might be localized in the temporal lobe, but an intricate and widespread system of associative connections throughout much of the brain. (The nature or presence of these connections cannot be determined in fossils.) Thus sensations of any kind derived from an external object or event can be generalized according to similarities with others. Each kind can then be associated with a distinctive symbol, which does not resemble the object or event at all but which arbitrarily stands for it. That symbol, a supreme element in the nature of man, is the word, and it is not surprising that words meaning "word," abstraction and symbolization on still another level, have acquired such mystical and philosophical overtones. (Λόγό!)

It is still possible but it is unlikely that we will ever know just when and how our ancestors began to speak. Yet it is certain that this ability depends on physical, structural, and chemical characteristics of the nervous system which evolved from our nonspeaking ancestors under the force of natural selection. The capacity for this unique kind of symbolization is quite general. It does not determine what symbol will be used for a given concept, but that any symbol can be associated with any concept. Thus we are all using exactly the same genetic capacity and symbolizing the same concept when various of us say "woman," "Weib," "femme," "mujer," "zhenshchina," or "imra," depending on whether we happen to have been raised in England, Germany, France, Spain, Russia, or Egypt. The words do not resemble the concept they stand for. Moreover, they can be written in different ways, as in Latin, Arabic, or Chinese characters, that do not resemble each other and that have no physical resemblance to the spoken words. They can even be associated with some symbol that is not verbal at all, as in this example with the simplified representation of Venus's mirror that biologists use to designate females: ♀ .

expressed by some vertebrate paleontologists, that the evolution of higher Primates, and of man in particular, is too controversial and confused a subject to be worth much serious attention. If this view remains common among those best equipped to interpret fossil species, such lack of interest will only prolong the controversy.

In spite of the fact that there are almost no members of the Dryopithecinae of Miocene-Pliocene age for which reasonably comprehensive osteological remains are known, the actual number of specimens of this period that have been discovered is considerable (about 550), and the geographic range of the specimens is extensive. Moreover, advances in geochronometric dating techniques (potassium-argon analysis in particular) now, or shortly, will enable us to make a far more accurate temporal arrangement of man's pre-Pleistocene relatives than we have had. Many of these relatives fall taxonomically within the pongid subfamily Dryopithecinae. Although the fossil record for most dryopithecines is scanty, restudy of this osteologically limited material has now become imperative, because it is adequate to clarify the evolutionary succession of pongids and hominids.

I wish to state initially that I have carefully examined the view that *Proconsul*, from the East African Miocene should be placed in a different subfamily from Eurasian dryopithecines and have found it unconvincing. Actually, there is hardly any morphological basis for separating Dryopithecinae *(Dryopithecus, Proconsul, Sivapithecus,* and related genera) from Ponginae *(Pongo, Pan, Gorilla).* Through the proper application of modern taxonomic principles, even without recovery of specimens more complete than those we now have, much more can be said about evolutionary relationships among the so-called dryopithecines than has been said to date. Dobzhansky (3) recently summed up the pertinence of good taxonomy as it applies to fossil man. His point is equally relevant to the taxonomy of earlier hominoids.

Does it really matter what Latin name one bestows on a fossil? Unfortunately it does. It flatters the discoverer's ego to have found a new hominid genus, or at least a new species, rather than a mere new race. But generic and specific names are not just arbitrary labels; they imply a biological status. Living men constitute a single species: *Homo sapiens.* Now, *Homo sapiens* can be descended from only one ancestral species living at any given time in the past. To be sure, some plant species arise from the hybridization of two ancestral species, followed by a doubling of the complement of chromosomes, but it is most unlikely that mankind could have arisen by such a process. It follows, then, that if two or several hominid species lived at a given time in the past, only one of them can possibly be our ancestor. All other species must be assumed to have died out without leaving descendants.

Undoubtedly a much more lucid picture of the Tertiary antecedents of man could be drawn on the basis of existing evidence were it not for the questionable nomenclatural practices of past years. Clearly, and regrettably, the taxonomic significance of the new systematics has been slower in gaining wide acceptance among anthropologists and paleontologists than among most biologists studying modern taxa. Of course, paleontologists have recognized for many years that the type individual of a fossil species is merely a specimen acquired through chance circumstances of fossilization and discovery from a population of variable organisms of which it may not even be a typical member. Types of fossil origin are thus chosen primarily as name-bearers for postulated species groups (4). Apparently it was less generally understood, until comparatively recently, that when one makes a specimen the type of a new species, or of a new genus and species, there is an obligation laid on the proposer of the new taxon to present a good deal of morphological or other evidence of probable genetic separation from any previously described species. This point applies particularly to Hominoidea, in which there is greater variability in dental pattern and relative tooth size than there is in many other mammal groups. Distinctions in dentition in a hominid specimen, sufficient to warrant designation of the specimen as the type for a new species, must be at least as great as the distinctions that occur between species of the closest living relatives of the fossil form.

SPECIATION

In order to understand what fossil species were and are, it is necessary to comprehend the processes of speciation and to be familiar with modern methods of species discrimination among living animals. Thus, in the case of the dryopithecines, in order to distinguish two fossil species of a given genus, one should be able to demonstrate that forms which are roughly contemporaneous show characters that fall outside the extreme range of morphological variability to be noted in comparable parts of all subspecies of present-day pongids, such as *Pan troglodytes* or *Gorilla gorilla*. High physical and dental variability in given species of man and apes has long been known (5), but it is clear that this has not been taken into account by the majority of past and recent describers of fossil hominoids. Beginning with Mayr (6) in 1950, or slightly earlier, several experienced taxonomists have drawn attention to the extreme oversplitting of the known varieties of Pleistocene hominids. Since the late 19th century this erroneous approach to taxonomy has produced approximately 30 genera and almost countless species. At the other extreme from this taxonomic prolixity stand such workers as Mayr and Dobzhansky, who, drawing on their knowledge of modern speciation, have adduced evidence for a single line of but a few species, successive through time, in this particular lineage (7). To alter their view it would only be necessary to demonstrate the occurrence of two distinguishable species of hominids in a single zone of one site, but, despite much discussion of possible contemporaneity, in my opinion such contemporaneity has not been satisfactorily established. There is fair morphological evidence that there were two species of *Australopithecus (A. africanus* and *A. robustus)*, but their synchronous existence has not been confirmed by finds of both at the same level in one site. Although the concept of monophyletic hominid evolution during the Pleistocene is now widely accepted, certain fallacies continue to affect thinking on probable pre-Pleistocene forms in this subfamily.

In the discussion that follows I attempt to outline and to clarify some of these fallacies. Changes in the taxonomy of fossil hominoids are suggested, on the basis of my direct observation of relevant original materials in America, Europe, East Africa, and India during the past 10 years (8). Among those acquainted with the traditional atmosphere of controversy that has surrounded the question of hominid origins there is often some reluctance to set forth an up-to-date survey of the implications of recent research on the subject. Clearly, all the points made here cannot be extensively supported by documentary evidence in this brief review. Nevertheless, it seems advisable to set some of the newer conclusions before the public at this stage.

OVERSPLITTING OF FOSSIL SPECIES

Apart from the widespread temptation to be the author of a new species or genus, there are three primary causes of the oversubdivision of many extinct taxa (in the case under consideration, fossil Pongidae and Hominidae). These are, (i) uncertainties resulting from incompleteness of the available fossils; (ii) doubts concerning the identity and relative age of species (whether two or more given "types" are time-successive or contemporaneous); and (iii) questions relative to the possible, or probable, existence in the past of ecologic barriers that could perhaps have brought about speciation between populations widely separated geographically.

In view of these and other sources of uncertainty, taxonomists of fossil Primates have generally sidestepped the question of reference of new finds to previously established species, maintaining that it is unwise to assign later discoveries to species named earlier when finds are not strictly comparable or when they consist only of fragments of the whole skeleton; they fequently describe as separate species specimens which appear to come from clearly different time horizons; and they usually draw specific or generic distinctions when materials are recovered from sites that are widely separated geographically, particularly if these sites are on different continents. With continued advances in the dating of past faunas by geochemical means, and with advances in paleogeography, it becomes increasingly possible to improve procedures and practices in the taxonomy of extinct Primates, and to resolve many of the above-mentioned problems.

Generic and specific distinctions of imperfectly known forms

In the past it has sometimes happened that a taxonomist proposing a new species or genus of fossil vertebrate has maintained that, although no characteristics that would, of themselves, warrant separation of the new fossil specimen (B) from a previously known type (A) could be observed, the recovery of more complete osteological data would show the forms concerned to be different. This sort of anticipation is poor scientific practice, and such an argument should never be used in an effort to distinguish a new taxon unless (i) there is clear evidence of a marked separation in time between the previously described species A and the putative "new" form B, or (ii) there is definite geological evidence of geographic or ecologic separation—for example, evidence of a seaway or a desert—which would greatly reduce or eliminate the possibility of morphologically similar specimens A and B being members of one widespread, variable, but interbreeding, population. Some students would not grant even these two exceptions but believe that morphological distinctions must be demonstrated. Generally, some small distinctions occur as a result of individual variation and can be misused as evidence of species difference. Therefore it is best to rely mainly on differences which can be shown to be probable indicators of distinctly adapted, and consequently different, species.

Abundant data on Recent and late Tertiary mammals show that many of the larger species were, and are, distributed in more than one continent, particularly throughout Holarctica. Moreover, the belief that there were fairly close faunal ties between Africa and Eurasia during Miocene-Recent times has been confirmed by the recovery and description, during the past 3 years, of new samples of continental vertebrates of this period from Kenya, Tanganyika, and the Congo (9), (10). Several of the mammals in these localities show close morphological similarity to Eurasian forms, and while many African species of the period do not show extra-African ties, the types which the two land masses have in common do show that increased intercommunication was possible. The fact that some stocks did not range outside Africa cannot offset the clear evidence that many of the same genera and even of the same species occurred in both Eurasia and Africa at this time.

Taxonomic uncertainty deriving from temporal differences

Many hominoid species were proposed in the past mainly on the strength of a posited time separation from a nearly identical but presumably earlier (or later) "species." Most of the "species" designated on this basis should be reinvestigated in an effort to determine their true temporal position and taxonomic affinities. A "new look" is needed because of recent improvements in the potassium-argon method of dating, and in other geochemical dating methods (11, 12) which should ultimately enable students of past species to discuss them in terms of an absolute time scale. Like other kinds of scientific evidence, dates obtained by the potassium-argon method can of course be misapplied. For instance, it must be demonstrated that dated sediments come from (or bracket) the same zones as the faunas they are supposed to date. There are other well-known sources of error in geochemical dating, but in my experience the strongest criticisms of this method come from persons relatively unacquainted with the analytical techniques involved.

One example of the application of geochemical dating techniques to the study of fossil hominoids will suffice to show what wide application such information may have. Simons (13) has proposed that, on morphological grounds, the primitive gibbon-like genera *Pliopithecus* and *Limnopithecus* can no longer be considered distinguishable. Newly recovered materials of *Pliopithecus* [subgenus *Epipliopithecus*] from Miocene Vindobonian deposits of Europe are closely similar, both in dentition and in postcranial structure, to *"Limnopithecus"* from the Rusinga Island beds of Kenya, East Africa. The fauna associated with this East African primate was regarded, at the time of Hopwood's proposal that a genus *"Limnopithecus"* be established, as being of earliest Miocene age and, therefore, older than the European *Pliopithecus* materials. In his fullest discussion of the generic characteristics of *"Limnopithecus,"* Hopwood (14) was able to list only a few slight features of distinction between the tooth rows, then known, of *Pliopithecus* and of *"Limnopithecus."* These are dental variations of a degree which have repeatedly been shown to occur even within members of one small population of such living pongids as *Pongo pygmaeus* and *Gorilla gorilla.* Hopwood further bolstered establishment of his new genus by remarking that additional bases for distinguishing the genera concerned "are the various ages of the deposits in which they are found and their widely separated localities." But he did comment, "apart from convenience neither reason [for placing the African species in a new genus] is particularly sound. . . ." The point I stress here is that taxonomic separations such as Hopwood proposed are not "convenient," for they create complexity where it does not exist.

Recently, Evernden and his associates (12) have reported a date of 14.9 ± 1.5 million years obtained by the potassiumargon technique from biotite samples of tufaceous sediments in the Rusinga Island series. Admittedly this is only a single datum, but if this sample is truly satisfactory for dating by the potassiumargon method, and if it does come from the same horizons as the *"Proconsul* fauna," it shows that the fauna which contains *"Limnopithecus"* *legetet* and *"L."* *macinnesi* could be contemporary with the European Vindobonian materials. Nevertheless, more dating of this fauna will be necessary before we have proof that it is as young as this. If this younger age becomes established, species of *"Limnopithecus"* may well fall entirely within the known temporal distribution of European members of *Pliopithecus.* Evernden and his coworkers also state that the evidences from relative faunal dating suggest a middle or late, rather than an early, Miocene age for the Rusinga fossils. In my opinion this view is supported by close similarities between three other Rusinga primate species (which I discuss later) and forms which occur in the Siwalik deposits of India, of probable middle or late Miocene age.

Finally, it should be stressed that Hopwood did exhibit considerable foresight in recognizing the basic unsoundness of attempting to reinforce a taxonomic separation by the argument of possible (but not proved) temporal difference. The foregoing example, and others which could be noted, show the danger of using the temporal argument when separating closely similar fossil specimens taxonomically. Moreover, it has been demonstrated that many extant mammalian genera have time ranges greater than the entire Miocene epoch, as estimated at present. Numerous instances of genera with long time ranges could be adduced. For instance, the perissodactyl genera *Tapirus* and *Dicerorhinus* in all probability extend back to the early Miocene or late Oligocene, about 25×10^6 years ago; members of some genera of carnivores (*Ursus, Bassariscus, Lutra, Felis,* and others) have all been described from deposits of late Miocene or early Pliocene age (10 to 15×10^6 years ago). Of course, we do not know that any hominoid genera survived as long as the genera in these categories, but most hominoid genera probably endured for at least 3 to 7 million years without much change of form. Consequently, even if it were known that European and East African *Pliopithecus* differed in absolute age by 4 or 5 million years, taxonomic separation at the generic level could not safely be based on this fact alone.

Migration, paleogeography, and past restrictions of species ranges

One of the most widespread assumptions in the study of the antecedents of man is that at some early period (Miocene, Pliocene, or "Villafranchian," depending on the author concerned) the species ancestral to *Homo sapiens* was restricted to a comparatively small geographic area. This restriction is taken by many scientists to account for the supposed "failure" to find pre-Pleistocene human forerunners. Such an assumption may be referred to as the "Garden of Eden illusion." Insofar as this widespread view is held as a scientific theory by some persons interested in the evolutionary history of man, it appears to be based on analogy with the restricted ranges of various recent mammal species, particularly, in this case, of higher Primates with limited distributions, such as orangutan *(Pongo pygmaeus)* or mountain gorilla *(Gorilla g. beringei).*

PLACE OF MAN'S ORIGIN

Some people believe that the place of hominid or human origin has not been discovered; conjectures, by others, as to its location have followed shifting vogues. Thus, when the first materials of *"Meganthropus"* were recovered in

Java from levels lower stratigraphically than those at which *"Pithecanthropus"* remains were recovered, many students favored the view that differentiation of the ancestral stock of mankind occurred in Southeast Asia. Later, with the realization that *Australopithecus* finds from the Transvaal were hominid remains, a case was made for initial hominid differentiation in South Africa (15). Now, new additions to our knowledge of early Hominidae, made in East Africa by Leakey and his associates, have shifted attention northward to that quadrant of the African continent.

It should be obvious that the oldest *known* localities of occurrence of human tools, or of given species of higher Primates, are probably not the first places where these technical developments or species arose. In order to report with confidence the exact regions of origin of the human species and of earliest cultural items, we would need 100 times the archeological and paleontological evidence that we now have, with absolute dates for all sites.

There are a number of possible reasons for the persistence of the "Garden of Eden" concept among scientists, but here I mention only a few of the misconceptions through which this point of view appears to have been initiated and sustained. Students who believe that ancestral species occurred in restricted areas may have in mind four well-known kinds of diffusion from local centers: (i) spreading of cultural items from specific places of invention; (ii) wandering of tribes, both historic and prehistoric, over great distances; (iii) spreading of advantageous gene mutations from individuals or local populations outward throughout an entire species population; and (iv) intercontinental faunal migrations across land bridges at various times in the past.

All these, and other, similar concepts, while pertinent in their own right, do not in my opinion validate the illusion that, through time, each species, as a unit, wanders widely from one region to another. Such a picture is particularly inaccurate in the case of Late Tertiary land-mammal species, such as species among the dryopithecines, whose main area of distribution was the tropical and warm-temperate portion of the Old World. Of course, given sufficient time, species ranges, particularly among the large Mammalia, do expand and contract, and do occasionally shift from one continent to another in response to environmental change. Nevertheless, movement of subpopulations is much greater than the range shifts of an entire species. Even within an evolving species lineage, time-successive species apparently do not appear from one of several populations of the antecedent species; in general, all populations of a single species tend to evolve together, the species changing as a whole because, as the environment changes, newly advantageous genes originating in various sections of the group spread through the species. Of course, if these streams of gene flow are broken for sufficiently long periods, speciation will ultimately occur. A single species, however, *is* a single species just because gene flow throughout all its members is (or recently has been) taking place.

RANGE OF LARGE MAMMAL SPECIES

Now, in applying these ideas to the evolution of large mammals in the Miocene-Recent period, primarily to mammals of the tropical and warm-temperate regions of Palearctica, certain points extremely relevant to the interpretation of dryopithecine evolution emerge. The first of these is illustrated in (Fig. 2-1), which shows a hypothetical model of the range of a large mammal species-series at three periods in the earth's history. The diagram is given as an abstraction because limitations in the distribution of sites yielding fossil land mammals (limitations that result from erosion of sediments or from nondeposition) are such that exact species ranges for past forms cannot now be drawn (and probably never can be). Nevertheless, this is the sort of distribution which recovered fossils indicate was characteristic, during the period with which we are concerned, of certain species of groups such as elephants, hyenas, the big cats, and ruminants. In this context it should be pointed out that the early supposition that many surviving species of large mammals have diminished

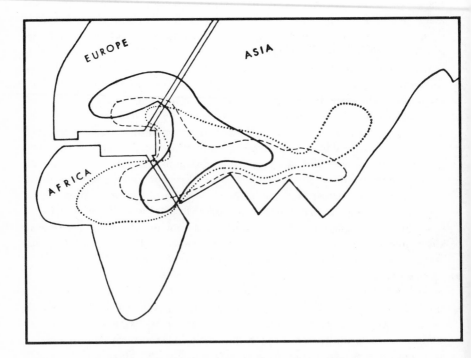

Fig. 2-1. Three species ranges, successive through time, of a hypothetical lineage of a large mammal, as they might have appeared in (dashed lines) the late Miocene, (dotted lines) the early Pliocene, and (solid lines) the late Pliocene.

ranges owing primarily to climatic fluctuations during the Pleistocene and to the activity of human hunters has, by now, been abundantly confirmed. Two examples, taken from dozens, illustrate this point. The lion, *Felis leo,* is now extinct in Eurasia except for a few small surviving populations in India. However, 15,000 to 20,000 years ago, *Felis leo* occurred widely in Europe and the Near East and was, presumably, then abundant in the Indian subcontinent and perhaps even further east. Ewer (16) has reported fossil remains closely resembling *Felis tigris* (but from a mammal slightly larger than the largest of modern tigers) from Olduvai Gorge in Tanganyika. Today, of course, the tiger exists only in Asia.

In the sort of species succession through time that is diagramed in (Fig. 2–1) is it not possible to say where the paleontological "species" came from— the population during, for example, the late Pliocene did not come *from* any one place and, strictly speaking, does not have a known place of origin. As nearly as can at present be determined, from the literature and from direct study of the relevant fossils in East Africa and in India, in Miocene-Pliocene times Eurasia and Africa had over 35 genera of land mammals in common. These included insectivores, anthracotheres, rodents, ruminants, monkeys, apes, hyracoids, hyenas, felids, mastodonts, deinotheres, and several other groups of mammals. Members of over 15 additional mammalian genera that now occur in Africa but have not yet been found in fossil sites on that continent have been found in Pliocene deposits of the Indian Siwalik Hills (17, 18). This total figure of half-a-hundred genera stands in spite of the early tendency to separate, at the generic level, African mammals from allied forms found else-where, just because they are of African provenance. Nevertheless, there are some distinct differences in African and Eurasian faunas of Miocene and Pliocene times.

Numerous groups do appear to have been prevented from crossing between the two areas, there is now evidence that certain mammal species had no difficulty in getting across whatever partial ecological barriers may have ex-isted between the two regions in Pliocene times. One of these is the probos-cidean species *Trilophodon angustidens,* which has been found as far east as Baluchistan, occurs in the Kenya Miocene, and has recently been reported by Hooijer from the Congo (10). There are enough such occurrences to indicate to me that there was reasonably free faunal interchange between these two major regions of the Old World at some time in the Miocene. I see no reason why certain species of dryopithecines or early hominids, or both, could not have par-ticipated in this interchange.

Nevertheless, one may ask whether higher Primates ever had range distri-butions as extensive as those of such later Tertiary Mammalia as I have men-tioned. Clearly, the range distribution of most present-day great apes is a re-stricted or relict distribution, but the fossil record of the pongids for the Miocene through the Villafranchian, as it now stands, is ample indication that certain varieties of these animals had much wider range distributions formerly than they have now. This also appears to be true for many animals of the later Pleistocene. For instance, *Pongo pygmaeus,* now restricted to the islands of Borneo and Sumatra, was then present in South China, and if the Siwalik Pliocene fossils reported by Pilgrim (19) are truly ancestors of this species, it probably had, at an earlier date, an extended range through the Malay Peninsula and Burma into India. Probable antecedents of the gibbons *(Plio-pithecus)* are known from several scattered localities throughout Europe and northern and eastern Africa; at one time they must have been distributed (in suitable habitats) between these areas and the present range of members of this genus, in Southeast Asia. Evidently the ranges of modern species of great apes have dwindled greatly as a result of environmental changes in the relatively recent past. Among such changes was shrinking of the type of forest cover that was necessary for their existence. In certain populations, such as those of *Pongo* in South Asia, extermination or restriction to isolated enclaves on offshore islands surely came about as a result of hunting by human beings.

One of the varieties of primates least affected by these types of constriction are the present-day species of the genus *Macaca.* Distribution of members of this genus (Fig. 2–2) illustrates the extremes of geographic range which members of a single stock of a prehominoid grade of partly arboreal primates have been able to achieve. It need not be assumed that man's ancestors had limited species range until they became terrestrial bipeds. In late-Pliocene and Villafranchian times, *Macaca* was nearly twice as widespread geographically as it is today. An acceptable evolutionary interpretation of this distribution would be that the ancestors of present-day *Macaca* reached the present extremes of their range (Japan, Gibraltar, and so on) when continental shelves were exposed during one of the Pleistocene glaciations, and that the far-flung present-day populations are descendants of perhaps no more than one widespread species that existed 1 to 3 million years ago. Of course, this species could have been already differentiating into genetically diverse populations (subspecies), with only moderate gene exchange between them, before and while the total range of the species was approaching its greatest extent. But it seems more probable that such species distinctions as exist in *Macaca* came about through relatively recent cessation of gene flow between various populations within the entire genus range (20). This would be particularly the case for populations isolated on islands since the last glaciation, or separated by late disappearance of suitable habitat, as between the western population of North Africa and its eastern allies. Members of *Macaca* appear to have been able to achieve such broad distribution mainly because its species have been ecologically plastic. Some varieties, such as the Japanese monkey, have remained relatively arboreal, while others, like the Barbary ape of Gibraltar, are almost

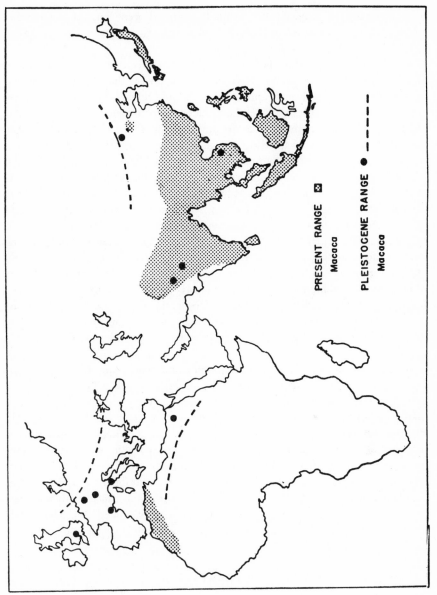

Fig. 2–2. Recent and fossil distribution of the species of *Macaca*.

entirely terrestrial. Conceivably, from the late Miocene on, the earliest hominids were at least as capable of extending their range as the species of
Macaca evidently were at a somewhat later date.

Thus, it can no longer be argued with confidence that the reason no pre-
Pleistocene forerunners of man have been discovered is that these prehominids
lived only in a limited geographical area of the Old World, and in a region
(perhaps of tropical forests) which has yielded no fossil remains. It is now quite
clear that the early hominoids as we know them from fossil remains ranged
widely in the Old World in Miocene and Pliocene times. In Fig. 2–3 the scattered occurrences of the hominoid genera are connected by straight lines,
forming rough approximations to range diagrams. Particulars of the sites and
species upon which Fig. 2–3 is based can be found in Piveteau (21). In spite of
three contrary factors—the rarity of fossil Primates, the enthusiasm of certain
taxonomists for subdividing at the generic level, and failure to discover fossil-
bearing localities in relevant areas—each of several "generic" units among
Anthropoidea of this period have now been reported from at least two Old
World continents, and some have been discovered in all three. That ancestors
of man are not included among these extensive materials is, in my opinion, no
longer an easily defended viewpoint. Moreover, the idea is equally controverted
on morphological grounds. Some dryopithecines do show hominid features.
The argument that human antecedents lived during pre-Pleistocene times in a
restricted area which remains undiscovered has another rather unlikely consequence. This assumption implies that apes and even some monkeys *(Dryopithecus, Pliopithecus, Macaca)*, although largely or partly arboreal, were able
to spread their range widely, while the forerunners of man were somehow
unable to do this. We are here concerned with a stock which, by the early
Pliocene, was probably experimenting with terrestrial living and bipedal locomotion. If, at this time, man's predecessors were not able to distribute themselves as readily as their contemporaries among the monkeys and apes could,
then it becomes necessary to conclude that man's evolutionary emergence from
his pre-human past was truly explosive. This conclusion becomes all the more
necessary if we assume that our supposedly poorly distributed antecedents sud-
denly outdistanced their more "primitive" contemporaries in the matter of
species-range extension.

SPECIES DISTINCTIONS

It should be noted that, although the particular specimens assigned by one
or more competent authorities to the genera indicated in Fig. 2–3 are adequately known for purposes of generic placement, students cannot tell definitely
whether the specimens assigned to a genus were members of the same or of
different species. The common practice has been to regard European, Asian,
and African finds of later Tertiary fossil Mammalia as belonging to different

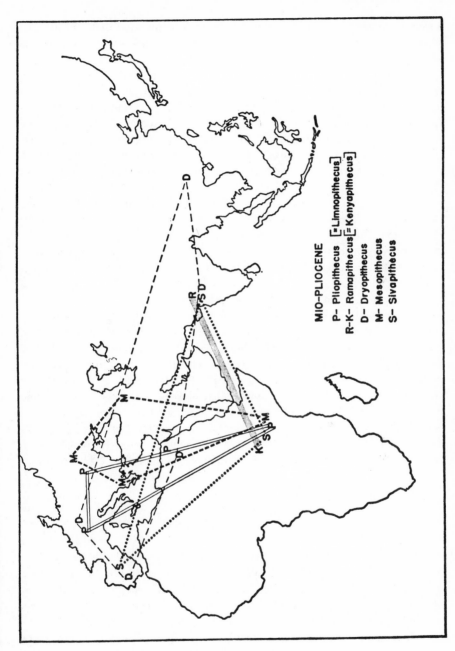

MIO-PLIOCENE

P– Pliopithecus [=Limnopithecus]
R-K– Ramapithecus [=Kenyapithecus]
D– Dryopithecus
M– Mesopithecus
S– Sivapithecus

Fig. 2–3. Occurrence and range distribution of some Miocene-Pliocene Hominoidea.

species, presumably in part because of the tacit assumption that ecologic barriers would, in nearly all cases, have prevented members of a species from reaching all three areas. Nevertheless, since these fossil forms are known primarily from fragmentary dentitions, it remains as difficult to prove that members of populations discovered in different continents represent distinct species as to demonstrate that they are members of the same species. Consequently, it will not be possible to test the validity of species distinctions among many such extinct mammals until much greater numbers of fossils of particular groups are known. In the case of these fossil "apes," for instance, when enough material has been recovered, statistical methods may be used in making species distinctions.

In connection with Fig. 2–3, it should also be pointed out that leading taxonomists of fossils differ as to the generic assignment of some of the species represented. For instance, after initial assignment of certain Spanish dryopithecine remains to the genus *Sivapithecus* (22) (an assignment followed here), this material was later referred elsewhere. On the other hand, Lewis (23) believes that materials currently assigned to *Dryopithecus* from the Miocene of Czechoslovakia should be placed in the genus *Sivapithecus*.

Consequently, I doubt that it has been established that *Sivapithecus* does not occur in Europe. Conversely, Fig. 2–3 does not indicate a range extension of *Pliopithecus* into Southeast Asia, but it seems entirely possible that the very fragmentary type of *"Hylopithecus"* from the Siwalik "series" may represent a primitive gibbon, perhaps assignable to *Pliopithecus*. With reference to this specimen, it seems instructive to quote what must be one of the most amazing passages in the history of bad taxonomic practice. This remark occurs as a conclusion to the description of the type species of *"Hylopithecus"* (24): "In preference to leaving the tooth now described without a generic name and so increasing the difficulty of reference I am giving it the name of *Hylopithecus*, although I am conscious that my material is quite insufficient for diagnosis."

ORIGIN OF THE HOMINIDAE

In 1910 Pilgrim was ready to state that Hominidae are descended from *Sivapithecus* (25). Later, in 1922, W. K. Gregory observed (26) "that man is a late Tertiary offshoot of the *Dryopithecus-Sivapithecus* group. . . ." Discoveries of hominoids during the half century which have elapsed since Pilgrim's writing have reinforced his viewpoint. Entirely apart from morphological considerations, such conclusions gain strength in the light of the taxonomic procedures and zoogeographic examples that I have discussed. It is curious that, in spite of numerous suitably cautious demonstrations in paleontological papers that the origins of man lay among the dryopithecines, it is still widely held by experts that next to nothing of definite value is known about the pre-Pleistocene forerunners of man (27). One is reminded of a possibly apocryphal comment said to have been made in 1860 by the wife of the Bishop of Worcester. On learning from her husband that T. H. Huxley had then recently argued that man had apelike ancestors, she observed (28): "Descended from apes! My dear, let us hope that it is not true, but if it is let us pray that it will not become generally known." Although the fact of human evolution is no longer doubted, the phyletic sequence before the Pleistocene has never been elucidated during the more than 100 years which separate us from the pronouncements of T. H. Huxley.

Briefly, the following relevant facts as to the origin of the family of man are known. Fossil "apes" of the *Dryopithecus-Sivapithecus* type have now been recovered from deposits distributed throughout a vast area of warm-climate regions of the Old World, including sites in Spain, France, central Europe, Turkey, Georgia, the U.S.S.R., Egypt, Kenya, Uganda, Pakistan, India, and China. Without undertaking a taxonomic revision of these forms at this juncture, but assuming for the moment that all these occurrences do in fact pertain to dryopithecines, I must point out that far too many genera have been proposed for them (29). Some of the genera which have been named are *Ankarapithecus, Austriacopithecus, Bramapithecus, Griphopithecus, Dryopithecus, Hylopithecus, Indopithecus, Kenyapithecus, Neopithecus, Paidopithex, Proconsul, Paleosimia, Ramapithecus, Rhenopithecus, Sivapithecus, Sugrivapithecus*, and *Udabnopithecus* (21, 30).

Such a large number of distinct genera implies an extensive adaptive radiation of sudden appearance in the early or middle Miocene, but in the case of the dryopithecines this diversification probably occurred more on paper than in reality. Direct study of nearly all of the original specimens of these Primates suggests to me that the dryopithecines should probably be assigned to only three or four distinct genera, perhaps even fewer.

Species of four of these "genera" *(Dryopithecus, Sivapithecus, Proconsul,* and *Ramapithecus)* are now fairly well known. To date, however, no student has adequately dealt with the possibility that not even all of these genera may be separable from each other. This is an important issue, for it now appears that the direct hominid lineage passed through members of at least two of these taxa.

Starting with the more *Australopithecus*-like of these forms and working backward through time, we can now draw some fairly clear inferences about the evolutionary appearance of Hominidae. *Ramapithecus brevirostris*, of probable early Pliocene (Pontian) age, from the Nagri zone of the Siwalik Hills of India, has long been known to possess several characters in the upper dentition and maxilla which significantly approach the dental conformation of Pleistocene species of tool-making man. Briefly, these characters, which distinguish this form from typical pongids and suggest hominid ties, are a parabolic (not U-shaped) dental arcade, an arched palate, a canine fossa, low-crowned cheek teeth, small incisors and canines, a low degree of prognathism, and a short face. Separately, almost all of these features can be found among pongids, but their occurrence in combination in *R. brevirostris* is a strong indication of hominid ties. Recently, Leakey has described a new East African primate specimen, *"Kenyapithecus wickeri,"* probably from about the same period or a little earlier, which is exactly like *R. brevirostris* in these and other features. In fact, in my opinion, not one *significant* character of difference exists between the two specimens (both are maxillae). This being so, the new form from Kenya should be assigned tentatively to *R. brevirostris,* at least until such a time as further material provides a basis for demonstrating that the two are different species. The conclusion that these two specimens are at least of the same genus has recently been supported by Frisch, who has also studied them directly (31). Perhaps the most extraordinary thing about Leakey's Fort Ternan, Kenya, specimen is its extreme similarity to the type specimen of *R. brevirostris*—an important and very significant fact that "generic" splitting only obscures. Greater differences than are to be noted here typically occur among members of a single-family social group within nearly all species of present-day hominoids. These two specimens indicate to me a considerable probability that in early Pliocene or latest Miocene times, or both, a single species of progressive dryo-pithecine (?) ranged all the way from northern India to East Africa, and perhaps farther. Personal examination of the specimens concerned also indicates that a third individual of this species, from the Nagri zone of the Siwalik Hills, in the Haritalyangar area, is represented by Pilgrim's specimen No. D 185—the right maxilla of *"Dryopithecus punjabicus"*—in the Indian Museum, Calcutta. This specimen agrees with the other two in significant details of dental morphology, and in the possession of a much-reduced rostrum and an extremely short canine root (alveolus). These three specimens of *Ramapithecus* strongly reinforce each other in indicating a valid species group. Moreover, all three specimens come from a stratigraphic level higher than that at which most of the more generalized dryopithecine remains are found.

The transitional nature of these specimens of itself raises the question of arbitrariness in separating the families Pongidae and Hominidae—a problem which has also been posed recently in connection with another event, the discovery of close biochemical similarities between man and the apes, in particular the African apes (32). Nevertheless, there do seem to be fairly good reasons for continuing to view the Pongidae and the Hominidae as distinct enough to be considered separate families. What I want to stress is the fact that the transitional nature of the *Ramapithecus* materials is such that they cannot be placed with finality in either group. Personally I do not see that it very much matters whether members of this genus be regarded as advanced pongids or as primitive hominids, but perhaps considerations of morphology slightly favor placement among the hominids. There is certainly no need to produce a new, higher category for such links—an alternative which has sometimes been resorted to in the past when a fossil taxon was determined to be roughly intermediate between two others.

TWO SERIES OF DRYOPITHECINES

To date, the most extensive series of dryopithecines come from two main areas, the Rusinga Island and Fort Ternan beds of Kenya and the Siwalik Hills of India and Pakistan. A primary difficulty in understanding the actual significance of these two series of Primates arises from the fact that the Indian dryopithecines were studied and described primarily in the period between 1910 and 1937, while the dryopithecines of Kenya have been dealt with mainly since 1951. No one has ever published the results of extensive comparative study of the two sets of materials. Lewis, in the most recent taxonomic treatment of the Siwalik "apes," in 1937, reduced the number of genera to four *(Bramapithecus, Ramapithecus, Sivapithecus, Sugrivapithecus)*, with ten contained species (33). Members of the first two of these genera he regarded as more manlike than members of the other two; *Sivapithecus* and *Sugrivapithecus* he regarded as being closer to the present-day great apes. Unfortunately, there was a lack of associations between upper and lower dentitions in the Siwalik material, and knowledge of some of these genera—such as *Bramapithecus*, known only from jaw fragments containing the last two molars—was very limited. There were no whole or nearly complete dentitions in which to study the range of variability. This situation has now changed, because of the recovery in Africa (1948–1962) of relatively complete portions of skulls, maxillae, and mandibles of several individual dryopithecines, together with postcranial bones and, in some cases, associated upper and lower jaws. Comparison of these two series of data indicate the following problems.

1) In both the Kenyan and the Indian sites (in the lower part of the section, in particular) is found a large form with large snout, protruding incisors, slicing anterior premolars, and rather high-crowned teeth. In the East African material the lingual molar cingula are more pronounced, but otherwise, characters of dentition, snout, and jaw do not differ significantly. Mainly, these Miocene varieties have been called *Sivapithecus indicus* (Siwaliks), and *Proconsul major* (Rusinga). May it not be that these two sets of fossils represent a single species that ranged fairly widely, and perhaps over a long period, but which in known populations (even from far-flung portions of its range) is not particularly variable? This large-snouted type of ape is temporally distributed from early or middle Miocene (Rusinga; Chinji, in the Siwaliks) to latest Miocene or early Pliocene (Fort Ternan; Nagri, in the Siwaliks), as is evidenced by a very large upper canine recovered at Fort Ternan,

at the same level as *"Kenyapithecus,"* reported by Leakey (9); perhaps by other teeth found at Fort Ternan, that have not been described; and by several discoveries in the Nagri Zone. Differences in the molar-crown patterns of the two populations are about as great within each area as between the two groups. A few successive species may be indicated by this material, or only a single species may be involved. This species could well be ancestral to the gorilla and chimpanzee. Ancestors of the African apes certainly need not always have been restricted to that continent.

2) A second primate form common to the Kenya and Indian areas in the Miocene is represented by the *Sivapithecus africanus* material (Kenya) and the "species" *Sivapithecus sivalensis* (India). In this group the teeth, particularly the canines, are relatively smaller than in *S. indicus,* and lingual cingula on upper molars apparently occur less frequently. The possibility remains high that other East African and Siwalik species, of the 15 accepted as valid in the more recent literature, will fall into synonymy with these two species as new data are recovered, or as a result of a fuller comparative study now in progress. The main distinction in dentition (and almost the only difference in known parts) between some *Sivapithecus* and modern *Pongo* is the higher degree of crenulation of the crowns of cheek teeth in *Pongo.* Several specimens of Indian *Sivapithecus* show rather crenulate molar crowns, and this may be assumed to indicate something about the origin of the orangutan. Such crenulations are particularly developed in the upper molar described by Pilgrim as *"Paleosimia,"* which may be a valid genus. In view of these crenulate teeth, it appears probable that a species that differentiated toward the Bornean great ape is represented in the Siwalik material, but this form has not been fully distinguished in taxonomic work to date. The probability that *Proconsul* cannot be separated generically from *Dryopithecus* is worth mentioning here. Both these genera, if indeed they are two rather than one, appear to be restricted to the Miocene. *Sivapithecus* apparently crosses the Mio-Pliocene boundary but is not easily separated from *Ramapithecus,* a conclusion indicated by Leakey's report on the East African material (9) and by my own studies on the Indian dryopithecines.

CONCLUSION

In concluding it seems advisable to make several observations as to the current state of knowledge of the origins of advanced hominoids.

The fossil hominoids of the Miocene of Kenya do not now appear to belong to the early part of that epoch, as had been previously believed, but may be of middle or, less probably, late Miocene age. Similarities between hominoids of the Miocene in India and Kenya, together with resemblances in other members of the two faunas, suggest that the Chinji Zone of the Siwaliks may be middle or late Miocene, as originally suggested by several early workers (see

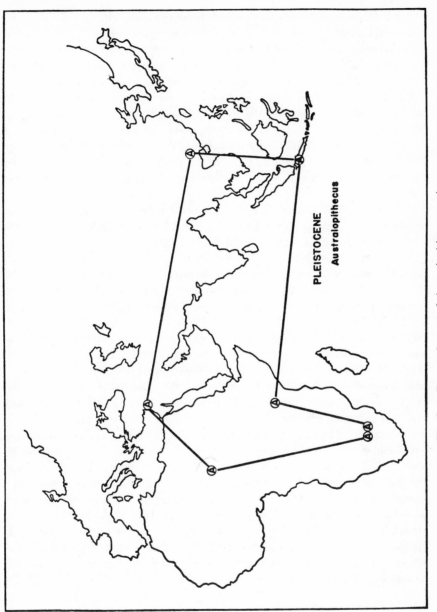

Fig. 2–4. Reported range of *Australopithecus* species.

18). At this time the "radiation" which produced the great apes of today and man seems barely to have begun. The possible occurrence of *Dryopithecus* in early Miocene equivalents of Egypt requires further investigation (34). There is now nearly universal agreement among those most competent to judge that *Oreopithecus* does not stand in the ancestral line of later pongids and hominids, although it is related to them (35). In view of these conclusions, the origins of man and of the great apes of Africa and Borneo are seen to lie directly among the dryopithecines. This conclusion supports the extensive discussions of Gregory as to the significance for human phylogeny of the *Dryopithecus* molar pattern and LeGros Clark's analysis of the morphological evidences favoring the occurrence of secondary canine reduction in the ancestry of Hominidae (36).

There is now adequate fossil evidence to indicate, (i) that, from about middle Miocene times, a few widely distributed species of the larger hominoids were present in both Eurasia and Africa and that successive differentiation of these species, through time, has occurred, with little branching or radiation; (ii) that the primary center of speciation among these animals was outside of Europe; (iii) that some dryopithecines in known parts entirely close the slight morphological gap between hominidae and Pongidae; and (iv) that, if reports as to localities of *Australopithecus* (37) by several serious students be accepted, the data now show that this earliest generally accepted antecedent of man was widely distributed in tropical regions of the Old World in the early Pleistocene (Fig. 2–4). Present archeological evidence does suggest that the use of tools may have occurred first in Africa, but this is not the same as to suppose that the initial species of man differentiated there, unless man be defined solely as a tool-manufacturing primate. To date, the latter supposition is an inference primarily supported by negative evidence—namely, the scanty recovery of australopithecines and of pebble tools in Southeast Asia and China. It must be remembered that one creditable occurrence is all that is needed to demonstrate the early presence of *Australopithecus* in the East. Such an occurrence apparently has now been confirmed by von Koenigswald, through his description of about a dozen teeth, assigned by him to a new genus, *"Hemianthropus,"* in materials recovered from Chinese drugstores (37). In my opinion these teeth are from members of the Australopithecinae assignable to the subgenus *Paranthropus,* but Woo (38) suggests that some of these teeth could belong to *Gigantopithecus* (39).

REFERENCES

1. W. E. LeGros Clark, *Proc. Am. Phil. Soc.* **103,** 159 (1959).
2. A few taxonomic terms used in this article may require definition for the general reader: Dryopithecinae, a subfamily of pongids which includes several species of

Miocene-Pliocene "apes"; Hominidae, the family of man and his immediate forerunners; Hominoidea (hominoids), a superfamily which includes the great apes and man, living and fossil, but excludes monkeys; Pongidae, the family of the fossil and living great apes. The term "Primates" is capitalized when the order Primates, as a major mammalian subdivision, is intended; "primates" (not capitalized) means some, but not all, members of this order.

3. T. Dobzhansky, *Sci. Am.* **208** (2) 169 (1963).
4. G. G. Simpson, *Am. J. Sci.* **40,** 413 (1940).
5. A. Remane, *Arch. Naturgeschichte* **87,** 1 (1922); A. Remane, in *Primatologia*, Hofer, Schultz, Starck, Eds. (1960), vol. 3, p. 637; W. K. Gregory and M. Hellman, *Anthropol. Papers Am. Museum Nat. Hist.* **28,** 1 (1926); A. Schultz, *Am. J. Phys. Anthropol.* **2,** 1 (1944).
6. E. Mayr, *Cold Spring Harbor Symp. Quant. Biol.* **15,** 109 (1950).
7. ———, *Am. Naturalist* **74,** 249 (1940); T. Dobzhansky, *Am. J. Phys. Anthropol.* **2,** 251 (1944).
8. My conclusions are documented at greater length in a monographic analysis of dryopithecines now in preparation.
9. L. S. B. Leakey, *Ann. Mag. Nat. Hist.* **13,** 689 (1962).
10. D. A. Hooijer, *Ann. Musee Roy. Afrique Central, Tervuren,* in press.
11. K. P. Oakely, *Advan. Sci.* **18,** 415 (1962).
12. J. F. Everndan, D. E. Savage, G. H. Curtis, G. T. James, *Am. J. Sci.,* in press.
13. E. L. Simons, *Genetic and Evolutionary Biology of the Primates* (Academic Press, New York, in press), chap. 2.
14. A. T. Hopwood, *J. Linnean Soc. Zool.* **38,** 31 (1933).
15. D. M. S. Watson, *Am. Scientist* **41,** 427 (1953).
16. R. F. Ewer, *Advan. Sci.* **18,** 490 (1962).
17. A. T. Hopwood and J. P. Hollyfield, *Fossil Mammals of Africa, Brit. Museum (Nat. Hist.)* **8,** 1 (1954).
18. E. H. Colbert, *Trans. Am. Phil. Soc.* **26,** 376 (1935).
19. G. E. Pilgrim, *Records Geol. Surv. India* **45,** 1 (1915).
20. Although several present-day species of *Macaca* surely must be valid—that is, genetically isolated—it is of some interest to observe that most of these living "species" of the genus *Macaca* have not been shown by cross-breeding experiments to be distinct species [see A. P. Gray, *Mammalian Hybrids* (Commonwealth Bureau of Animal Breeding and Genetics, Edinburgh, 1953)].
21. J. Piveteau, *Traite Paleontol.* **7,** 167 (1957).
22. J. F. de V. Comella and M. C. Pairo, *Bol. Inst. Geol. Espan.* **91,** 1 (1947).
23. Personal communication, and Yale Peabody Museum records.
24. G. E. Pilgrim, *Mem. Geol. Surv. Ind.* **14,** 12 (1927).
25. ———, *Records Geol. Surv. Ind.* **40,** 63 (1910).
26. W. K. Gregory, *Origin and Evolution of the Human Dentition* (Williams and Wilkins, Baltimore, 1922), vol. 1. p. 548.
27. F. C. Howell, *Science* **130,** 831 (1959).
28. M. F. Ashley Montagu, in T. H. Huxley, *Man's Place in Nature* (Univ. of Michigan Press, new ed., 1959), intro.
29. I am currently engaged in a taxonomic revision of Dryopithecinae, based on direct study of nearly all known European, African, and Indian materials.

30. W. K. GREGORY, M. HELLMAN, G. E. LEWIS, *Carnegie Inst. Wash. Publ.* **495** (1938),p. 1; E. L. SIMONS, *Postilla* **57,** 1 (1961).

31. J. E. FRISCH, *Anthropol. Anz.* **25,** 298 (1962).

32. E. ZUCKERKANDL, R. T. JONES, L. PAULING, *Proc. Natl. Acad. Sci. U.S.* **46,** 1349 (1960); M. GOODMAN, *Ann. N.Y. Acad. Sci.* **102,** 219 (1962).

33. G. E. LEWIS, *Am. J. Sci.* **34,** 139 (1937).

34. R. FORTEAU, *Ministry of Finance, Survey Department, Cairo* (1920), vol. 1.

35. W. L. STRAUS, JR., *Clin. Orthopaed.* **25,** 9 (1962).

36. W. E. LeGROS CLARK, *The Fossil Evidence for Human Evolution* (Univ. of Chicago Press, Chicago, Ill., 1955).

37. In addition to major finds in Olduvai Gorge, Tanganyika, and the Transvaal, South Africa, the reported assignments of fossils to the Australopithecinae and specifically to *Australopithecus* (subgenera *Australopithecus* and *Paranthropus*) are as follows. (i) Stekelis *et al., Bull. Res. Council Israel Sect.* G **9,** 175 (1960), teeth found in association with a Villafranchian fauna at Tell Ubeidiya, Jordan Valley, Israel; (ii) Y. Coppen, *Compt. Rend.* **252,** 3851 (1961), *Australopithecus* cranial fragment found near Largeau, Lake Chad, North Africa; J. T. ROBINSON, *Am. J. Phys. Anthropol.* **11** (1953), transfer of Javan *"Meganthropus"* to *Australopithecus* (subgenus *Paranthropus*); G. H. R. VON KOENIGSWALD, *Koninkl. Ned. Akad. Wetenshap. Proc.* **B60,** 153 (1957), description of *Australopithecus (Hemianthropus) peii,* from China.

38. J. K. WOO, *Palaecontol. Sinica* **146,** 1 (1962).

39. I thank the Wenner-Gren Foundation of New York and the board of the Boise fund of Oxford University for financial support in the preparation of this article. I also thank W. E. LeGros Clark, A. L. McAlester, B. Patterson, C. L. Remington, M. C. McKenna, and W. L. Straus, Jr., for critical reading of the manuscript. Illustrations were prepared by Mrs. Martha Erickson.

3 · New Fossil Primates: A Review

Elwyn L. Simons
Yale University

The distinct rarity of fossil primates maintains the development of studies regarding the evolutionary appearance of man and allied forms in an intriguing
but often frustrating state. Nevertheless, some of the mists obscuring the past of
the order to which man belongs have recently been clearing. The years since
1950 stand as the most productive of new finds and new reports of any equal
time period since the first fossil primate *Adapis* was described by Cuvier in
1822. Moreover, the steady climb in rate of recovery of new types and more
complete individuals suggests that paleontologists and paleoanthropologists will
augment the series of ancient primates which came to light in the first two-
thirds of this century by at least an equal number during the remainder. Discoveries of particular value include several of nearly complete skulls together
with postcranial remains. Such discoveries, belonging to a number of species
previously known only from jaws and teeth, recently established another dimension for osteological comparison between fossil and living types.[1] For reasons of brevity, not all the significant new types of primates described from
dentitions alone can be considered in this report.

In spite of the additions to knowledge of primate history discussed here,
many basic problems of the evolutionary differentiation of the order as a whole

Revised from E. L. Simons "New Fossil Primates: A Review of the Past Decade," *American
Scientist,* June 1960, Vol. 48, No. 2, pp. 179–192. Copyright 1960 by The Society of the Sigma
Xi, New Haven, Conn. By permission of the author and the publisher.

[1]See Table 3–2.

need clarification. A few such problems are: When and where did the common ancestor of the Old World monkeys, apes, and man arise? What are the nearest relatives, among known early Tertiary families, of surviving primates? At what time did the ceboids, or New World monkeys, branch off from the line of the higher primates of Europe, Asia, and Africa? Which of the many groups of North American Eocene primates make the most likely candidates for the ancestry of the Ceboidea? When did the ape and human stocks diverge? What is the relationship of the ape-like creatures *Aegyptopithecus* from the Oligocene of Egypt and *Dryopithecus* species (subgenus *Proconsul*) from the early Miocene of Kenya to this differentiation? How should the earliest primates be distinguished from allied insectivores? What characteristics typified pre-Pleistocene hominids? How many of the genera and species currently assigned to Pleistocene man have taxonomic validity?

With such a variety of unsolved problems regarding the origin and radiation of the primates, much further geological exploration and collecting is needed. Some long-known localities for Old World fossil primates remain most likely to yield specimens which could answer a number of these problems and deserve further attention. Such areas include the Miocene and Pliocene beds of the Siwalik Hills in northwestern India and eastern West Pakistan, the Miocene deposits of Kenya and Uganda, and the Oligocene terrestrial deposits of the Fayum, southwest of Cairo, Egypt. In all these sediments primates which might pertain to the line of hominid differentiation occur. Recent collections show that fossil primates can be found abundantly in these three areas among many other potential sites in the Old World.

Apart from the distinct need for additional collecting lies the matter of interpretation and careful analysis of species now known. A remark attributed to the great paleoanthropologist Franz Weidenreich, even if apocryphal, serves to emphasize this aspect of the subject. When asked where the fossil ancestors of living man are, Weidenreich is said to have replied: "On our desks." The same possibility obtains for a number of fossil nonhominid primates, already available in museum collections. Restudy, and more critical comparison, pending recovery of new connecting links, stand as desirable objectives for correct assessment of currently known fossil specimens. Such projects may require a more constructive spirit of international cooperation among paleontologists and anthropologists than has sometimes prevailed. One improvement would be a freer exchange of specimens for description and study among competent researchers. A good example of such cooperation is the efficient and prompt reporting of new fossil mammals (including many primates) collected in Kenya and Tanzania in recent years and described by Butler, Leakey, LeGros Clark, Napier, Tobias, Simpson, Witworth, and a number of other colleagues.

Terminology in classification of primates varies greatly. Here catarrhine and platyrrhine are used as equivalents for Old and New World higher primates, respectively. This procedure, by placing Cercopithecoidea and Hominoidea in one infraorder, avoids the cumbersomeness of having always to use both terms when contrasting (as a group) the monkeys, apes, and men of the Old World with other primates. In order to avoid additional confusion the classification followed here, except for insertion of Catarrhini and Platyrrhini as infraorders, is that of Simpson (1945), which is as indicated in Table 3–1.

Table 3–1. Major Subdivisions of Primates

Suborder	Infraorder	Superfamily	Family
Prosimii (lower primates, or prosimians)	Lemuriformes (lemurs) Lorisiformes (lorises) Tarsiiformes (tarsiers)		
Anthropoidea (higher primates, or simians)	Catarrhini (Old World higher primates)	Cercopithecoidea (Old World monkeys, or cercopithecoids)	
		Hominoidea (hominoids)	Pongidae (apes, pongines, dryopithecines)
			Hominidae (hominids, or humanoids, men and allied forms)
	Platyrrhini (New World higher primates)	Ceboidea (New World monkeys, or ceboids)	

Discussion of the more significant new fossil primate finds is here divided into the chronological sequence of Tertiary epochs. As a supplement to the text, Table 3–2 lists known partial or complete skulls of Tertiary primates. From this series four species are figured, together with one Pleistocene type, as illustrative of a temporal, not phyletic, sequence among Cenozoic primates.

PALEOCENE

During the last few years two almost complete skulls of Paleocene primates have been identified. These supply the first foundation for cranial comparisons between Paleocene and subsequent species. One of the two, currently under study by R. W. Wilson, South Dakota School of Mines, comes from mid-Paleocene deposits in New Mexico. This cranium has been provisionally assigned to one of the oldest known primates, *Palaechthon,* having an age of about 7 times 10^7 years. A second skull from sediments of Paleocene age was described by D. E. Russell (1960). Belonging to a species of *Plesiadapis* (a specialized lemur-like prosimian, known from both Europe and North America), this specimen was collected from late Paleocene beds near Cernay-les-Rheims in France (Fig. 3–1). Neither the European nor the American Paleocene primate skull belongs to a species with much possibility of being ancestral to any surviving members of the order, but even so, comparisons of these with Eocene and later primates should help clarify opinions regarding early cranial morphology in the order.

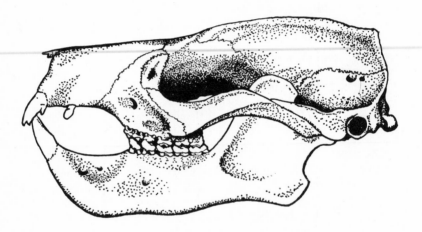

Fig. 3–1. Skull of a Paleocene primate *Plesiadapis,* ×1. Age about 6.5 × 10 years. (Cranium with some correction for distortion.)

An interesting lesson to be learned from examination of these two skulls is that, although ancient, they are not generalized. Truly primitive features, like absence of a postorbital bar, are combined with specializations such as premolar reduction. In fact, the structural alterations and partial loss of antemolar teeth in *Plesiadapis* are greater than in most of the more recent primates. A relatively complete series of limb and foot bones of this animal, also found at Cernay, is now being studied at Yale. A preliminary reconstruction of this skeleton is indicated in Figure 3–2. The significance of a primate skeleton of such antiquity is evident, and preliminary observations show that some features of the postcranial anatomy of the Cernay species would not have been postulated for a primate.

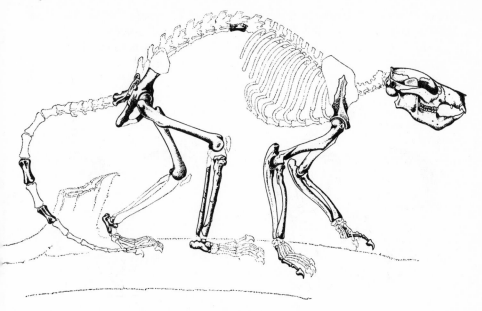

Fig. 3-2. Preliminary reconstruction of the skeleton of *Plesiadapis.*

EOCENE

Significant additions to knowledge of anatomy of Eocene forms came recently through recovery of a magnificent series of skulls and other materials from the North American middle Eocene belonging to two primitive lemur-like primates, *Notharctus* and *Smilodectes*, reported recently by Gazin (1958, 1965). Together with remains of previously known lemuroids of the late Eocene of France and Switzerland these crania provide a broader basis for study of anatomical and zoogeographical relationships among Lemuriformes. Of about the same age as the lemuroid skulls discovered by Dr. Gazin are two partial crania, recently reported on by McKenna (1966) of the American Museum of Natural History. These two specimens, belonging to a family of ancient mammals, the microsyopids, show that this little-known group of insectivore-like primates or primate-like insectivores can be related with some certainty to archaic primates like *Plesiadapis*. They represent yet another branch of early separation—one of the many stocks which grade, almost insensibly, away from undoubted primates toward insectivores, and which clearly indicate the derivation, among placental mammals, of primates. Restudies of a number of primate species of Eocene age have also attempted to trace the origins of certain surviving prosimians, particularly in the case of the French tarsioid *Necrolemur* (Fig. 3-3) (see Simons and Russell 1960, and Simons 1961*a*).

Other lemur-like Eocene primates were reviewed by Simons (1962a). Species of two genera, *Anchomomys* and *Pronycticebus*, although presently classified in the Eocene family Adapidae, show interesting resemblances to the modern lorises, and this may indicate that the differentiation of the lorisiform primates goes back at least this far.

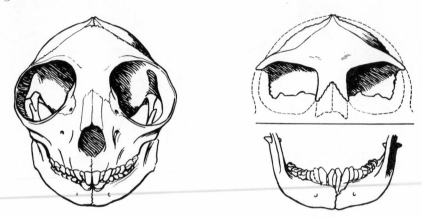

Fig. 3–3. Left, skull of an Eocene primate, *Necrolemur*, × 1.2 approx. Right, parts of two Oligocene Primates, × 1.2 approx.: above, an anthropoid frontal fragment from the Egyptian Fayum deposits; below, the mandibles of *Parapithecus*, a small Fayum species of uncertain taxonomic position.

Simpson (1955) reviewed the aberrant prosimian *Phenacolemur,* and related forms, in a beautifully illustrated monograph. This curious, slightly rodent-like genus occurs in the late Paleocene and early Eocene of North America, and has also been identified in early Eocene collections from France. To date, only *Plesiadapis, Phenacolemur, Homo,* and perhaps *Pelycodus* occur, or are known to have occurred, in both the Old and the New Worlds. Distribution of all these genera demonstrates that in the late Paleocene, or slightly before, climate and land bridges made possible a Holarctic distribution for some primates. In the virtual absence of Asian specimens, the probability that some other early Tertiary prosimians of North America were also existing in Eurasia increases the importance of New World types as possible indicators of the nature of early Old World stocks.

OLIGOCENE

The Oligocene epoch was almost certainly a critical age for diversification of higher primates. Before the Yale expeditions of the 1960's and discovery of an Oligocene primate skull in west Texas in 1964, the known world primate fauna of that time consisted of only seven or eight individual specimens, all from the Fayum early Oligocene of Egypt, and of a further three types, *Macrotarsius*, *"Kansupithecus,"* and *Anagale* (found elsewhere), which were thought to belong in this order. A small, but nearly complete, frontal bone from the Fayum desert (collected in 1908) was reported by Simons (1959). This skull fragment, the oldest of any known catarrhine primate, shows that postorbital closure, a distinctive feature of subsequent Anthropoidea, had been attained by the early Oligocene (Fig. 3–3). Also, a mandibular fragment from the Fayum beds (at the American Museum of Natural History and from which tooth crowns have been lost) was described morphologically by Simons (1961*b*). This indicated another genus, somewhat larger than *Propliopithecus*, but differing from it through possession of an elongated third lower premolar as in later catarrhine monkeys and apes. Subsequent to this, finds in the Fayum made by members of the Yale expeditions under the author's direction made it possible to describe the genus and species represented by this jaw as *Aegyptopithecus zeuxis* (Simons, 1965). In addition, three other new primates from the Fayum, *Oligopithecus savagei*, *Apidium moustafai* (1962*b*), and *Aeolopithecus chirobates* (1965), have been described and reported on extensively elsewhere by Simons (1962*b*, 1963*a* and *b*, and 1965). Together with previously described Fayum primates these new species strengthen the impression that Anthropoidea may have been reasonably diversified by the early Oligocene. Absence of any antecedents for catarrhines in the late Eocene of Europe (although prosimians are numerous there) suggests a non-European and Asian or African origin for the group.[2] One problematical and very fragmentary primate *"Kansupithecus"* reported from the province of Kansu, China, by Bohlin in 1946 had been thought to represent an Oligocene Asiatic hominoid, but a more recent faunal correlation suggested by Thenius (1958) would place the Kansu fauna in the Miocene.

Anagale, long thought to represent an Oligocene occurrence of the treeshrews, has been shown by McKenna (1963) not to belong to the order Primates. This leaves only two species of the order of Oligocene occurrence outside the Fayum. These are both North American monotypic genera, *Macrotarsius* and *Rooneyia*. New and unpublished finds of *Macrotarsius* should soon add to knowledge of its relationships. Simons (1961*c*) has pointed out that the lower jaw of this primate shows a morphologically intermediate stage between more primitive omomyid prosimians and later South American monkeys. Quite the most exciting recent addition to North American paleoprimatology was the finding of an Oligocene omomyid skull in 1964 by J. A. Wilson of the University of Texas. Wilson (1966) shows this cranium to be a mosaic of "primitive" and "advanced" features. Absence of postorbital closure, possession of simple molar cusp patterns, a somewhat backward directed foramen

[2]*Alsaticopithecus*, from the Eocene of Alsace, for which hominoid relationships have been suggested, has been shown by McKenna (1960) to be more probably a microsyopid.

magnum, and placement of the lacrymal foramen outside the orbit are all primitive features of this skull. In contrast with these, the skull shows some features otherwise typical only of higher primates. These include an ossified external auditory meatus and absence of the foramen lacerum medius.

MIOCENE

Additions to knowledge of Miocene hominoids during the last fifteen years have been substantial. Studies by LeGros Clark and Leakey (1951) on a skull and other remains of the early Miocene form of *Dryopithecus* (subgenus *Proconsul*)[3] were most recently enlarged by description of a forelimb of this primate by Napier and Davis (1959). Simons (1961*d*) demonstrated that the supposed dryopithecine *Ramapithecus* is on dental grounds perhaps better placed with hominids. In 1962 Leakey distributed a paper describing a new probable early Pliocene or late Miocene site, Fort Ternan, Kenya, and named a supposed new genus and species of primate *Kenyapithecus wickeri* from this locality. Simons (1963*c*, 1964*a*) pointed out that known species of *Ramapithecus* and *Kenyapithecus* are not dryopithecines and are all referable to the species *Ramapithecus punjabicus*. If species distinctions exist between the finds made in Africa and North India they cannot be demonstrated from known material. Simons and Pilbeam (1965) reviewed the twenty-eight genera with fifty contained species which had been considered members of the fossil ape subfamily Dryopithecinae, Of these, many were synonyms of *Ramapithecus punjabicus*, the earliest probable hominid species. The remainder were either *nomena vana, nomina nuda,* or were assignable to one of eight species of *Dryopithecus* or to the one species of *Gigantopithecus*. Several studies of limb bones and parts of crania of two other gibbon-like Miocene apes both belonging to subgenera of *Pliopithecus (Limnopithecus* and *Epipliopithecus)* were also published during this period (Fig. 3–4). As a result of these reports one can now consider postcranial anatomy of mid-Tertiary hominoids in some detail. Perhaps the most striking findings to be drawn from study of the skeleton of Miocene apes is that, unlike surviving pongids, some at least of these ancient apes lacked a fully ossified auditory meatus, may have had a tail, and had forelimbs shorter than hind limbs. Miocene apes had apparently not yet acquired the elongated forelimbs which characterize brachiating anthropoids of the present day. Intermembral indices (combined length of radius and humerus relative to total length of femur and tibia) in both *Epipliopithecus* and *Limnopithecus* lie near 95. This figure is higher than in man and cercopithecoid monkeys (range 70–90), lower than that of living pongids (range 112–145).

[3]Classification of fossil apes followed is that of Simons and Pilbeam (1965).

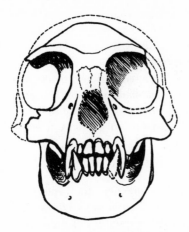 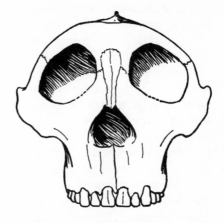

Fig. 3—4. Left, skull of a Miocene primate *Pliopithecus*, an early relative of the gibbons, after Zapfe (1958); × 0.6 approx. Right, skull of a Pleistocene hominid primate *Zinjanthropus*, after Leakey (1959); × 0.3 approx.

LeGros Clark and Thomas (1951) estimated the brachial index (length of radius in relation to humerus) in *Limnopithecus* as about 103, and limb bones of *Epipliopithecus* figured by Zapfe (1958), collected near Neudorf an der March in Czechoslovakia, have virtually the same index. The latter species is of mid-Miocene age. Of some interest is the fact that the brachial index of both these Miocene apes falls in an intermediate position between its mean in gibbons and those of the remainder of known hominoids, which reinforces the suggestion of gibbon affinities for species of these two genera, a relationship formerly based largely on dental comparisons. Recently an important study by Ankel (1965) has shown that because of the large diameter of the sacral canal in *Epipliopithecus*, this animal presumably had a long tail. From a monographic review of this primate by Zapfe (1960) it also emerges that in this Czechoslovakian ape there was only partial ossification of the ectotympanic tube, which is more extensively ossified in all living catarrhines. These primitive features led Remane (1965) to remove *Pliopithecus* to a separate, supposedly aberrant, family, Pliopithecidae. Nevertheless, one must realize that recovery of early forms of extant mammal families can and usually does necessitate expansion of the familial definition. By allocating these early apes to a distinct family without living descendants Remane has shifted attention away from the highly probable conclusion that these animals show us much about the condition of our own ancestors and in fact, of all hominoids at that time. There is little reason to doubt that these Miocene apes are in or near the ancestry of modern gibbons.

Considering, on the other hand, pongids of the genus *Dryopithecus*, the brachial index of *Dryopithecus (Proconsul) africanus*, lies considerably lower (86). Such a figure falls between the mean brachial index of the gorilla and that of the chimpanzee. However, this estimate derives from a juvenile *Dryopithecus africanus* and, as the brachial index typically increases with age in Anthropoidea, it was probably nearer 90 in the adult—a considerable remove from its mean in man, at about 76. Although presentation of a few indices of this sort cannot, of itself, serve to outline possible interrelationships of these pongids, it does represent one useful type of analysis made available by newly found limb bones. The relation of subgenus *Proconsul* to hominid differentiation continues to be obscure. In view of their generalized anatomy it seems unlikely that species of *Dryopithecus* would have looked very different from any hominids contemporary with them to an untrained eye, assuming that a dichotomy of the two families had occurred by then.

Another interesting observation derived from the new foot and hand skeletons of *Limnopithecus, Epipliopithecus,* and *Dryopithecus (Proconsul)* (noted by many who have studied them) is that the extremities of these early pongids retain many monkey-like features. In fact, it has been suggested that some of these bones would have been assigned to monkeys had they not been recovered in association with dentitions of essentially pongid type. In an analogous manner, the postcranial skeleton of *Homo sapiens* shows less differentiation from that of *Australopithecus* or *Homo erectus* than does the skull and dentition. Most discussions of australopithecine postcranial anatomy have been concerned with showing its manlike and non-ape-like construction. Relative to the broad stream of primate history this practice looks through the wrong end of the telescope. Living man retains, evidently with some additional refinements, the structural modifications for bipedality of *Australopithecus*. Thus, as bipeds, men could be said to be *Australopithecus*-like, and not the other way round. The broad pelvis and femoral conformation of *Oreopithecus* (see below), to the extent that these indicate bipedality, implies that bipedal trends in some lines of hominoids are of pre-Pliocene origin.

That Old World Anthropoidea were already considerably diversified and of wide distribution in this epoch is indicated by discovery of forms apparently assignable to the Indian subgenus of *Dryopithecus, Sivapithecus,* and to the Indian genus *Ramapithecus* in the Miocene Kenya deposits (LeGros Clark and Leakey 1951) and Leakey (1962). Moreover, in April 1965, Louis Leakey announced that teeth of something resembling *Oreopithecus* have been found at Fort Ternan, Kenya, along with at least two kinds of monkeys. Monkeys resembling *Mesopithecus* have also been reported from the Kenya Miocene beds by MacInnes (1943), but these may represent a new genus. *Mesopithecus* has been found at a number of localities in Europe and in the Near East. Recent reports on Miocene hominoids include that of Thenius (1954), a restudy of *Austriacopithecus* from Central Europe, and that of Burtschak and Gabachvili (1950) on a Dryopithecine(?) *Udabnopithecus* from Georgia, USSR. As mentioned above, Zapfe (1960) has fully illustrated the *Pliopithecus* skeletal material from Czechoslovakia, and knowledge of this ape has been further amplified by Ankel's study (1965) of the sacral canal and its implication that this was a tailed ape. Woo (1957, 1958) has discussed new materials of this genus from Keiyuan, Yunnan, China. Chow (1958) has demonstrated that this Hsolungtan coal field fauna probably correlates with the fossil ape-yielding deposits of the Chinji-Nagri zone of the Siwalik Hills, North India. These Chinese finds are not new species or are not demonstrably so. One specimen is evidently *Dryopithecus indicus*, the smaller, probably *Ramapithecus punjabicus*.

Relationships between early and late Cenozoic prosimian primates are hard to determine because of the rarity of Oligocene and Miocene species. Several new finds have been made. Jaw fragments and parts of two skulls of a Miocene prosimian were described by LeGros Clark and Thomas (1952) and by LeGros Clark (1956). These belong to an early Miocene genus *Progalago*, from Kenya, which can definitely be assigned to the lorisiform division of lower primates. Recovery of a primate of loris type of such antiquity indicates that the divergence of Madagascan lemurs and lorisiform prosimians cannot have occurred later than sometime in the Oligocene. Simons (1963*b*) noted the discovery in the Yale Siwalik collections of a mandible of the genus *Indraloris*. Recently Simpson (1967) has reviewed the African Miocene and Pleistocene lorisoids including *Progalago, Mioeuoticus* (Leakey, in Bishop, 1962). In this paper he also describes two new genera of African lorisids, *Komba*, from the Kiswahili name for species of *Galago*, and *Propotto*, from its evident similarity to the living Pottos. He concludes that these many new Miocene lorisids do not help much in closing the morphological gap between recent Lorisiformes and Eocene prosimians because in parts preserved they are only slightly more primitive than living relatives.

Stirton and Savage (1951) have contributed to knowledge of early platyrrhine monkeys in a study of a partial cranium of a Miocene Columbian primate *Cebupithecia*. Little definite information is available regarding earlier New World monkeys. Present evidences are that, by Miocene times, platyrrhines were of essentially modern type.

PLIOCENE

One of the most fascinating single finds in recent years was the skeleton of *Oreopithecus* recovered (1958) from the Grosseto lignites of Tuscany, Italy, by the Swiss paleontologist Hürzeler. This skeleton, as well as many more fragmentary specimens previously collected, comes from rocks deposited just after most scientists draw the Mio-Pliocene boundary and is, therefore, about 1.2 times 10^7 years old. Unlike all the remainder of pre-Pleistocene catarrhines, *Oreopithecus* possesses a number of dental and osteological characters that occur elsewhere only in undoubted hominids, such as relatively small canines, very short face, and broad pelvis. Careful analyses of some of these, and other features, have been made by Hürzeler (1954, 1958; and earlier) and by Butler (1959). Several studies now published help to clarify the problematic taxonomic position of this hominoid. Straus (1963) shows that hip and foot structure in this animal indicates that bipedal walking may have been possible. The form of the anterior inferior iliac spine and the large heel with reduced basal tubercle of calcaneus are more like the conformation seen in man in these regions than like any other hominoid. More recently, Kummer (1965) has emphasized that both femora of the 1958 *Oreopithecus* skeleton show laterally flexed distal condyles and a comparatively acute angle between the femoral shaft and the main axis of the femoral head and neck, both resemblances to bibedal man. Although aware of the possibility that these features could in part have been caused by crushing, he feels this unlikely to have occurred in the same manner on both sides. A consensus of current opinion is that this animal, if a hominid, is not on, or even very near, the ancestral line of living man. Such a conclusion is justified by a number of morphological features seen in this primate which would not be expected so late in man's ancestry, including marked increase in molar length posteriorly, highly cuspidate teeth, and long forelimbs. An alternative taxonomic placement which has wide support is to consider *Oreopithecus* as representing a separate hominoid family. Whatever its relationship to modern man may be, this find clearly raises the question: Do we really know what sort of anatomy to expect to find in a ten-million-year-old human ancestor? It should be mentioned in passing that, when contrasting this Tuscan primate with *Epipliopithecus* and the Miocene anthropoids of Kenya, it is well to remember that almost certainly *Oreopithecus* stands closer in time to the present day than it does to some at least of these earlier hominoids. Pronounced morphological alterations in various hominoid lines could have come about between early Miocene and the end of this epoch. *Oreopithecus* had comparatively long forearms and curved phalanges. Since the most distinctive skeletal alterations for brachiation among Anthropoidea are seen in the gibbon and siamang, one might expect to find more evidence of this in their Miocene forerunners. Instead, the earliest real elongation of the forelimb occurs later and in a possible hominid, *Oreopithecus*. However this may be, Hürzeler is to be commended for strikingly demonstrating the value of application to the task of collecting better osteological materials. If his example is followed elsewhere, students can look forward to the early accession of more extensive knowledge of the radiation and deployment of this order.

PLEISTOCENE

So many new reports on Pleistocene humans, and subhuman primates as well, have appeared in recent years that it is impossible to consider more than a few of the most significant early Pleistocene finds here. As they pertain to fossil man, the major middle to late Pleistocene discoveries have been discussed by LeGros Clark (*American Scientist,* September 1959). In general, it can be said that the extensive series of Pleistocene hominids now known gives evidence of a progressive morphological and temporal succession leading up to present-day man. No doubt many details of this sequence, so fascinating in an anthropocentric world, will be further refined, but the broad outlines of man's evolutionary development throughout most of the Pleistocene Epoch can now be drawn.

The beginning of the Pleistocene is today conventionally demarcated by the widespread appearance in the Old World of a characteristic fauna called the Villafranchian, at a time perhaps 2.0 to 2.5 times 10^6 years ago. It was apparently in this earliest part of the Pleistocene, in a world inhabited by an exotic series of giant mammals, as well as by the generally smaller ancestors of surviving forms, that the first modest evidences of human ingenuity appear. These take the form of crudely worked stone tools of a type called Oldowan pebble tools or pre-Chelles Acheul culture. Opinions vary as to the geographic distribution of this industry, but it may have occurred in Eurasia as well as at Olduvai Gorge and elsewhere in Africa. For decades, students of Paleolithic Man searched without clear success for an association of human remains with these earliest artifacts, and although a few tools of Oldowan type had been recovered from the South African brecchias containing *Australopithecus* (see Robinson and Mason 1957), it remained possible to question the assumption that *Australopithecus* was the tool-maker concerned.

All this was changed on July 17, 1959, when, at Olduvai Gorge in Tanzania, East Africa, a human skull which was almost complete, was found in association with a few tools, flint flakes, and parts of splintered bones of the animals upon which this "Oldowan Man" fed. The cranium, found by Mrs. Leakey, has been assigned (1959) by Dr. Leakey to a new genus *Zinjanthropus* ("Zinj" being an Arabic word for East Africa). Dr. Leakey has pointed out that *Zinjanthropus* shows distinct similarities to *Australopithecus*, and is an australopithecine, but these resemblances were not adequate in his opinion to indicate that the two types are congeneric. Later, most students came to realize that this was not a new genus but like the old familiar *Australopithecus* (or *Paranthropus*) *robustus* of South Africa. At first it seemed that this find, associated as it was with definite artifacts, demonstrated that the australopithecines could not be as far off the line of human ancestry as has sometimes been maintained. One of the most unique aspects of the original *"Zinjanthropus"* discovery is that the skull, a tibia, and perhaps other parts of the skeleton were in place on the living-floor inhabited by what were definably primitive men.

After further work at Olduvai, however, the Leakeys found evidence of another hominid species in Olduvai Bed I. These are by far the most ancient finds of hominid remains at camping sites in the open. Present evidence suggests that, in the early Pleistocene, man's ancestors did not know the use of fire, and therefore they probably did not consistently inhabit caves. Life in the open was apparently not conducive to the preservation of human remains at living sites, so that the majority of previous early finds, for instance those of Heidelburg, Swanscombe, Steinheim, and Java, consist of skeletal parts scattered by stream action. With luck, perhaps further very ancient associations of archaeological and osteological remains will be recovered from open sites; at least the finds at Olduvai Gorge show that this can be done.

More recently Leakey and his associates (1964) proposed the name *Homo habilis* for the second type of hominid found in Beds I and II Olduvai. To date, this taxon has not met with general acceptance, as has been discussed in some detail in Pilbeam and Simons (1965). Briefly, the situation is that the hominids from Olduvai Bed II included as paratypes of *H. habilis* are not the same morphologically and are perhaps almost a million years younger than the type jaw and other referred material from Bed I. Actually the Bed II hominids seem to be *Homo erectus* as is indicated by the detailed comparisons of Tobias and von Koenigswald (1964). As Robinson has repeatedly pointed out, most recently in 1965, the type mandible of *H. habilis* possesses all the morphological features of *Australopithecus*, not *Homo*. Robinson and a number of other scientists, including myself, have stressed the point of view that the minor differences from various *Australopithecus* specimens seen mainly in the premolars of the type specimen of *H. habilis* do not establish convincingly that this jaw is something other than a jaw of that genus. Moreover, compared to premolar size the lower canines in this type jaw are relatively huge for a hominid. This must be considered a primitive feature and is certainly not a resemblance to members of genus *Homo*. In any case, it is not a jaw that can be referred to the genus *Homo* unless the definition of this genus be enlarged to include all *Australopithecus* as well. Such a broad mandibular-dental definition of the genus is unworkable for it would cause one also to have to include *Ramapithecus* species (some of which date from the late Miocene) in the genus *Homo*. Nevertheless, in spite of these problems of terminology, the discovery of very ancient hominid material at Olduvai is particularly timely, coming as it does soon after the period in which two possible candidates as early Pleistocene ancestors of man, *Eoanthropus* and *Gigantopithecus*, were for different reasons eliminated from such a position.

The exposure as a forgery of the problematic Piltdown Man or *"Eoanthropus"* announced (1953) by Weiner, LeGros Clark, and Oakley requires little additional comment here, except to stress that elimination of this creature from the family tree removed a form with a morphology increasingly out of step with new finds of the last quarter century. Far from this detection being a scientific embarrassment, it demonstrated that, under the exacting scrutiny made possible by modern techniques, there is little need to suppose that deceptions of this sort will ever again pass unnoticed.

In connection with recent studies of mandibles of *Gigantopithecus* found *in situ* in caves in Kwangsi, South China (Pei 1957; Pei and Li 1959), it is advisable to consider the hypothesis of Weidenreich that the forms *Gigantopithecus*, *Meganthropus*, *Pithecanthropus* represent a successive evolutionary series of decreasing size. Pei suggests on the basis of faunal correlation that *Gigantopithecus* is of Villafrachian age and, insofar as such far-flung correlations have value, would therefore be an approximate contemporary of the australopithecines of Olduvai Bed I. Weidenreich's opinion that *Gigantopithecus* might stand in the line of human ancestry was derived from a few isolated teeth that were rather different from apes like *Dryopithecus*, but which also differ from *Australopithecus* and *Homo*. At that time (1946), when much less was known of the South African man-apes, such a conjecture was possible, but it has not been confirmed by the new South China mandibles. Following Weidenreich's idea that *Gigantopithecus* was a near-human type, Weinert suggested in 1950 that it should be called *Gigantanthropus*. Since this point has been brought up again more recently (Heberer 1959) perhaps it should be mentioned that, according to the international rules of nomenclature, changes of generic names as the taxonomic position of a given form is changed are not allowed, (see Linneus "Critica Botanica" 1737, aphorism 243). The report that *Gigantopithecus* and the large-jawed australopithecines were huge animals has been widely circulated, but has little basis. In the case of the latter group, such a conclusion has been seriously weakened by the absolute size of australopithecine pelves (now five in number) and other skeletal parts recovered in the past few years from the South African brecchias. These postcranial remains show some australopithecines possessed, together with massive jaws, a body the size of a modern pigmy. Whether or not this was the case in *Gigantopithecus* remains purely speculative. Pei's opinion (1957) that *Gigantopithecus* does not belong among hominids gains support from the construction of a third jaw, described by Pei and Li (1958), which shows a short diastema behind the large lower canines, coupled with a slightly sectorial lower premolar following it. The creature possessed a simian shelf and elongate lower molars having distinct central constriction. On the other hand, the comparatively small and vertically placed incisors and curious wear on the lower canines suggest that the anterior upper dentition of *Gigantopithecus* may not have been particularly typical of apes at any stage, indicating a fairly long separate lineage for this Chinese primate. The possibility of a relationship with *Oreopithecus* should be examined.

A final issue that may be worth considering here is the question of the place of origin of mankind. Of course, this depends on how one defines humanity, but a second source of confusion derives from a rather widespread misunderstanding of species population distribution. Large mammals seldom occur in one place, being found throughout a large area. The prehistoric distribution of wolf, aurochs, horse, and lion are examples that come to mind. Taking the association of patterned tools with the hominids of Olduvai Bed I as evidence of the attainment of human status among australopithecines, it is then possible to

Table 3–2. Partial or Complete Skulls of Tertiary Fossil Primates

Epoch and Approx. Years Since Beginning	Genus	Group	Continent
Pliocene 1.2 x 10⁷	Dolichopithecus	cercopithecoid	Europe
	Libypithecus	cercopithecoid	Africa
	Mesopithecus	cercopithecoid	Europe, Africa
	Oreopithecus*	hominoid	Europe
Miocene 2.6 x 10⁷	Cebupithecia*	ceboid	S. Amer.
	Pliopithecus* [Epipliopithecus]	hominoid	Europe
	Dryopithecus* [Proconsul]	hominoid	Africa
	Progalago*	lorisiform prosimian	Africa
	Komba*	lorisiform prosimian	Africa
	Mioeuoticus*	lorisiform prosimian	Africa
Oligocene 4.0 x 10	Fayum frontal* [? Apidium]	catarrhine	Africa
	Rooneyia*	prosimian	N. Amer.
	Aegyptopithecus*	hominoid	Africa
Eocene 6.0 x 10⁷	Adapis	prosimian	Europe
	Anchomomys	,,	Europe
	Cynodontomys*	,,	N. Amer.
	Hemiacodon*	,,	N. Amer.
	Microchoerus	,,	Europe
	Microsyops*	,,	N. Amer.
	Nannopithex* [Pseudoloris]		Europe
	Necrolemur	advanced prosimian	Europe
	Notharctus	prosimian	N. Amer.
	Phenacolemur*	prosimian	N. Amer.
	Pronycticebus	,,	Europe
	Protoadapis* [Megatarsius]	,,	Europe
	Pseudoloris	advanced prosimian	Europe
	Smilodectes* [Aphanolemur]	prosimian	N. Amer.
	Tetonius	adv. prosimian	N. Amer.
Paleocene 7.5 x 10⁷	Plesiadapis*	prosimian	Europe
	Palaechthon* (undescribed)	prosimian	N. Amer.

* Specimens identified, described or reassigned since 1950.

consider the zoogeographic distribution of this group (rather than the disputed problem of occurrences of Oldowan artifacts), as evidence of the range of the earliest known humans. When this is done, the points made by Robinson (1953) in favor of *Meganthropus* from Java being congeneric with *Paranthropus* gain in importance. Since the latter is usually considered only a sub-genus of *Australopithecus*, it becomes possible to maintain that distribution of this group stretched from South Africa to Southeast Asia. There has, however, been a general hesitancy to do this because of the fragmentary nature of the specimens of *Meganthropus*. Due to their proximity, one practice has been to rank *Meganthropus* as a subgenus of *Pithecanthropus*. *Pithecanthropus erectus* itself, however, is now commonly ranked only as a species of *Homo*, *H. erectus*. Description of a new hominid genus *Hemanthropus* by von Koenigswald (1957), based on a number of isolated upper and lower teeth from China drug-stores, raises this issue anew.[4] *Hemanthropus* is a *Paranthropus*-like form which evidently occurred in South China. Unless both of these assignments eventually prove to be incorrect, it would appear that australopithecine distribution covered a large area of the Old World. Clearly, more evidence will have to be recovered before theories as to which continent was the cradle of mankind gain a sound foundation. Arambourg's genus *Atlanthropus* (1954) poses a similar situation in a slightly later period. This North African human, and perhaps *Telanthropus* from the Sterkfontein locality in South Africa (see Broom and Robinson 1949, 1950) are not very different in known parts from *Pithecanthropus*. It is time that the often repeated stricture that few genera of Pleistocene men are well based taxonomically had an effect on terminology. The idea that the bases for generic distinctions among Pleistocene men are weak is hardly new, E. D. Cope having remarked in "The Primary Factors of Organic Evolution" (1896:169) with reference to the Java ape-man: "He [Dr. Dubois] proposes for him a new genus *Pithecanthropus* (after Haeckel), and even a new family, Pithecanthropoidae, without having shown that he is not a member of the genus *Homo*."

[4]For centuries the Chinese have used fossils, called "dragon bones," in powdered form as medicinal agents. The first identified teeth of *"Sinanthropus"* and *Gigantopithecus* were also located in collections made for this purpose.

REFERENCES

ANKEL, F., 1965, Der canalis sacralis als indikator für die länge der caudalregion der primates. *Fol. Primat.*, 3:263–276.

ARAMBOURG, C., 1954, L'hominien fossile de Ternifine (Algerie). *C. R. Acad. Sci. Paris.* **239**:72–74.

BISHOP, W. W., 1962, The Mammalian Fauna and Geomorphological Relations of the Napak Volcanics, Karamoja. *Records Geol. Surv.* Uganda, Entebbe, for 1957–1958:1–18.

BOHLIN, B., 1946, The fossil mammals from the Tertiary of Tabun-buluk. *Rept. Sino-Swed. Scient. Expd. N. W. Prov.* China, 6, 4.

BROOM, R., and J. T. ROBINSON, 1949, A new type of fossil man. *Nature,* 164:322.

————, and ————, 1950, Man contemporaneous with Swartkrans apeman. *Amer. Journ. Phys. Anthrop.,* 8:151–155.

BURTSCHAK-ABBAMOVITSCH, N. O. and E. G. GABACHVILI, 1950, "Discovery of a fossil anthropoid in Georgia." *Priroda,* 9:70–72 (Moscow).

BUTLER, P. M., and J. R. E. MILLS, 1959, A contribution to the odontology of Oreopithecus, *Bull. Brit. Mus. (Nat. Hist.) Geol. Ser. 4(1):1–26.*

COPE, E. D., 1896, The primary factors of organic evolution (the Open Court Publishing Company, La Salle, Ill.).

GAZIN, C. L., 1958, A review of the Middle and Upper Eocene Primates of North America, *Smiths. Misc. Coll., 136,1:1–112.*

————, 1965, An endocranial cast of the Bridger Middle Eocene primate, *Smilodectes gracilis. Smiths. Misc. Coll.,* 149, 4:1–14.

HERBERER, G., 1959, The descent of Man and the present fossil record. *Cold Spring Harbor Symposia on Quan. Biol. 24:235–244.*

HUZELER, J., 1954, Zur systematischen Stellung von *Oreopithecus. Verh. naturf. Ges. Basel,* 65:88–95.

————, 1958, *Oreopithecus bambolii* Gervais. A preliminary report. *Verh. naturf. Ges. Basel, 69:1–48.*

KOENIGSWALD, G. H. R. VON, 1957, Remarks on *Gigantopithecus* and other hominoid remains from Southern China. *Proc. Koninkl. Nederlandse Akad. Wetenschappen, Amsterdam,* ser. B, 60,3:153–159.

LEAKEY, L.S.B., 1959, A new fossil skull from Olduvai. *Nature,* 184:491–493.

————, 1962a, A new lower Pliocene fossil primate from Kenya. *Ann. Mag. Nat. Hist.* Ser. 13, 4:689–696.

————, 1962b,(See Bishop, W. W.).

————, P. V., TOBIAS, and J. R. NAPIER, 1964, A new species of the genus *Homo* from Olduvai Gorge, Tanganyika. *Nature,* 202,4927:7–9.

LE GROS CLARK, W. E., 1956, A Miocene lemuroid skull from East Africa. *Brit. Mus. (Nat. Hist.) Foss, Mamm. of Afr.,* 9:1–6.

————, 1959, The crucial evidence for human evolution, *Amer. Sci.,* **47** 3:229–313.

————, and L. S. LEAKEY, 1951, The Miocene Hominoidea of East Africa., *Brit. Mus. (Nat. Hist.) Foss, Mamm. of Afr.* 1:1–117.

————, and D. P. THOMAS, 1951, Associated jaws and limb bones of *Limnopithecus macinnesi., Brit. Mus. (Nat. Hist.) Foss, Mamm. of Afr.* 3:1–27.

————, and ————, 1952, The Miocene lemuroids of East Africa., 5:1–20.

MACINNES, D. G., 1943, Notes on the East African Miocene primates. *J. East Afr. Uganda Nat. Hist. Soc.,* **17**:141–181.

MCKENNA, M. C., 1960, Fossil Mammalia from the early Wasatchian Four Mile fauna, Eocene of Northwest Colorado. *Univ. Calif. Publ., Geol. Sci.* 37:1.

————, 1963, New evidence against tupaioid affinities of the mammalian family Anagalidae. Amer. Mus. Nov. 2158:1–16.

————, 1966, Paleontology and the origin of the Primates. *Folia primatologica,* **4,** 1:1–25.

NAPIER, J. R., and P. R. DAVIS, 1959, The fore-limb skeleton and associated remains of

Proconsul africanus. Brit. Mus. (Nat. Hist.). Foss. Mam. of Afr., 16:1–69.

PEI, W.-C., 1957, Discovery of *Gigantopithecus* mandibles and other material in Liu-Cheng district of central Kwangsi in South China. *Vert. Palasiatica, Peking*, 1,2:65–72.

———, and Y.-H. LI, 1959, Discovery of a third mandible of *Gigantopithecus* in Liu-Cheng, Kwangsi, South China. *Ibid.*, 2,4:198–200.

PILBEAM, D. R. and E. L. SIMONS, 1965, Some problems of hominid classification. *Amer. Sci.*, 53,**2**:237–259.

REMANE, A., 1965, Die Geschichte der Menschenaffen in *Menschliche Abstammungslehae*, Gustav Fischer Verlag, 249–309.

ROBINSON, J. T., 1953, *Meganthropus*, australopithecines and hominids. *Amer. Jour. Phys. Anthrop.*, 11:1–38.

———, 1965, Homo '*habilis*' and the australopithecines. *Nature*, 205, 4967:121–124.

———, and R. J. MASON, 1957, Occurrence of stone artifacts with *Australopithecus* at Sterkfontein. *Nature*, 180:521–524.

RUSSELL, D. E., 1960, Le crâne de *Plesiadapis*; note préliminaire, *Bull. Soc. Geol. Fr.*, Ser. 7, 1, 3:312–314.

SIMONS, E. L., 1959, An anthropoid frontal bone from the Fayum Oligocene of Egypt: the oldest skull fragment of a higher primate *Amer. Mus. Nov.*, 1976:1–16.

———, 1961a, Notes on Eocene tarsioids and a revision of some Necrolemurinae. *Bull. Brit. Mus. (Nat. Hist.), Geol. Ser.*, 5, 3:45–69.

———, 1961b, An anthropoid mandible from the Oligocene Fayum beds of Egypt. *Amer. Mus. Novitates*, 2051:1–5.

———, 1961c, The dentition of *Ourayia*: Its bearing on relationships of omomyid prosimians. *Postilla*, Yale Peabody Museum, 54:1–20.

———, 1961d, The phyletic position of *Ramapithecus*. *Postilla*, Yale Peabody Museum, 57:1–9.

———, 1962a, A new Eocene primate *Cantius*, and a revision of early Cenozoic lemuroids of Europe. *Bull. Brit. Mus. (Nat. Hist.) Geol. Serv.*, **7,** 1:1–36.

———, 1962b, Two new primate species from the African Oligocene, *Postilla*, Yale Peabody Museum, 64:1–12.

———, 1963a, A critical reappraisal of Tertiary Primates. Chapter 2 in *Genetic and Evolutionary Biology of the Primates*, Ed. J. Buettner-Janusch. 65–129 (Academic Press, Inc., New York).

———, 1963b, Current research on fossil vertebrates in India, Society Vertebrate Paleontology Bulletin, June 1963:5–7.

———, 1963c, Some fallacies in the study of hominid phylogeny. *Science*, **141**, 3584:879–889.

———, 1964a, On the mandible of *Ramapithecus*. *Proc. Nat. Acad. Sci.* **51**,3:528–535.

———, 1965, New fossil apes from Egypt and the initial differentiation of Hominoidea. *Nature*, **205,**4967:135–139.

———, and D. R. PILBEAM, 1965, Preliminary revision of Dryopithecinae (Pongidae, Anthropoidea). *Folia Primatologica*, **3,**2–3,1–70 (Karger, Basel).

———, and D. E. RUSSELL, 1960, The cranial anatomy of *Necrolemur*. *Breviora*, Mus. Comp. Zool., Harvard, 127:1–14.

SIMPSON, G. G., 1945, The principles of classification and a classification of mammals. *Bull. Amer. Mus. Nat. Hist.*, 85:1–350.

————, 1955, The Phenacolemuridae, new family of early primates. *Bull. Amer. Mus. Nat. Hist.*, 105,5:415–441.

————, 1967, The Tertiary Lorisiform Primates of Africa. In press, *Bulletin of Museum of Comparative Zoology.*

STIRTON, R. A., and D. E. SAVAGE, 1951, A new monkey from the La Venta late Miocene of Columbia. Ministerio de Linas y Petroleos, Servicio Geol. Nac., *Compilacion de los Estudios Geologicos Oficiales en Columbia*, 7:347–356.

STRAUS, W. L., JR., 1963, The classification of *Oreopithecus*. In *Classification and Human Evolution. Viking Fund Publ. Anth.*, 37:146–177.

THENIUS, E., 1954, Die Bedeutung von *Austriacopithecus*. Ehrenberg fur die Stammesgeschichte der Hominoidea. *Anz. Oster. Akad. d. Wissensch.*, 13:191–196.

————, 1958, Tertiärstratigraphie und tertiäre Homminoidenfunde. *Anthrop. Anz.*, Stuttgart, 22,1:66–77.

TOBIAS, P. V. and G. H. R. VON KOENIGSWALD, 1964, A comparison between the Olduvai hominines and those of Java and some implications for hominid phylogeny. *Nature*, 204,4958:515–518.

WEIDENREICH, F., 1946, Apes, giants and men. Univ. Chicago Press.

WILSON, J. A., 1966, A new primate from the Earliest Oligocene, West Texas, Preliminary Report, *Folia Primatologica*, 4,227–248.

WOO, J.-K., 1957, *Dryopithecus* teeth from Keiyuan, Yunnan province. *Vert. Palasiatica*, 1:25–32.

————, 1958, New materials of *Dryopithecus* from Keiyuan, Yunnan. *Vert. Palasiatica*, 2,1:38–42.

ZAPFE, H., 1958, The skeleton of *Pliopithecus (Epipliopithecus) vindobonensis.* Zapfe and HURZELER. *Amer. Jour. Phys. Anthrop.*, 16:441–458.

————, 1960, Die Primatenfunde aus der miozänen Spaltenfüllung von Neudorf an. der March. *Schweizerische Palaeontologische Abhandlungen*, 78:1–293.

4 · An Early Miocene Member of Hominidae

L. S. B. Leakey

National Museum Centre for Prehistory and
Palaeontology, Nairobi, Kenya

In 1934, G. Edward Lewis (1) described a new genus of fossil primate from the Siwalik deposits in India under the generic name of *Ramapithecus,* with *brevi-rostis* as the specific name of the genotype. He emphasized that *Ramapithecus* possessed some hominid characters but classified it, in his official diagnosis, as a member of the family Simiidae, cautiously adding "(Hominidae?)." In 1938, Gregory and Hellman, in a joint paper with Lewis, (2) remarked about this genus: "While the Siwalik genus *Ramapithecus* and the South African *Austra-lopithecus* are still apes, by *definition,* they are almost on the human threshold in their known anatomical characters."

In 1961, Elwyn Simons (3) stated that he believed that *Ramapithecus* might be a member of the Hominidae, but he did not make a definite claim to this effect. He regarded its geological age to be "within the Nagri zone, which is of Pliocene—early Middle Siwalik—age."

In 1961, I published (4) a preliminary note on what I considered to be a new genus and species of primate from Fort Ternan, Kenya. I named this *Kenya-pithecus wickeri* and provisionally gave the geological age as Early Pliocene (Pontian in the English sense). Because the fossil fauna from the same site and level has become better known, I have more recently referred it to the Upper Miocene (5). The fauna of Fort Ternan is rather more primitive than the Early Pontian fauna from such sites as Pikermi, Samos, etc. In my paper of 1961, I

From *NATURE,* January 14, 1967 Vol. 213, No. 5072, pp. 155–163. Reprinted by permission of the author and publisher.

noted similarities between *Kenyapithecus wickeri* and *Ramapithecus brevirostis*, and mentioned its resemblance to the Hominidae. I left the familial position open, however, and described it as "Family, *incertae sedis.*"

During the past few years, most authorities have come to agree that *Kenyapithecus wickeri* and *Ramapithecus brevirostis* should both be regarded as early respresentatives of the Hominidae. It is also widely accepted that both belong, geologically, to the closing stages of the Miocene and/or to the very early Pliocene. Evernden and Curtis (6) have indicated a potassium-argon date for the Fort Ternan deposits, which yielded *Kenyapithecus wickeri,* of about 14 million years. A glass fission track date can be expected soon.

Simons and Pilbeam (7), as well as Simons (8), have recently advanced the opinion that *Kenyapithecus wickeri* should be regarded as a synonym of *Ramapithecus brevirostis*. At the same time, they have suggested that Pilgrim's *Dryopithecus punjabicus* is also identical. Because the name of this species has priority, they have proposed that the Mio-Pliocene representatives of the Hominidae should be known as *Ramapithecus punjabicus* (Pilgrim). In their view (p. 136), moreover, *Dryopithecus fontani (partim), Bramapithecus thorpei* and *Bramapithecus sivalensis,* as well as Woo's far eastern *Dryopithecus keyunanensis*, should now, also, be regarded as synonyms of *Ramapithecus punjabicus* (Pilgrim). This seems to be a somewhat extreme example of taxonomic lumping. Although it is possible—but by no means certain—that all the Asiatic representatives listed may belong to the single genus *Ramapithecus,* the generic distinctiveness of the East African *Kenyapithecus* will be demonstrated in this article.

In my view, the species *Kenyapithecus wickeri* differs from the Asiatic forms at the generic as well as the specific level.

It must also be noted that although the original type of Lewis's *Ramapithecus brevirostis* came from the Nagri zone, which is usually regarded as of early Pliocene age, Pilgrim's *Dryopithecus punjabicus* was listed as from the Chinji formation, which is usually regarded as Uppermost Miocene rather than Early Pliocene. On the evidence of the palaeontological data which are so far available, both are probably geologically slightly younger than *Kenyapithecus wickeri* of Kenya.

In 1951, Le Gros Clark and Leakey (9) described a small maxillary fragment of a primate from site *R*.106 on Rusinga Island, Kenya, tentatively placing it in the genus *Sivapithecus* with *africanus* as a specific name. It was shown to differ markedly from any of the material representing the various species of *Proconsul* from Kenya, while it seemed to share certain features in common with some of the specimens which were described as *Sivapithecus sivalensis*. It was also regarded as differing from the genus *Dryopithecus* of Europe and Asia as described in the literature. This was a view based only on the small maxilla fragment which formed the Type, which came from deposits usually regarded as of Lower Miocene age.

In 1961, I suggested that when the time came to classify the primate which I had named *Kenyapithecus wickeri* into a zoological family it would have to be joined in that same family by *Sivapithecus africanus*. This view was supported at one time by Simons, for he wrote in 1963: *"Sivapithecus* apparently crosses the Mio-Pliocene boundary but *is not easily separated from Ramapithecus*, a conclusion indicated by Leakey's report." In his most recent work with Pilbeam, however, Simons has withdrawn from this view. He now treats all known *Sivapithecus* material as falling within the genus *Dryopithecus* with the name *"Sivapithecus"* reduced to sub-generic rank. He even goes so far as to claim that Le Gros Clark and Leakey's *Sivapithecus africanus* is both generically and specifically "identical" with *Sivapithecus sivalensis* of India. I shall endeavour to show that this cannot be the case.

There is thus a growing consensus of opinion that *Ramapithecus* and *Kenyapithecus* both represent primitive members of the Hominidae; if this is correct and as they were already present in India and East Africa respectively, in Mio-Pliocene times we should expect to find still earlier ancestral members of the family Hominidae either in Middle or even in Lower Miocene deposits. This could be either in Africa or in Asia or in both continents, and the origin of the family Hominidae may even be found to extend back to the Oligocene.

In consequence of pondering this idea, I recently began a detailed re-examination and re-evaluation of the large collection of Lower Miocene primates from Rusinga, Songhor, Koru, etc., which is in Nairobi. This resulted in an examination of some specimens which had been collected since the last study and others which had been overlooked previously, as well as a review of certain others which might have been wrongly identified in earlier publications. The report which follows deals with the recognition, within this collection, of a number of specimens which seem to me to be unquestionably representatives of the family Hominidae. All but one are, moreover, on geological as well as faunal evidence, older than both *Ramapithecus brevirostis* and *Kenyapithecus wickeri*. The specimens to be discussed come from deposits which are usually regarded as of Lower Miocene age, and they include the type specimen of what was formerly called *Sivapithecus africanus*. There is also one specimen from Maboko Island which is regarded as representing *Kenyapithecus sp. indet.*

The Genus *Kenyapithecus*

FAMILY	Hominidae	
GENUS	*Kenyapithecus*	Leakey 1961

My original diagnosis of the genus *Kenyapithecus* was as follows:

A genus within the Superfamily HOMINOIDEAE, with low crowned molars and premolars; the upper canines are small and set vertically in their sockets. There is a well defined canine fossa and the root of the malar element of the malar-maxillary process is set just above the first molar.

For purposes of comparison with both my 1961 diagnosis of *Kenyapithecus* and also with the revised diagnosis of the genus, which will be given later, Lewis's generic diagnosis of *Ramapithecus* is included in full. Similarly Simons and Pilbeam's new diagnosis of *Ramapithecus* will also be quoted in full.

Lewis's original diagnosis of *Ramapithecus* read as follows:

Simiidae (Hominidae?) in which the dentition parallels the hominid type in its broader aspects. The dental arcade of the upper jaw is parabolic rather than "U" shaped as in recent Simiidae, and hence the palate broadens posteriorly. The cheek teeth of opposite sides of the jaw are more widely separated posteriorly than anteriorly rather than approximately equidistant from M^2 to P^3. The face is very slightly prognathous, as contrasted with recent Simiidae. There are no diastemata in the dental series. The canine is small, not an antero-posteriorly elongated trenchant tusk, but of hominid type with a transverse dimension exceeding the antero-posterior dimensions.

In place of this generic diagnosis, Simons and Pilbeam have recently suggested the following:

[*Ramapithecus*] differs from *Australopithecus* and members of the *Dryopithecus* group in the following general features:

Slightly smaller overall size (except for *Dryopithecus africanus*) [by which they mean *Proconsul africanus* of other authors], shallower mandible, less complex patterns of tooth crenulation, little or no evidence of cingula or Carabelli's cusps and shorter face. Incisors and canines reduced in relation to cheek-tooth size when compared to *Dryopithecus* but not as markedly as in *Australopithecus*; incisor procumbancy intermediate. Differs from *Dryopithecus* and other apes in showing more widely spaced and much lower molar cusps, so that the central or occlusal fovea of the molars covers more of the crown surface of the tooth (even so these features show some variability in *Ramapithecus* and *Dryopithecus* as well as in modern *Homo* and *Pan*); sides of the upper molars, particularly, are more vertical; also differs from *Dryopithecus* in showing a larger and lower canine fossa, an arched palate, arcuate tooth row and a much shorter rostrum.

Although this generic definition of *Ramapithecus* by Simons and Pilbeam is much lengthier than that of Lewis, it cannot be regarded as satisfactory for the following reasons:

(*a*) It makes size a generic character in that it states "slightly *smaller* overall size than *Dryopithecus* and *Australopithecus*," but immediately refers to an exception. Moreover, should a larger species of the genus be discovered, it would automatically be excluded by this diagnosis. It must, therefore, be emphasized that size is never really valid as a generic character.

(*b*) It states that the mandible is "shallower" than in *Australopithecus* and *Dryopithecus*. It does not say whether this is in relation to the overall size, or whether it is shallower only relative to the length of a tooth row. This feature again makes size, for example, "shallower," a generic character, which is taxonomically unsatisfactory.

(c) It goes on to say "shorter face," but because no complete face of *Dryopithecus* (other than in the *Proconsul* group) has been found and certainly no complete face from gnathion to nasion in *Ramapithecus*, this seems to be a most unwise diagnostic character to attribute to the genus, in the present state of our knowledge.

(d) The character "incisors and canines reduced in relation to cheektooth size when compared with *Dryopithecus*" may be valid for Asia but it is not true for specimens from East Africa which Simons and Pilbeam wish to include in *Ramapithecus*. While it may be true in respect of *Ramapithecus punjabicus* (*brevirostis*) (if indeed incisors of this genus and species are known in Asia, of which I am not aware) when compared with the more classical *Dryopithecus* species, it is certainly not true (see below) in respect of comparisons of the incisors as between *Kenyapithecus* and the *Proconsul* group, which Simons and Pilbeam insist on including in the genus. One thing is clear: neither the original East African species *Kenyapithecus wickeri* nor the new species of *Kenyapithecus*, which is to be described below, can be accommodated within the genus *Ramapithecus*, as it is now diagnosed by Simons and Pilbeam. *Kenyapithecus* must, therefore, on their own showing, be retained as a distinct and separate genus.

REVISED DIAGNOSIS

The following new diagnosis for the genus *Kenyapithecus* is now proposed. It is the result of examining not only the original type as well as other more recently recovered additional Fort Ternan specimens, but also the specimens which are now to be placed in a second and geologically rather older species of *Kenyapithecus*, from Songhor and Rusinga.

Hominidae in which the dentition closely resembles that of *Homo* in the broader aspects, but not in the crown structure of the canines, nor that of the upper 3rd premolars. The upper canines have short crowns with compressed and relatively short roots, the crowns are not of the *Homo* type, but more primitive. The upper incisors are shovel-shaped, and closely resemble those of some members of the genus *Homo*. The dental arcade of the maxilla is arcuate, not U-shaped as in the Pongidae, while the alignment of the cheek teeth in the maxillae and also in the mandible diverges posteriorly. The face is only slightly prognathous. There is no diastema in the upper or lower dental series. The premolars and molars, including both upper and lower, either have no cingulum, or else a very reduced one. The lower molar cusps are widely spaced and crowns of the teeth lower relative to crown size than in Pongidae. A true fossa canina is present and is morphologically somewhat of the general type seen in *Homo sapiens*. In this character, *Kenyapithecus* differs very markedly from the Pongidae, but resembles *Ramapithecus*. The cross-section through the symphysis of the mandible resembles that of primitive species of the genus *Homo*, and is quite unlike that to be seen in *Dryopithecus*, *Sivapithecus* or *Proconsul*, or in modern Pongidae.

Kenyapithecus wickeri (Leakey)

The first species of *Kenyapithecus* to be described is *Kenyapithecus wickeri*, Leakey.[1] It comes from the Upper Miocene deposits of Fort Ternan, Kenya, and was announced in 1961. Since then an additional upper central incisor has been found from the same site and level as the original material. The description and measurements of this incisor are as follows:

Crown width	10 mm
Crown height (lablal)	9·25 mm
Crown height (lingual)	9·25 mm
Diameters of root at junction with crown	
Labio-lingual	6·5 mm
Bilateral	7·5 mm

This left upper central incisor of *Kenyapithecus wickeri* from Fort Ternan was recovered after the original type specimen had been described. It was found the following year a few feet further into the cliff at the same horizon. It is very well preserved except for the root, the distal end of which is missing.

This tooth is remarkably like that of *Homo* and differs in a number of characters from the corresponding teeth of *Proconsul* (Fig. 4–1). Moreover, it has characters in common with the australopithecines, in particular in the cross-section of the root where it meets the crown. In the upper central incisors of *Proconsul*, the root at the junction with the crown is approximately trihedral, and has a greater diameter from the labial to the lingual aspect than from side to side. In the *Kenyapithecus wickeri* specimen, the cross-section is not trihedral but much more oval with the maximum diameter from side to side, while the labial-lingual diameter is reduced. The height of the crown of this tooth, which is practically unworn, is less than the width, and it is more compressed labio-lingually compared with corresponding teeth of *Proconsul*. The region near the cutting edge is very thin providing a fine chisel edge very different from the upper incisors of *Proconsul*, where a marked medial thickening extends almost to the top of the crown.

The upper central incisors of *Proconsul* are not known for the species *Proconsul major*, but we have well preserved examples of both *Proconsul africanus*

---

[1]A new mandible of *Kenyapithecus wickeri* was recently found on Rusinga, and a report will appear in *Nature*, February 1968.

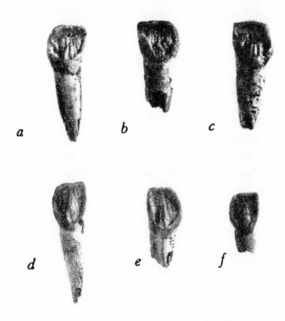

Fig. 4-1. Comparisons of upper central incisors. *a, Kenya-pithecus africanus; b, Kenyapithecus wickeri; c, Kenya-pithecus sp. indet.; d, e,* and *f, Proconsul nyanzae.*

and *Proconsul nyanzae*, some of them found in direct association with the rest of the upper dentition, so that identification is certain (see Fig. 4–1). MacInnes[10] described the upper central incisors of a specimen found in 1932–33 on Rusinga Island. At that time, *Proconsul nyanzae* had not been recognized as distinct, so that he provisionally attributed the specimen to Hopwood's *Proconsul africanus*. Subsequently, Le Gros Clark and Leakey showed that it belonged to the species *Proconsul nyanzae*. These authors accepted MacInnes's description of the incisors as adequate, and did not, therefore, elaborate on them in their own report. MacInnes's description is reproduced here for convenience. It reads as follows:

The root and base of the crown of the first incisor is roughly trihedral in section, with a flat surface to the front. The apex of the crown is sharply constricted from front to back, the anterior surface being gently convex from above downwards, while the posterior surface is rather sharply concave, producing a flat chisel edge. The median surface shows a pressure facet produced by contact with the first incisor of the opposite side, which lies at right angles to the cutting edge of the tooth, while the outer angle of the cutting edge is more rounded. From each of these two angles a very distinct crest curves downwards and backwards and inwards, the two uniting posteriorly. From the middle front of the posterior surface a massive enamel buttress extends from the base of the crown to a point about half-way to the cutting edge. The enamel is considerably wrinkled, particularly on the posterior surface.

New *Kenyapithecus*

The second and new species of the genus *Kenyapithecus* has, as its Type, the maxilla provisionally described in 1951 by Le Gros Clark and Leakey as *Sivapithecus africanus*.

Kenyapithecus africanus (Le Gros Clark and Leakey)

The *africanus* species of the genus *Kenyapithecus* differs from the genotype (*wickeri*) in the following characters: the canine fossae are present, but are less developed; the upper 3rd premolars exhibit two strongly developed and divergent labial roots; their crowns are markedly wider labially than lingually, giving a triangular outline when viewed from the occlusal surface. Traces of anterior internal cinguli are present in the molars and premolars; the upper canines are larger relative to the premolars and molars than in the species *wickeri*. The following additional characters can be seen in the mandible. The corpus in the region of the 4th premolar and 1st molar is deep and very slender, in marked contrast to all Pongidae, including *Proconsul* and *Dryopithecus*; the anterior face of the mandible has a rounded contour, which projects forward in front of the gnathion; the cross-section through the symphysis is markedly hominid in shape, and quite unlike *Proconsul*, *Dryopithecus* or *Sivapithecus*. The available evidence suggests marked sexual dimorphism.

Type. The type specimen is *CMH* 6, Nairobi, from Rusinga site *R.* 106. 1948. It is in the British Museum (Natural History), London.

This specimen was originally described in some detail, and therefore only a few additional features need to be commented on. In the first place, definite evidence of the presence of a canine fossa can be seen on the maxilla. Second, the root of the malar-maxillary process is set forward over the 1st upper molar as in *Kenyapithecus wickeri* and in *Ramapithecus*, not as in the Pongidae or *Proconsul*. Both these features seem to be characteristic of the early Hominidae and are missing in *Dryopithecus* and *Proconsul*. The upper 3rd premolar has two pronounced labial roots (Fig. 4–2).

Additional Material

The following seven specimens which are in the collections in the Centre for Prehistory and Palaeontology, Nairobi, are now referred to *Kenyapithecus africanus*. (1) Part of the right side of a mandible No. *CMH* 142 from Rusinga, site 106. (2) Part of a mandible from Rusingion; the cross-section through 1948—specimen No. 276. (3) Two incomplete maxillae of a single individual, from Songhor, specimen Nos. *Sgr.* 52 and *Sgr.* 111 of 1948. (4) A fragment of

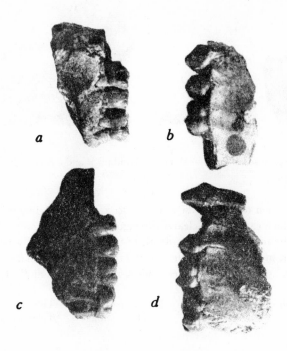

Fig. 4–2. Comparisons of buccal view of maxillae. *a* and
b, Kenyapithecus africanus; *c, Ramapithecus brevirostis*;
d, Kenyapithecus wickeri.

a mandible from Songhor, specimen *Sgr.* 417 of 1951. (5) An incisor from Rusinga, site *R.*106. (6) An isolated right upper 2nd molar from Songhor, specimen 404 of 1948. (7) A maxilla fragment from Songhor, No. 748 of 1962. (8) A maxilla fragment from Songhor No. 1377 of 1962. (9) Part of a clavicle from Rusinga, site *R.* 106 of 1947.

(1) Mandible fragment, specimen No. CMH 142. Specimen No. *CMH* 142 comes from the same site (*R.* 106) as the Type, but was found on the surface nearby. It consists of part of the right corpus of a large mandible which is broken anteriorly in the region of the root of the right lateral incisor, and posteriorly through the roots of the 1st molar. All the crowns of the teeth are missing, but the corpus is well preserved from the alveolar margin to the lower border (Fig. 4–3).

The mandible fragment was provisionally referred by Le Gros Clark and Leakey to *Proconsul major* on account of the very great depth of the corpus, which measures 39·5 mm in the region of the lower 4th premolar, compared with 41 mm in the large mandible which is the paratype of the *Proconsul major*. The crowns of the teeth were all missing and, in view of the very scant knowledge of the fauna in 1951, it therefore seemed preferable at that time to

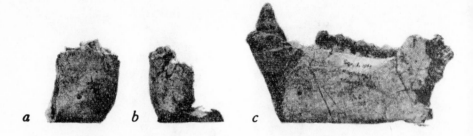

Fig. 4–3. Comparisons of anterior slope of inandibles. *a* and *b Kenyapithecus africanus;*
c, Proconsul major.

refer this specimen to the largest of the *Proconsul* species. The most important
differences which can now be clearly distinguished are:

(*a*) At the level of P_4M_1 the depth of the corpus is only very slightly less
than that seen in *Proconsul major*, but the thickness of the mandibular, at this
point, is totally different; the corresponding measurements at P_4M_1 are:

Proconsul major	Depth 41 mm	Thickness 22 mm
Kenyapithecus africanus	Depth 39·5 mm	Thickness 12 mm

(*b*) In the known mandibles of *Proconsul major* there is a clearly defined
diastema between the lower 3rd premolar and the lower canine; in this
specimen the anterior lingual root of the lower 3rd premolar is set far forward
and extends well beyond the posterior rim of the alveolus of the canine, and
there is no diastema (Fig. 4–4).

(*c*) In *Proconsul major* (as also in both the other species of the genus) the
furthest posterior projection of the symphyseal region is set high in the mid-line
and extends well back, so that its limit is almost in line with the lower 4th
premolar. In this specimen the most backward part of the symphysis is not
further back than the level of the front of the 3rd premolar, and may be even
further forward.

(*d*) In *Proconsul major* the inner wall of the corpus, in the region of the
premolars, slopes slightly inwards, and the corpus itself is very thick. In this
specimen the outer wall is at first straight, then turns slightly outwards.

(*e*) The area of the root of the canine in *Proconsul major* is marked by a
strong surface swelling of the anterior face of the mandible, giving a clear line
of demarcation between the "chin" region and the lateral wall of the corpus. In
this specimen, there is no such swelling and the root of the canine is much less
massive.

(*f*) The roots of the lower canines are more laterally compressed than in
any *Proconsul*, and are orientated more antero-posteriorly and less transversely
than in any species of *Proconsul* or Pongid.

Fig. 4–4. Comparison of occlusa views of mandibles. *a* and *b*, *Kenyapithecus africanus* (males?); *c*, *Kenyapithecus africanus* (female?); *d*, *Pronconsul nyanzae; e, Pronconsul major.*

(*g*) The whole mandibular structure is gracile even though the corpus is very deep (39·5 mm).

(*h*) The mental foramen lies relatively low on the corpus, and is situated beneath the 4th premolar, instead of below the 3rd premolar as in *Proconsul major.*

(*2*) *Mandible fragment, specimen No. 276.* The second specimen now referred to *Kenyapithecus africanus* is the anterior part of another mandible. It is somewhat weathered and was found on the surface. As such, it was not considered of much importance when the 1951 report was prepared. Its morphology, however, is of such a nature that it now becomes clear that it cannot represent the genus *Proconsul*. It displays a number of features, especially in the cross-section of the symphysis and on the anterior face of the "chin" region, which indicate a remarkably hominid structure (Fig. 4–3).

Because it clearly does not represent a *Proconsul*, and because it shares so many features in common with other specimens now referred to *Kenyapithecus africanus*, it seems wise to consider this specimen as representing the latter genus and species. This decision is reinforced by the fact that a wholly comparable, but rather smaller, fragment of mandible (see later) has been found at Songhor, close to the point where two maxillae specimens of this same species had been discovered (see following section).

In this second referred specimen, all the crowns of the teeth are missing. The preserved part extends from the anterior edge of the alveolus of the 4th premolar on the right side round to the alveolus of the left 4th premolar. While both the 4th premolars are only represented by parts of the roots, the lower 3rd premolars, both canines and all four incisors, have their roots intact. There is no trace of a diastema between the lower 3rd premolars and the canines. This is a marked contrast to the conditions to be seen in the various *Proconsul* species. Instead of a diastema, we find that the anterior root of the 3rd premolar is pushed well forward beyond the posterior rim of the alveolus of the canines (see Fig. 4–4).

The arrangement of the incisors in the alveolus is clearly to be seen along the alveolar margin, and differs very markedly indeed from the crowded condition to be seen in any mandible of any species of *Proconsul*. The four incisor teeth were set more or less in a straight line between the canines instead of with the two central incisors being more forwardly placed (Fig. 4–4). In this character there is close resemblance both with *Homo* and with *Australopithecus*, but not with *Proconsul* or *Dryopithecus*. The roots are set vertically in the mandible and are not procumbent. The preserved roots of the canines indicate somewhat robust, but not very large, teeth. They are strongly compressed bilaterally, and are placed more antero-posteriorly than in *Proconsul*. Viewed from the front the chin region differs most markedly from that of any species of *Proconsul*, in all of which the anterior region suggests an inverted triangle with the base of the triangle along the alveolar margin of the incisors and the apex of the triangle near the middle point of the lower border of the symphysis. In *Proconsul* there is also a marked backward slope of the anterior face of the mandible in the chin region. In the specimen now referred to *Kenyapithecus africanus* the morphology of the anterior part of the mandible is remarkably like that in a primitive *Homo*, such as the Mauer jaw. The most forward projecting part lies below the alveolus of the central incisors. The whole shape of this region is, moreover, well rounded and filled out (Fig. 4–3), quite unlike any *Proconsul* or *Dryopithecus*. The cross-section through the symphysis is also different (Fig. 4–5) and recalls that of the more primitive members of the genus *Homo* and of some australopithecines.

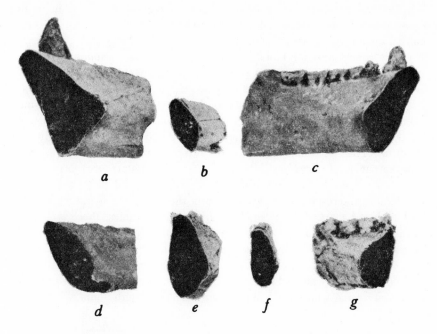

Fig. 4–5. Comparisons of cross-section of mandibles at symphysis. *a, Pronconsul major*; *b, Proconsul africanus*; *c, Proconsul nyanzae*; *d, Pan satyrus*; *e, Kenyapithecus africanus* (male?); *f, Kenyapithecus africanus* (female?); *g, Homo habilis.*

(3) Incomplete maxillae, specimens Nos. Sgr. 52 and Sgr. 111. Two parts of the palate became separated before they were embedded in the deposit in which they were found. The fracture of one premolar is, however, subsequent to the specimen having been eroded from the deposits. Specimen No. 52 consists of a part of the right maxilla. It contains both premolars and the 1st molar. The root of the canine is preserved in the alveolar wall, but the crown has broken off. The specimen has also been broken away some 15 mm above the alveolar margin, in an irregular fracture. In this region, a cross-section of the canine root near the tip is exposed. Above the upper 4th premolar and the upper 1st molar, the maxillary sinus can be seen, filled with matrix. On the palatal aspect the fracture is just short of the palatal surture, which is not preserved. The two cross-sections through the root of the canine (one near the tip and one at the alveolus) reveal that this tooth was orientated in the maxilla with its long axis in much the same direction as that of the molar-premolar series. The labio-lingual width is almost equal to the antero-posterior measurement. At the fracture near the alveolar margin the measurements of the root are 11 mm (antero-posteriorly) and 10·5 mm (bucco-lingually). At the fracture near the tip of the root, about 15 mm above the alveolar margin, the corresponding figures are 8 mm and 6 mm, respectively.

The 3rd premolar has a crown which is roughly triangular in outline when viewed from the occlusal surface—it is very much wider on the labial than on the lingual aspect. The greater labial width is linked with the presence of a very robust anterior labial root and with a rather pronounced anterior cingulum (Figs. 4–2 and 4–6). A somewhat similar morphology can be seen in certain specimens from Asia which are classified as *Sivapithecus sivalensis*, and is also present in the Type specimen of *Kenyapithecus africanus*. The single lingual root of the 3rd premolar is very robust and is directed at a wide angle into the palatal area, instead of nearly vertically into the alveolar margin as in *Proconsul*. The two labial roots of this tooth are strongly developed as in the Type specimen of *Kenyapithecus africanus*. The contact area between the crowns of the upper 3rd and 4th premolars is large and flat, as a result of considerable antero-posterior compression of the teeth, which in turn is correlated with the marked facial shortening. In this character, there is a strong resemblance to the position to be seen in the other and geologically younger species of the genus—*Kenyapithecus wickeri*, from Fort Ternan. The crown area of this upper 3rd premolar is unfortunately rather worn so that the details of the cusp pattern cannot be clearly studied. The measurements of this tooth are: bucco-lingual width 10·25 mm, antero-posterior length 9 mm.

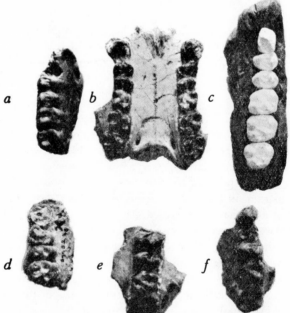

Fig. 4–6. Comparisons of upper dentition from occlusal view. *a, Remapithecus brevirostis* (cast); *b, Proconsul africanus*; *c, Sivapithecus sivalensis* (cast); *d and e, Kenyapithecus africanus*; *f, Kenyapithecus wickeri*.

The 4th premolar is narrow antero-posteriorly (both on the lingual and labial aspects) and is wide bucco-lingually. Like the upper 3rd premolar, it has two labial and one lingual root. The labial enamel surface of the crown is very convex antero-posteriorly, and there is no trace whatever of a cingulum. The contact facet of the crown with the upper 1st molar is also large and flat.

The 1st molar, while roughly rectangular in outline viewed from the occlusal surface, is slightly less wide labially than lingually. All four cusps are worn, but the two on the lingual aspect much more so than those on the labial side. No trace of a cingulum is visible. The cusp pattern of this molar is entirely different from that of any species of *Proconsul*. On the labial face of the crown, moreover, there is a clear valley which separates the anterior from the posterior cusp area. This valley extends halfway down the side of the crown.

The second maxilla fragment, *Sgr.* 111, comes from the left side of the same individual. Only the 4th premolar is intact; the 3rd premolar is represented by its roots and by a small portion of the crown. The canine is represented by a broken root which is still in the socket. This root is clearly set in a much more vertical position in the maxilla than in any species of *Proconsul*, or for that matter in any member of the Pongidae. The length of this canine root can be estimated to have been about 24 mm. It has a similar cross-section to that which has been described in the other maxillary specimen.

An interesting feature of *Sgr.* 111 is the presence of a well marked *fossa canina* on the maxillary surface, above the 3rd and 4th premolars. This does not exhibit quite the same depth, or morphology, as in *Kenyapithecus wickeri*,

Table 4–1

	M^1		P^4		P^3	
	L^*	B^*	L	B	L	B
Kenyapithecus africanus	10	11	7·5	10·5	9·5	11·5
Kenyapithecus wickeri	10·5	10·5	6	10·25		
Ramapithecus brevirostis (cast)	9·2	10·9	6·7	10·0	6·9	10·3
Sivapithecus sivalensis (cast)	10·5	11·5	7·0	11·0	9	10·5

All measurements are in mm.
Note. Measurements made on casts may not be very reliable because the degree of accuracy of the cast is unknown.
$^*L$, antero-posterior length; B, bucco-lingual width.

where the position is nearly like that in *Homo*. Nevertheless, it is much more developed and more manlike than in any fossil or living pongid. A trace of a similar canine fossa occurs in the type specimen, but unfortunately the main part of the relevant area is broken away. On this second maxilla fragment the fracture of the palate is at or near the palatal suture and the palate is seen to have been rather flat and shallow.

Table 4–1 sets out the measurements of the teeth of the type of *Kenyapithecus africanus* compared with the type of *Kenyapithecus wickeri*, as well as the type of Lewis's *Ramapithecus brevirostis* and a comparable specimen of *Sivapithecus sivalensis*.

(4) Mandible fragment, specimen No. Sgr. 417. The fourth referred specimen is a mandibular fragment which was found at Songhor near the maxillae described above. It may perhaps represent the same individual. It clearly comes from a mandible that must have been considerably smaller than the first and second referred specimens, and this may, perhaps, be regarded as evidence of sexual dimorphism. It has been noted that the Songhor maxillae fragments found nearby are also somewhat smaller than the type specimen from Rusinga site *R.* 106. This specimen consists of the anterior segment of a mandible of small size, embracing the broken right canine, the roots of all four incisors and the fractured root of the left canine. The canine roots are very small. The whole depth at the symphysis is preserved and the inferior border is intact. One of the most striking characters, and one which clearly places this specimen outside the genera *Proconsul, Limnopithecus* and *Dryopithecus*, is the cross-section through the symphyseal region (Fig. 4–5) together with the shape and fullness of the anterior face of the mandible in the mid-line. In this character the present specimen duplicates what has already been described in the second referred specimen.

The nature of the cross-section through the symphysis of this specimen is very similar to that in the second referred specimen of the *Kenyapithecus africanus* mandible. The roots of the canines and of the incisors are placed nearly vertically in the corpus, and the incisor roots are noticeably less crowded together than in a *Proconsul* of comparable size.

(5) Upper central incisor, specimen No. CMH 9. In 1951, Le Gros Clark and Leakey figured an upper central incisor from Rusinga Island as a possible incisor of *Proconsul nyanzae*, but more detailed study shows that it does not agree in its overall morphology with specimens which can be shown to belong to *Proconsul*. On the other hand, it agrees remarkably, in structure with the upper central incisor of *Kenyapithecus wickeri* (see Fig. 4–2). It is slightly less like a shovel-shaped incisor of the genus *Homo* than the corresponding tooth of *Kenyapithecus wickeri*, but we have already seen that in other characters also *Kenyapithecus africanus* is somewhat less evolved in the hominid direction than

the geologically younger species *wickeri* from Fort Ternan. The tooth is large, with a maximum crown diameter of 10 mm and a labial-lingual diameter at the base of the crown of 7·25 mm. It exhibits only a small degree of wear on the crown, and the dentine is not exposed. The lingual surface of the crown is rather concave in longitudinal section and slightly so in transverse section. The cutting edge is straight, and on the median side the lateral edge is almost at right angles at first, and then curves inwards to the neck. The lateral edge, in contrast to the median edge, descends in a smooth curve outwards before turning inwards to the neck of the tooth, at the commencement of the root. In these characters the crown parallels the upper central incisor of *Kenyapithecus wickeri* to a remarkable degree (Fig. 4–1). The root is rather less compressed labio-lingually than in *Kenyapithecus wickeri* and is more nearly trihedral. In this single respect it resembles the roots of *Proconsul* incisors but the labial face of the root, near the neck, is slightly convex from side to side. The measurements of the root at the neck are labio-lingual width 7 mm, bilateral width 7 mm.

The morphology of the lingual aspect of the crown is perhaps the most interesting character, and here the resemblance is wholly with *Kenyapithecus wickeri*, and not at all with *Proconsul nyanzae* or *africanus*. The typical structure of the labial aspect of the upper central incisors of *Proconsul* as described by MacInnes (10) has already been quoted.

There are now six additional *Proconsul nyanzae* upper central incisors available for study in the Nairobi collection. Although they show minor points of variation, they all conform to the same morphological pattern, which has at its most marked feature a convex buttress running centrally from the base of the crown almost to the tip on the lingual face.

(6) Upper right second molar, specimen No. 404. Closely resembling the 1st upper molar of specimen *Sgr.* 52 is an upper right second molar from Songhor. Nevertheless the condition of wear on the occlusal surface and examination of the contact facets on either side indicate that it belongs to another individual. It is probably female. The measurements of this tooth are bucco-lingual diameter 11·5 mm, antero-posterior diameter 10 mm.

(7) Maxilla fragment, specimen No. 748. This maxilla fragment is from the right side. It contains the 3rd and 4th upper premolars, which are beautifully preserved and only very slightly worn. As in the other specimens of *Kenyapithecus africanus*, the width of the 3rd premolar is much greater on the labial than on the lingual aspect so that the tooth viewed from the occlusal aspect is slightly triangular in outline. There are two labial roots to this tooth and, as in the type specimen from Rusinga site *R.* 106, the anterior one is very massive. The contact with the 4th premolar is large and flat. The 4th premolar is wide bucco-lingually and narrow antero-posteriorly, the respective measurements being 11·5 mm and 7 mm. In size and morphology these two teeth conform

closely with the corresponding teeth in the type specimen and probably represent a male.

(8) Maxilla fragment, specimen No. 1377. The maxilla fragment No. 1377 from Songhor is from the left side and, like No. 7, also contains only the two premolars. It is distinctly smaller than No. 7 and the teeth are comparable in size, as well as in morphology, with the corresponding two teeth in *Sgr.* 52 of 1948 (see section 3). It is presumed to be female.

The measurements of these two teeth are as follows:

P^3—Antero-posterior length 8·5 mm; bucco-lingual width 10 mm
P^4—Antero-posterior length 6 mm; bucco-lingual width 10 mm

Besides the specimens listed, which certainly represent *Kenyapithecus africanus*, there are some eight other speciments which, possibly, should also be referred to this genus and species, but the evidence is less certain. When more complete material has been discovered it may be possible to diagnose these specimens further.

(9) Part of a clavicle, specimen No. 604, 1947. Le Gros Clark and Leakey (9) briefly noted a part of a clavicle from Rusinga site *R.* 106, No. 604. It was found close to the type specimen and to specimens 1–5 here, and may belong to the same individual.

Kenyapithecus, SPECIES INDET.

In 1951 Le Gros Clark and Leakey provisionally referred an upper first molar found on Maboko Island to what they then called *Sivapithecus africanus*. The question therefore arises as to whether this specimen represents the genus *Kenyapithecus* and, if so, which species.

The deposits at Maboko Island are no longer regarded to be of the same age as those of Rusinga, Songhor and Koru. They are usally now either referred to the uppermost Miocene, or to the early Pliocene, and are considered to be of roughly the same age as those of the Fort Ternan site.

The molar tooth in question conforms in all respects to molars of *Kenyapithecus* and must certainly be regarded as representing that genus. For the moment it seems better not to assign it to any particular species. It was illustrated in Plate VI, Fig. 44, of Le Gros Clark and Leakey.

During the current study an upper left central incisor from Maboko Island (Fig. 4–1) was discovered. It clearly also represents the genus *Kenyapithecus* and is also, for the moment, treated as species indet. The measurements of this incisor tooth *MB*. 142 (*CMH* 11) are as follows: labio-lingual width at base of crown 7·25 mm; transverse diameter of crown 9·75 mm; anterior height of crown 11·00 mm; internal height 11·5 mm.

DISCUSSION

Status of Kenyapithecus africanus

Although in 1963 Simons supported the view that what Le Gros Clark and Leakey called *Sivapithecus africanus* would prove to stand very close to *Kenyapithecus wickeri*, he abandoned that idea in 1965. He and Pilbeam have now jointly suggested that specimens which they group together as the "Sivapithecus" group of Primates are no more than a sub-genus of *Dryopithecus*. They suggest that there are two distinct species of this "sub-genus": one *Sivapithecus indicus* and the other *Sivapithecus sivalensis*.

I consider that it would be much wiser to retain the generic name *Sivapithecus* for the truly Asiatic members of Dryopithecinae, reserving the generic name *Dryopithecus* for the European forms belonging to this sub-family. This is purely a matter of definition and it is never easy to decide just what should constitute a genus or what a sub-genus. It is, however, important to bear in mind that the differences between *Sivapithecus indicus* and *Sivapithecus sivalensis* appear to be marked, and that what is known as *Sivapithecus sivalensis* is possibly not a *Sivapithecus* at all. There seems to be no doubt that the species *Sivapithecus sivalensis* in India may stand much closer to the genus *Ramapithecus* than it does either to *Sivapithecus indicus* or to the true European *Dryopithecus* specimens, or even to the East African *Proconsul* stock. This can be clearly established by examining the morphology of the molar and premolar teeth.

Simons and Pilbeam have expressed their opinion that the specimen which Le Gros Clark and Leakey originally called *Sivapithecus africanus* is indistinguishable "both generically and specifically" from the Asiatic *Sivapithecus sivalensis*. They also maintain that *Kenyapithecus wickeri* is identical with *Ramapithecus punjabicus*. In the light of the foregoing study, I strongly reject both these opinions as having no adequate foundation in the light of the data which are now available. The following are two of the principal reasons for the rejection of Simons and Pilbeam's views on this matter:

(*a*) The diagnosis of *Ramapithecus* which has been given by Simons and Pilbeam states that, in the genus *Ramapithecus*, the mandible is "shallower" than in *Dryopithecus* and *Australopithecus*. This is certainly not true of *Kenyapithecus africanus*, where we have a mandibular fragment which is 39·5 mm deep at the level of the 4th premolar.

(*b*) They further state that the incisors and canines are "reduced in relation to the cheek teeth when compared with those of *Dryopithecus*." I do not know what incisor teeth of the Asiatic *Ramapithecus* they have examined as a basis for this statement, but it is emphatically not the case when the size of the upper central incisor of *Kenyapithecus wickeri* or of *Kenyapithecus africanus* is compared with the premolars and molars of the same individual.

Table 4–2

	Upper Central Incisors		Upper 4th Premolars		Upper 1st Molars	
	Crown bilateral width	Bucco-lingual width at base of crown	Antero-posterior diameter	Bucco-lingual width	Antero-posterior diameter	Bucco-lingual width
K. wickeri	10	6·5	6	10·25	10·5	10·5
K. africanus	10	7·5	7·5	11·5	10·6	11·3
P. nyanzae	7	8·0	7·0	10·5	10	11·0
P. africanus	6	6·4	7·5	9·7	7·9	9·6

The corresponding modules comparing central incisors with 4th premolars are 8·25–8·125 and 8·625–9·65 in *Kenyapithecus* and 7·5–8·75 and 6·2–8·6 in the *Proconsuls*. Similarly the modules comparing measurements of the first molars are 8·25–10·5 and 8·625–10·9 in *Kenyapithecus* and 7·5–10·5 and 6·2–8·75 in the *Proconsuls*.

Table 4–2 sets out the relative measurements of the upper central incisors, upper 4th premolars and upper 1st molars (in each case in a single individual) from specimens representing *Kenyapithecus wickeri* and *Kenyapithecus africanus* (Hominidae) and *Proconsul nyanzae* and *Proconsul africanus*. Reference to the upper 3rd premolars is omitted because we do not have this tooth in *Kenyapithecus wickeri*. Table 4–2 shows that in *Kenyapithecus* the upper central incisors are not reduced relative to premolars and molars, but are large relative to them when compared with the *Proconsul* group.

While it is readily agreed that *Ramapithecus* should be regarded as a member of the Hominidae—an Asiatic member—the new evidence suggests that is should not—at least at present—be treated as identical to *Kenyapithecus*. Good specimens of the symphyseal region of the mandible of *Ramapithecus* are required, as well as information about its upper incisors, before we can be certain.

It has been proposed in this article that the former "*Sivapithecus africanus*" should now be regarded as a Lower Miocene representative of the genus *Kenyapithecus*, and called *Kenyapithecus africanus*, because it clearly stands close to *Kenyapithecus wickeri*. It has among other things (a) an incipient *fossa canina* of *Homo* type, (b) a very thin mandibular ramus relative to depth, (c) no diastema in the lower dental series, (d) transverse section through the symphysis of hominid type, and (e) an upper central incisor of hominid structure. Until *Sivapithecus sivalensis* can be shown to share all these features, identity cannot be accepted.

Geological age

The geological age of the Rusinga deposits and also of those at Songhor is usually regarded as Lower Miocene. The fauna of even the youngest part of the series is regarded as at least two "faunal stages" older than the fauna of Fort Ternan (11), which is considered to be Upper Miocene. The Fort Ternan fauna includes primitive Bovidae with well developed horn cores, while even in the youngest deposits of Rusinga and Songhor there are no true Bovidae with horns. Ungulates are represented, instead, by several hornless members of the Tragulidae.

While dealing with the question of age, it is necessary to consider briefly certain suggestions that have been made that the fauna of Rusinga, Songhor and Koru, etc., ought not to be regarded as of Lower Miocene age, but as somewhat younger. The most serious argument which has been advanced against a Lower Miocene age for the Rusinga formation has come from Evernden, Curtis and Savage, and this must, therefore, be critically examined. They have, in effect, expressed the view that an age of about 15×10^6 yr, which was obtained by the potassium-argon method of dating on a specimen collected in the *R.* 106 region of Rusinga, near the foot of the Kiahera Hill, should be regarded as the date for the whole Rusinga series. Kiahera Hill consists mainly of rocks which belong to Shackleton's "Kiahera Series"[12] which he believes to represent the oldest part of the Rusinga sequence. Curtis and Evernden's sample certainly came from "near the foot of Kiahera Hill" and it has been assumed that it must, therefore, belong to a low level in the Kiahera series. This is not necessarily the case. There are a number of faults and unconformities in the area, and the Kathwanga series, which Shackleton regarded as possibly the youngest part of the Rusinga rock sequence, rests against Kiahera Hill in several places. The sample that was used to obtain a potassium-argon age of about 15×10^6 yr may perhaps have come from the Kathwanga series.

Of greater significance than this single potassium-argon figure, for the purpose of accurate dating, is the fact that the fauna of even the youngest part of the Rusinga Miocene series (as already stated) differs markedly from the Upper Miocene fauna of Fort Ternan. It differs, in fact, by at least two "faunal stages." If the Fort Ternan deposits are correctly dated by potassium-argon dating, as about 14×10^6 yr, than the age of 15×10^6 yr given for the deposits at Rusinga, near to the base of Kiahera Hill, must be wrong. The possibility cannot, however, be wholly excluded that the uppermost part of the Rusinga sequence, the Kathwanga series, may be of Middle Miocene age, but even this seems to me somewhat unlikely, on the basis of the faunal evidence.

The real question, for the purpose of this present article, is not only the question of the age of the Rusinga Island deposits but also those at Songhor, whence some of the specimens now referred to *Kenyapithecus africanus* have come. At the present time the Songhor deposits are usually regarded to be of the same general age as the main Rusinga series. It must, however, be noted that there are distinct differences in the faunal assemblages between those from Songhor and those from Rusinga. These differences have usually been explained by suggesting that the two sites represent different ecological settings, rather than that they are due to a real difference in geological age because there are certain well defined faunal elements in common. It is, however, possible that the Songhor beds may only represent the upper part of the Rusinga series, and that both may be of Middle Miocene age, leaving the main Rusinga deposits in the Lower Miocene.

Another reason which has been put forward in support of a later age for the Rusinga formation was that advanced by Savage in 1964. The argument runs as follows: *Pliohyrax, Mesopithecus, Sivapithecus*, together with members of the Tenrecidae, occur in the faunal assemblage from Rusinga and these prove that the age is younger than Lower Miocene, because they are creatures which occur in Middle and Upper Miocene beds elsewhere. This view overlooked the following points:

(1) The identification of *Pliohyrax* has been shown by Whitworth (13) to have been incorrect and the material formerly referred to under that name is, in reality, a *Megalohyrax*.

(2) The specimen which MacInnes very tentatively identified in 1943 as "*Mesopithecus*" was a mandible which came from the site on Maboko Island, and not from Rusinga. This site has since been shown by Simpson to be younger than the Rusinga series, and is probably of Pliocene age. In any event the specimen is not a "*Mesopithecus*." This specimen, therefore, has no bearing whatever on the age of the Rusinga deposits.

(3) The specimen which Le Gros Clark and Leakey called "*Sivapithecus*" was only very tentatively placed in that genus, and it has now been shown not to be a *Sivapithecus*.

(4) The presence of Tenrecidae supports rather than contradicts a Lower Miocene age, because this family no longer exists on the African mainland but only on Madagascar Island, which was cut off from Africa during Lower Miocene times, or even earlier.

While the available evidence suggests, therefore, that *Kenyapithecus africanus* carries the Hominidae back to the Lower Miocene, the possibility that it might be of Middle Miocene age cannot be wholly ruled out, but it is emphatically not of Upper Miocene age. It is, therefore, distinctly older than *Ramapithecus* and *Kenyapithecus wickeri*, and is the oldest member of the family Hominidae known at the present time.

One of the results of the discovery of remains of a genus of the Hominidae,

Kenyapithecus africanus, at Songhor and on Rusinga Island, is that it is no longer possible to treat certain of the post-cranial skeletal material which was formerly attributed to *Proconsul* as necessarily belonging to that genus. As Le Gros Clark and Leakey observed on p. 87 of their 1951 report: "A few isolated limb bones attributable to some of the large Homindae have come to light. Although they are from sites which have also yielded teeth and jaws of *Proconsul*, *none of those to be described in this section* was found in such close association with those other remains as to permit any assurance that it belonged to the same individual."

The talus and calcaneum (*CMH* 145 and 146) from Songhor and a very similar talus from Rusinga (*CMH* 147) were assumed to belong to *Proconsul* and referred provisionally to the species *nyanzae* (on account of their size), but it was recognized in 1951, and must be again emphasized here, that these specimens could just as well belong to some other primate.

The incomplete femora and the shaft of the humerus from the Maboko Island site were also assumed to belong to *Proconsul*, but we now know that the Maboko deposits are younger than the main Rusinga series, and are probably of an Upper Miocene or Early Pliocene age. While *Proconsul* (species indet.) is known to persist as late as the Upper Miocene in East Africa (compare with Fort Ternan and Maboko), it is also clear that at least one incisor tooth of *Kenyapithecus* has been recorded from the Maboko beds, while a primate related to *Oreopithecus* is also present at both sites.

A tibia fragment from Rusinga was also described by Le Gros Clark in 1952 (ref. 14). This, too, can no longer be regarded as necessarily representing the genus *Proconsul*.

Two incomplete clavicles were reported by Le Gros Clark and Leakey; one of them was from Maboko Island, the other was found on Rusinga at site *R.* 106, which is the site also yielding the mandible fragment and the type maxilla fragment of *Kenyapithecus africanus*, and an incisor of this species. Of these two clavicle fragments, the specimen from site *R.* 106 is particularly interesting, in view of its close association with material representing *Kenyapithecus africanus*. It has been provisionally referred to that genus. It will be sent to a specialist for study and report.

The work on Rusinga Island and at Songhor was carried out with the aid of grants from the Royal Society (1948), the Boise Fund, and the Wenner-Gren Foundation, while the Fort Ternan site was studied under the auspices of the National Geographic Society. The help of all these bodies is gratefully acknowledged.

REFERENCES

1. LEWIS, G. E., *Amer. J. Sci.,* **27**, 161 (1934).
2. GREGORY, W. K., HELLMAN, M., and LEWIS, G. E., *Fossil Anthropoids of the*

Yale-Cambridge India Expedition of 1935 (Carnegie Institute of Washington, 1938).

3. SIMONS, E. L., *The Phylectic Position of* Ramapithecus. Postilla (Yale, 1961).

4. LEAKEY, L. S. B., *Ann. Mag. Nat. Hist.,* Series 13, **4** (1961).

5. LEAKEY, L. S. B., in Wenner-Gren Symposium on "The Origin of Man" (1965).

6. EVERNDEN, J., SAVAGE, D., CURTIS, A., and JAMES, T., *Amer. J. Sci.,* **262** (1964).

7. SIMONS, E. L., and PILBEAM, D. R., *Folia Primatologica,* **3**, 81 (1965).

8. SIMONS, E. L., *Proc. U.S. Nat. Acad. Sci.* (1964).

9. LE GROS CLARK, W. E. and LEAKEY, L. S. B., *The Miocene Hominoidea of East Africa, Fossil Mammals of Africa* No. **1** (Brit. Mus. Nat. Hist., 1951).

10. MACINNES, D., *J. East African and Uganda Nat. Hist. Soc.,* **17,** Nos. 3 and 4 (November, 1943).

11. SIMPSON, G. G. *Amer. J. Sci.,* **263** (1965).

12. SHACKLETON, R. M., *Quart. J. Geol. Soc. London.* **106** (1951).

13. WHITWORTH, T., *The Miocene Hyracoids of East Africa, Fossil Mammals of Africa,* No. **7** (Brit. Mus. Nat. Hist., 1954).

14. LE GROS CLARK, W. E., *Proc. Zool. Soc. Lond.,* **122**, Part II (August, 1952).

5 · A Classification of Primate Locomotor Behaviour

J. R. Napier
Smithsonian Institution

It might appear from the classification of locomotor patterns (Table 5–1) that primates fall into a number of discrete behavioural categories such as Vertical Clinging, Brachiation and so on, and that field or captivity observations of a particular species would serve to pinpoint their precise category. This is far from the truth. Locomotor differences between groups of primates are quantitative rather than qualitative. The differences lie principally in the degree to which the forelimbs and the hindlimbs are used to jump, swing, climb or run, and the frequency with which each type of behaviour is employed by a particular species in different ecological situations within a single biome.

Any classification within a relatively homogenous group showing continuous variation, inevitably leads to an over-simplification as a result of the need to compromise. Classifications however are necessary to provide a perspective, a basis for discussion and a framework on which further investigations can be built.

BIOMECHANICAL CLASSIFICATIONS

Primates are a fairly uniform group in respect of the anatomy of the limb skeleton, particularly of the hindlimb. The similarity of hindlimb structure is

Reprinted with permission from *A Handbook of Living Primates* by J. R. and P. H. Napier, London, Academic Press Ltd., 1967, where it appeared under the title "Locomotion in Primates."

Table 5-1. Locomotor Categories

Category	Subtype		Activity	Primate Genera
1. Vertical clinging and leaping			Leaping in trees and hopping on the ground.	Avahi, Galago, Hapalemur, Lepilemur, Propithecus, Tarsius, Indri.
2. Quadrupedalism	(i)	Slow climbing type	Cautious climbing—no leaping or branch running.	Arctocebus, Loris, Nycticebus, Perodicticus.
	(ii)	Branch running and walking type	Climbing, springing, branch running and jumping	Aotus, Cacajao, Callicebus, Callimico, Callithrix, Cebuella, Cebus, Cercopithecus, Cheirogaleus, Chiropotes, Lemur, Leontideus, Phaner, Pithecia, Saguinus, Saimiri, Tupaia.
	(iii)	Ground running and walking type.	Climbing, ground running.	Macaca, Mandrillus, Papio, Theropithecus Erythrocebus.
	(iv)	New World semibrachiation type	Arm-swinging with use of prehensile tail; little leaping	Alouatta, Ateles, Brachyteles, Lagothrix
	(v)	Old World semibrachiation type	Arm-swinging and leaping.	Colobus, Nasalis, Presbytis, Pygathrix, Rhinopithecus, Simias.
3. Brachiation	(i)	True brachiation	Gibbon type of brachiation	Hylobates, Symphalangus.
	(ii)	Modified brachiation	Chimpanzee and orang-utan type of brachiation	Gorilla, Pan, Pongo
4. Bipedalism			Human type of walking (Heel-toe striding)	Homo

apparent both osteologically and osteometrically. A series of femora from a wide variety of species show, apart from allometric considerations, a remarkable similarity of form. Measurements of lower limb proportions (the Crural Index for example) show very little variation between taxa or between functional locomotor groups and are therefore of extremely limited value as diagnostic indices. The hindlimbs of primates are primarily supporting structures and their anatomy is in accordance with biomechanical requirements for resisting the compression forces exerted by the ground during walking and running. All primates walk, and therefore they all possess the same basic structural characters. Variation in these characters will depend on how often and under what circumstances they use their hindlimbs for walking and how often for other purposes. For example the hindlimbs of chimpanzees and orangs are adapted for suspension, having a notably free range of movement, particularly at the hip, ankle, mid-tarsal and toe joints. These special prehensile adaptations of the feet permit them to scramble and climb among the slender branches of trees supporting the body weight at very bizarre angles. Chimpanzees and orangs very often use their hindlimbs alone to suspend the body. On the ground however chimpanzees walk quadrupedally and even bipedally, their legs in this situation supporting the body from below. Other primates such as the quadrupedal howlers, spider monkeys and woolly monkeys of South America, also occasionally use their hindlimbs for suspension; so also do galagos and pottos. In fact, it would be true to say that the majority of primates can, and sometimes do, suspend themselves by their feet. Since all primates support themselves on the hindlimbs and many suspend themselves in this manner, a classification of locomotion simply in terms of the supporting and suspending functions of the hindlimbs is unlikely to be very satisfactory.

The situation with regard to the forelimbs is very similar. The limbs are used for both support and suspension, and are therefore subject to both compression and tensile forces. All primates, except the gibbons and man, walk quadrupedally using their forelimbs as props. Equally all primates, with again few exceptions, use the arms to suspend the body from above. The most striking examples of arm-swinging primates are of the gibbons and the siamangs; in certain ecological situations these primates use arm-suspension exclusively. The New World spider and woolly monkeys and some of the African and Asian Colobinae frequently employ arm suspension as a means of locomotion. Other primates such as the guenons and the macaques only occasionally use this method of locomotion. Arm-suspension in the primates therefore, comprises a *spectrum* of activity from the habitual to the occasional and can not be used very meaningfully, as it stands, as a means of classifying locomotion. However it is possible, using the same criteria of suspension and support, to grade the *degree* of these activities as demonstrated by different groups of primates; this involves an arbitrary segmentation of a continuous spectrum of activity as shown in Table 5–2. Such a method can help to dif-

Table 5-2. Analysis of Limb Function in Anthropoidea

	Forelimb		Hindlimb	
	Suspension	Support	Suspension	Support
Brachiators	+++	+(+)	++	+++
Semibrachiators New World	++	++	+	+++
Semibrachiators Old World	+(+)	+++	-	+++
Quadrupeds	(+)	+++	-	+++

Analysis of limb function in Anthropoidea. The plus signs indicate the relative extent to which the limbs are used for suspension and support.

ferentiate limb function in certain groups but it contributes little to classification or primate locomotion as a whole.

A much more meaningful method of quantification of supporting and suspensory activities has been developed by Ashton and Oxnard (1963, 1964a, 1965, and Oxnard, 1963). They have undertaken extensive studies into the stress patterns of primate forelimbs in terms of both muscular and osteological form and proportions, and have subjected their results to appropriate statistical techniques. Theirs is essentially a metrical method and the results provide a quantitative assessment of the whereabouts in the spectrum of forelimb use (from suspension to support) of any particular species, living or fossil.

BEHAVIOURAL CLASSIFICATION

A classification by means of total locomotor pattern (Table 5-1) involves the consideration of both fore- and hindlimbs together; it is in fact concerned with locomotor behaviour of living animals rather than simply with their biomechanical adaptations. In adopting this method of classification, the basic problem—the segmentation of a continuous phenomenon into discrete categories—is by no means solved, but the available categories are wider; such factors as speed of movement, use of tail, body and limb postures and ecological situation can be woven into classification. The principal categories (Table 5-1) can be defined as follows:

1. *Vertical clinging and leaping*: A type of arboreal locomotor behaviour in which the body is held vertically at rest and pressed to the trunk or main

branch of a tree; movement from place to place is effected by a leap or jump from one vertical support to another. The forelimbs take no part in propelling the body during leaping. Vertical clinging and leaping primates usually hop bipedally when moving rapidly on the ground, but assume a quadrupedal gait when moving slowly.

2. *Quadrupedalism:* A type of locomotion which can take place on the ground or in the trees; its principal component is four-legged walking or running. In an arboreal situation the hands and feet may be used, in a prehensile fashion, to provide stability. The movements of springing, jumping and leaping are associated with this mode of locomotion. Quadrupedalism also involves the vertical movement of climbing, using all four extremities. Movement may be repid as in galloping on the ground or it may be cautious and slow. Quadrupedal primates in certain situations show a variable amount of arm-swinging with or without the additional use of a prehensile tail.

Subtypes of Quadrupedalism Category

i. *Slow climbing.* A type of quadrupedal locomotion in which either three or four of the extremities are applied to the branch at any given moment. Movement is always slow and cautious. The limbs may act to suspend the body or to support it.

ii. *Branch running and walking.* Generalised quadrupedal locomotion in which running or walking in trees usually involves prehensile grasp with forelimbs or hindlimbs or both. The hand is usually plantigrade. Climbing, jumping or leaping in a dog-like fashion is also seen.

iii. *Ground running and walking.* running and walking. Generalised quadrupedal locomotion in which running or walking on the ground does not usually involve prehensile grasp of limbs. The hands usually digitigrade in posture. Branch walking, frequently with a digitigrade hand posture, is seen, and also climbing and dog-like leaping.

iv. *New World semibrachiation.* A type of arboreal locomotion in which the forelimbs are used extended above the head to suspend the body or to propel it through space. The forelimbs may be used alone or in association with the hindlimbs and the prehensile tail. Quadrupedal walking and running constitute a major part of the habit. Leaping is uncommon.

v. *Old World semibrachiation.* Differing from the New World type mainly in the extent to which leaping is employed. During leaping the arms reach out ahead of the body to grasp a handhold or to check momentum. Hand over hand progression is seldom seen.

3. *Brachiation.* A form of locomotion in which the typical component is arm-swinging by which means the body suspended from above, is propelled through space. The hindlimbs are used to support the body in trees or on the ground either in the erect or in the quadrupedal position. In some brachiating primates the hindlimbs may be used to suspend the body.

Subtypes of Brachiation Category

i. *True Brachiation,* A form of arboreal locomotion in which the forelimbs alone are used fully extended above the head to suspend or to propel the body through space by means of hand over hand progess. Arm-swinging may be used to provide momentum to cross considerably wide gaps between forest trees. Bipedal walking on branches and bipedal walking on ground constitute part of the total pattern.

ii. *Modified Brachiation.* A form of arboreal locomotion in which the forelimbs extended above the head play a major role in suspending the body or propelling it through space. The hindlimbs contribute to the pattern to a greater lesser extent, being used to provide partial support for the body from below. Hindlimbs may also be used to suspend the body from above. On the ground quadrupedal walking, the weight of the forebody being taken on the knuckles or bunched fists, is commonly seen; bipedalism is also seen.

4. *Bipedalism.* A form of locomotion in which the body is habitually supported on the hindlimbs which move alternately to propel it through space. The quintessence of the movement is a striding, heel-toe gait. The forelimbs are only occasionally used to suspend the body. Quadrupedalism in bipedal primates is seldom employed except in infancy.

All four locomotor categories are serially linked by some facet of locomotor pattern common to each successive pair. Vertical clingers when moving slowly on the ground are quadrupedal. Quadrupeds may suspend themselves by the arms alone, in the manner of brachiating primates. Brachiating primates when on the ground and in the trees adopt bipedalism for short distances. Thus, the sequence Vertical Clinging–Quadrupedalism–Brachiation–Bipedalism forms a continuum of locomotor activity which only arbitrarily can be segmented into discrete categories. In terms of living primates a number of transitional forms are found which it is difficult to assign to a particular group. *Lemur catta* for instance is generally regarded as quadrupedal but field and captivity studies (Napier and Walker, 1967a and 1967b) indicate that a considerable element of vertical clinging and leaping behaviour figures in its repertoire. Spider and woolly monkeys though quadrupedal frequently swing by their arms for considerable distances as Erikson (1963) has pointed out. Ashton *et al.* (1965) have shown that, in the morphological characters of the shoulder girdle, *Ateles* occupies an equivocal New World position intermediate between Brachiation and Semibrachiation. Among the brachiating primates, the gibbons adopt a bipedal gait when on the ground. There are many other examples of primates which are intermediate in their locomotor patterns between one category and another. The significance of this state of affairs however is more easily understood if the sequence Vertical Clinging to Brachiation noted above is looked upon as a phylogenetic succession.

One would need to suppose that Vertical Clinging constituted the principal locomotor pattern of the Eocene primate stock from which the lemurs, monkeys and apes evolved. A somewhat generalised vertical clinger having the characteristic short arms and long legs but possibly lacking the extreme specialisation of *Tarsius* then evolved into a quadrupedal form simply by a relative increase in the length of the forelimb and a relative decrease in the length of the hindlimb. These changes would give rise to an animal something like the modern genus *Lemur* whose forelimbs are still rather short and hindlimbs rather long relative to trunk length. Further adaptive change in relative limb-length would produce a more generalised quadrupedal morphology such as is seen in the Asian langurs and the African *Colobus* monkeys. These Old World monkeys are termed semibrachiators, a subtype of the Quadrupedalism category; their locomotion involves a major element of leaping and a minor element of arm-swinging. As has been suggested elsewhere (Napier and Davis, 1959; Napier, 1963), modern semibrachiators may represent a stage in primate locomotor phylogeny when brachiation in its fullest expression was evolving. In the palaentological record it has been suggested (Napier and Davis, 1959) that *Proconsul africanus* was the representative of this stage.

The derivation of bipedalism is somewhat equivocal. There appear to be two possibilities. Firstly that bipedalism evolved from quadrupedalism; and secondly that it evolved out of an early stage of brachiation. Most authorities now agree that human bipedal gait could not have been derived from fully evolved brachiation as Keith (1923) and many others at one time believed. The two alternatives noted above are not really alternatives at all. As has been already mentioned, quadrupedalism and brachiation are not wholly discrete categories. The quadrupedalism sub-type—semibrachiation—contains elements of both categories. Washburn (1950) stated "Spider monkeys brachiate [*sic*]. . . . They also move in a quadrupedal fashion . . . . The combination of brachiation and quadrupedal locomotion . . . shows how the ape-type of locomotion may have arisen . . . " Straus (1949) stated that man's catarrhine ancestors "probably indulged in some swinging by the arms and in that sense might be regarded as primitive brachiators."

Whether in fact bipedalism evolved out of specialised quadrupedalism or unspecialised brachiation is entirely unimportant inasmuch as these two locomotor categories constitute a continuum of morphological and behavioural variation.

Locomotion among living primates must be viewed in the light of phylogeny in order to understand the significance of its continuous nature.

Bridging forms that do not comfortably sit in one category or another are the modern descendants of ancestral primates whose locomotor evolution came to a halt at a point best suited to their ecological needs; it is not surprising that this halt should often lie *between* major categories.

Field studies of primates in their natural habitats very often reveal the variety of their locomotor habits. Langurs for instance are known to run, walk, leap, jump, hop and even swing by their arms (Ripley 1967). Baboons run, walk, jump and climb. Chimpanzees run and walk bipedally, climb, hop and brachiate. In the face of such a plethora of activities, all of which are adaptive for their particular way of life, it is difficult purely on behavioural grounds to place them in a single, meaningful category. It is important to assess their behaviour as far as it is possible in the light of their past evolution, a procedure which naturally involves a consideration of morphology. The question that needs to be asked is what element within the broad range of the locomotor potentialities of any one species has been of major significance in their past history as reflected in the palaeontology of the group and in the present morphology of the species? In other words, on what particular aspect of their locomotion has natural selection operated?

While locomotor categories are expressed here in behavioural terms, their basis is essentially morphological. In order to recognize the brachiating affinities of the gorilla amid its secondary specialisations for ground life, for instance, recourse to morphology must be made as there is little in its behaviour which would support such a classification.

REFERENCES

Ashton, E. H., and C. E. Oxnard, 1963, The musculature of the primate shoulder. *Trans. zool. Soc. Lond.* **29**:553–650.

——, and ——, 1964a, Functional adaptations in the primate shoulder. *Proc. zool. Soc. Lond.* **142**:49–66.

——, and ——, 1964b, Locomotor patterns in primates. *Proc. zool. Soc. Lond.* **142**:1–28.

Erikson, G. E., 1963, Brachiation in New World monkeys and in anthropoid apes. *Symp. zool. Soc. Lond.* **10**:135–164.

Hill, W. C. Osman, 1956, Behaviour and adaptations of the Primates. *Proc. R. Soc. Edinb.* B **66**:94–110.

Napier, J. R., 1963, Brachiation and orachiators. *Symp. zool. Soc. Lond.* **10**:183–195.

——, and P. R. Davis, 1959, The fore-limb skeleton and associated remains of *Proconsul africanus*. London, *British Museum (Natural History) Fossil Mammals of Africa, No. 16*.

——, and A. C. Walker, 1967a, Vertical clinging and leaping, a newly recognised category of locomotor behaviour among primates. *Folia Primat.* **6**:180–203.

——, and ——, 1967b, Vertical clinging and leaping in living and fossil primates.

In *Progress in Primatology*, Ed. D. Starck, R. Schneider, H.-J. Kuhn. (Gustav Fischer Verlag, Stuttgart).

OXNARD, C. E., 1963, Locomotor adaptations in the primate fore-limb. *Symp. zool. Soc. Lond.* **10**:165–182.

PRIEMEL, G., 1937, Die platyrrhinen Affen als Bewegungstypen unter besonderer Berücksichtigung de Extremformen *Callicebus* und *Ateles*. *Z. Morph. Ökol. Tiere.* **33**:1–52.

REYNOLDS, VERNON, and FRANCES REYNOLDS, 1965, Chimpanzees of the Budongo Forest. In *Primate Behaviour*, Ed. I. De Vore. (Holt, Rinehart and Winston, Inc., New York).

RIPLEY, S., 1967, The leaping of langurs. *Am. J. Phys. Anthrop.* **26**:149–170.

STRAUS, W. L., 1949, Riddle of man's ancestry. *Q. Rev. Biol.* **24**:200–223.

WASHBURN, S. L., 1950, Thoracic viscera of the gorilla. In *Anatomy of the Gorilla*, Ed. W. K. Gregory. (Columbia University Press, New York).

6 · The Origin of the Hominids: An Immunological Approach

Vincent M. Sarich

University of California, Berkeley

Who our closest living relatives might be and the nature of our relationship to them have been subjects of controversy for well over a hundred years (Huxley 1863). The absence of a definitive fossil record has forced students of the

Research supported in part by United States Public Health Service Fellowship No. 1–FI–GM–30, 454–01 to the author, and National Science Foundation Grant No. GB–3839 and GB–6420 to Allan C. Wilson.

The success of this study has been greatly aided by the cooperation of a number of individuals and institutions who made available such serum samples as they had. The generosity of these responses greatly gratified me, for it indicates a community of interest in a set of problems—an interest which places them that much closer to solution. To all of these contributors I express my special gratitude: Dr. Morris Goodman, Wayne State University; Drs. Robert W. Cooper and Lester W. Nelson, San Diego Zoological Society; Dr. Michael Crawford, University of Pittsburgh; Dr. T. Hayashida, University of California Medical Center, San Francisco; Dr. Robert Hummer, Southwest Foundation for Research and Education; the Delta Regional Primate Center, and the Davis National Primate Center.

This article is an abridged and slightly altered version of an unpublished doctoral dissertation presented to the University of California, Berkeley, June 1967. I would like to thank Dr. Allan C. Wilson in particular for making his laboratory facilities available, demonstrating many of the investigative approaches used, supplying financial support for the study, and acting as a friend and critic throughout. I also thank Dr. S. L. Washburn for my introduction to anthropology, valued advice and guidance throughout, financial support, and the major insights into the nature of primate evolution which only he could provide. Valuable technical assistance has been provided by Linda Ferguson, Jule Griebrok, and Karen Reinheimer.

problem to evaluate the phylogenetic significance of morphological and behavioral characters in the living species. These evaluations have led to widely varying estimates of the time of origin of the hominid line. Whereas Washburn placed this time at no more than 2 to 4 million years ago (1965:10), Schultz has suggested that a date in the earliest Miocene would be more appropriate (1966:24). This range of dates only samples two of the more reasonable views of primate evolution—a more complete survey of proposed dates would bear out the statement made by Simpson (1945:17): "The student of classification is likely to feel that almost all arrangements for which there is any reason, and a good many for which there is none, have been proposed."

I think it can be agreed that no consensus on this question is likely in the near future on the basis of the evidence previously used. What is necessary is the application of information from new sources to the solution of this long outstanding problem.

The objective is an understanding of the origin and evolution of the hominid line. In order to begin, data are required from which clear conclusions may be drawn as to the phyletic relationships among the various groups under consideration. Only when this basic task is accomplished can the nature of the evolutionary process that shaped the development of the hominid line be properly appreciated within a realistic network of relationships.

The first step in the construction of the network is the choice of a standard of measurement. The most important part of the task of measuring the distances that separate species is the selection of what is to be measured. What must be selected is a constellation of characters whose properties and change reflect that of the species in both time and space. In other words, these characters must retain within themselves the essence and record of the evolutionary process; they must be continuously variable within a framework of continuous change.

The first hint that comparative molecular data might prove useful in this regard came with the pioneering work of Nuttall more than sixty years ago. At that time it was beginning to be appreciated that biochemically similar and functionally equivalent compounds could be demonstrated to be different in different species. Once such differences had been shown it was only a short step for Nuttall to consider them as a source of phyletic or taxonomic information. His comparative method was immunological and he noted in 1902 after completing a series of tests:

I do not wish these numbers to be taken as final, nevertheless they show the essential correctness of the previous crude results. To obtain a constant it will be necessary to make repeated tests with the blood of each species with different dilutions and different proportions of antiserum. I am inclined to believe that with care we shall perhaps be able to "measure species" with this method, for it appears that there are measurable differences in the reactions obtained with related blood, in other words, determine degrees of relationship which we may be able to formulate (quoted in Boyden 1951:2).

As Nuttall perceived so long ago, the basic problem is not so much in demonstrating molecular differences as in measuring them. Today the ideal datum for such a measurement is usually considered to be the number of amino acid residues by which the two molecules differ in primary structure. However, a number of practical and theoretical difficulties stand in the way of such determinations. The major problem is that the elucidation of a primary structure is very time-consuming and still something of an art. In addition, the informational value of a biological macromolecule increases at least in direct proportion to its size since molecular evolution is generally slow; larger molecules more rapidly accumulate absolute differences. Yet the longest polypeptide chain sequenced up to the present contains only 243 amino acids. This problem rather severely limits the usefulness of primary structure comparisons for probing any but the most distant relationships and has led to the search for more rapidly applied comparative methods.

This means that differences at higher structural levels must be measured; that is, the properties of the intact molecule must be studied. This requirement logically leads us back to the original approach of Nuttall—an immunological one. Immunological comparisons of related molecules have the important advantages of speed and sensitivity, but because a second and imperfectly understood biological system is being used as the detector and measurer of differences, it is necessary to demonstrate the relationship between real and measured differences. The major effort in the application of any new methods to the solution of old problems necessarily lies in the validation of the approach and methods used.

The rationale of applying an immunochemical study to the resolution of phylogenetic questions is that biological macromolecules, such as serum albumin, evolve over time just as do the species of which they are a part. Thus we may speak of the common ancestor of, for example, human and chimpanzee serum albumin molecules, this ancestral molecule being present in the common ancestor of man and chimpanzee. From the time that the human and chimpanzee lineages separated, their albumins, like the organisms themselves, have been evolving independently under what we may assume to have been differing selection pressures until today they are recognizably different but homologously related molecules. Such homologies are recognized by immunological procedures, for antibodies made against human serum albumin (HSA) will react not only with HSA, but also with similar structural features in chimpanzee serum albumin. The measure of the degree of this structural similarity is then the magnitude of their immunological cross-reactivity.

The technique used to measure the degree of this cross-reaction was micro-complement fixation (MC'F). Complement is a functional unit composed of a sequentially acting series of compounds present in vertebrate sera which have the property of binding (fixing) antigen-antibody lattices. Such a lattice is formed when cross-linking occurs; that is, complement is not fixed by antigen-antibody complexes where the antigen is monovalent (contains only one antigenic site). The degree of fixation is dependent on the size of the lattice and so is proportional to the strength of the antigen-antibody reaction. This reaction, or complement fixation, is used at dilutions where precipitation does not occur and is assayed by the use of a second reaction. The complement unfixed by the lattice can then lyse properly sensitized red cells which are added after the reaction mixture has been incubated for a specified length of time. The amount of hemoglobin released is determined spectrophotometrically and is inversely proportional to the degree of the antigen-antibody reaction; that is, the more fixation occurring the less the amount of complement left free for lysis. The application of this technique to the study of primate albumins and its advantages have already been discussed (Sarich and Wilson 1966).

The availability of a sensitive and economical immunological tool makes possible the reliable measurement of differences; the next problem is the selection of the molecule whose evolutionary changes are to be studied. A molecule suitable for the application of immunochemical data to the resolution of phylogenetic problems is not readily found. Such a molecule should show minimal polymorphism at the lowest taxonomic levels that are to be differentiated. A situation where intraspecific variability is comparable to interspecific variability (allelic evolution is one such) is clearly to be avoided. The more complex situation, where a number of homologously related molecules of similar function are present in a single species (for example, the hemoglobins), is of course even more of a problem. Albumin, in contrast, seems to be a single polypeptide chain coded at a single locus with no evidence of multiple forms or ontogenetic variation (Putnam 1965). As one might expect, however, polymorphism must exist in an evolving molecule within a species. Thus albumin polymorphism exists among the primates in *Homo sapiens* (Melartin and Blumberg 1966), *Papio anubis* (Kitchin, Barnicot, and Jolly 1967), and *Aotus trivirgatus* (Sarich, unpublished observations).

The molecule should be well defined and readily characterized. Albumin is perhaps the best studied large nonenzyme protein known and has been used in a tremendous variety of research procedures. It is relatively readily purified and its properties are well known. It also appears to contain no other potentially antigenic components such as carbohydrates and lipids (Putnam 1965).

The molecule should be antigenic and large enough to provide a statistically reliable sample of differences between the forms to be studied. Albumin, with almost 600 residues, is among the largest polypeptide chains known. Except for myosin, all well-characterized larger proteins seem to have subunit structure (Klotz 1967).

The molecule should evolve rapidly enough so that differences accumulate at a useful rate. It has been known for many years that albumin differences among certain closely related forms could be demonstrated immunologically; *e.g., Homo—Pan* (Boyden 1958) and *Ovis—Capra* (Marable and Glenn 1965).

These considerations, along with the purely practical matter of the ready availability of serum or plasma, made the choice of albumin a relatively simple one at the beginning of the research. The degree of suitability and the relative freedom from experimental difficulties that this choice insured was not fully appreciated at that time. In retrospect, and with the advantage of two years of experience in this field, it appears that no better choice could be made today.

The albumins used in this study, with two exceptions (*Presbytis* and *Galago*), were purified from the serum of a single individual of each species. The experimental details have already been discussed (Sarich and Wilson 1966). The following primate serum albumins have been purified for immunization purposes:

> HOMINOIDEA: *Homo sapiens, Pan troglodytes, Hylo-bates lar*
> CERCOPITHECOIDEA: *Macaca mulatta, Papio papio, Cercocebus galeritus, Cercopi-thecus aethiops, Presbytis entellus*
> CEBOIDEA: *Cebus capucinus, Ateles geoffroyi, Cacajao rubicundus, Aotus trivirgatus, Saguinus oedipus*
> PROSIMII: *Nycticebus coucang, Galago crassicaudatus*

Antisera were prepared in rabbits and characterized as discussed in the paper already referred to. Immunoelectrophoresis demonstrated the presence of antibodies to other serum components besides albumin. However, these impurities did not affect the nature of the micro-complement fixation (MC'F) reaction as they were too dilute to contribute to complement fixation when the concentration of antiserum was in the correct range for the albumin antialbumin reaction. Thus the MC'F procedure effectively purifies slightly impure systems and helps insure that only a single molecular species is being compared.

The measurement of cross-reactions with heterologous species is shown in Fig. 6–1., Antiserum 6_F (rabbit 6, final bleeding) was reacted with the serum albumins of *Homo, Pan, Macaca,* and *Cebus*, which form a series of decreasing phylogenetic relationship to man. At an antiserum concentration of 1:11000 (Fig. 6–1a) chimpanzee serum albumin gave a peak 67 percent as high as that given by the homologous human serum albumin (HSA), but rhesus albumin gave no reaction at all. To obtain a reaction with rhesus albumin the antiserum concentration had to be raised by a factor of approximately 2.5 (Fig. 6–1b), and *Cebus* serum albumin did not give a MC'F peak comparable to the homologous one until the concentration of antiserum was raised by a factor of 4.5

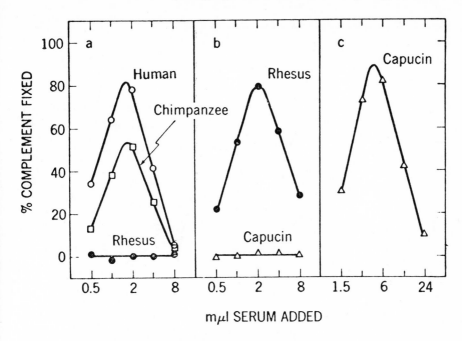

Fig. 6–1. The reactivity of antiserum 6_F to human serum albumin with human, chimpanzee, rhesus, and capucin albumins. The antiserum concentrations were (a) 1:11000, (b) 1:4600, (c) 1:2500. It should be noted that the shapes of the curves given by the nonhomologous albumins are essentially identical to that given by HSA when the antiserum concentration is adjusted appropriately. From Sarich and Wilson (1966:1564).

(Fig. 6–1c). It should be noted that the peak of the homologous curve was obtained upon the addition of only 1.8×10^{-9} ml of human serum, which corresponds to approximately 72 picograms of albumin, at an antiserum concentration of 1:11000. Even when weaker antisera are used and more distant cross-reactions are measured, it is possible to set up thousands of cross-reactions with an antiserum derived from a single bleeding of a single rabbit. This insures comparability of data from day to day or even year to year and in addition conserves rare serum samples.

The sharp dependence of MC′F reactions on antiserum concentration is shown in (Fig. 6–2). For any one species of serum albumin, the peak height of the complement fixation curve bears a linear relationship to the log of the antiserum concentration over a range of 20 percent to 90 percent fixation. The slope of the line is identical for human, rhesus, and capucin albumins. This slope does vary somewhat when other antigen-antibody systems are studied and appears to bear some relationship to the size of the subunits in the antigen being studied (Sarich, Wilson, and Arnheim, unpublished observations).

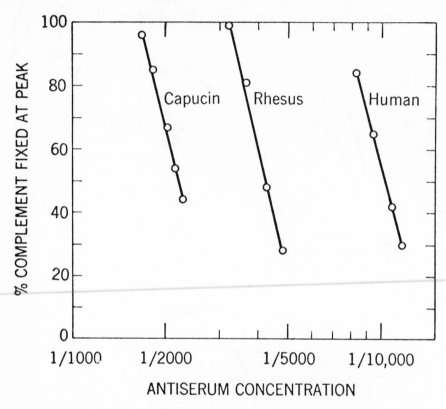

Fig. 6-2. The degree of complement fixation as a function of antiserum concentration for three different primate albumins. The antiserum was 6_F and the antigens were the human, rhesus, and capucin albumins present in the respective sera. Each point represents the peak height of a C'F curve for a particular antiserum concentration. The slopes of the lines are identical and appear to be characteristic for serum albumin. Slopes for other antigen-antibody systems vary somewhat (Sarich, Wilson, and Arnheim, unpublished observations). From Sarich and Wilson (1966:1564).

The fact that the slopes are alike provides a basis for measuring the immunological distances between different species of albumin. Although many immunological methods employ a fixed antiserum concentration and express cross-reactions as a percentage of the homologous reaction, it is obvious that this is not appropriate for the MC'F method. For example, it was possible to demonstrate the heterologous rhesus reaction only when the antiserum concentration was increased. As a measure of cross-reactivity we use the factor by which the antiserum concentration must be raised in order for a particular albumin to give a degree of complement fixation equal to that given by the homologous one (human albumin in this case). This number is called the index of dissimilarity (Wilson *et al.* 1964) or immunological distance (ID). The ID is independent of the actual peak heights at which the comparison is made because the slopes shown in (Fig. 6–2) are identical. With 6 F the ID's are: human, 1.0 (by definition); *Pan*, 1.17; *Macaca*, 2.38; and *Cebus*, 4.64. The experimental error to which these measurements are subject is no more than ±2 percent and the measurement is reproducible within these limits over long periods of time (up to 18 months in these cases).

Though the preliminary work was done with unpooled antisera and showed antiserum variation to be a much more minor problem than the literature and general discussion would have led one to believe would be the case, it was decided to use antiserum pools for maximum reliability. The pools were made by mixing the individual antisera in reciprocal proportion to their MC'F titers (the MC'F titer of an antiserum is defined as that concentration required to fix 75 percent of the available complement at the peak of the C'F curve for the reaction with the homologous antigen). It was hoped in this way to sample the different antibody populations of the various antisera and so obtain a more comprehensive view of the albumin surface. In other words, even though one would expect no single rabbit to make antibodies against all the antigenic sites on the albumin molecule, it is probable that each rabbit "sees" a somewhat different proportion of that molecule. The fact that the titer of the pool is always that expected on the assumption that each antiserum is contributing equal amounts of complement-fixing antibody to the pool indicates that this assumption is probably valid.

A few MC'F indices have already been mentioned—a more complete list based on data obtained with an antiserum pool directed to human serum albumin is given in Table 6–1. Every ape albumin reacted strongly with the pooled antisera, the indices ranging from 1.09 to 1.28. As noted by other authors, the albumins of the African apes react more strongly than those of the Asiatic ones, nevertheless, all the hominoid indices are far lower than those given by the Old World monkeys. These gave indices ranging from 2.23 to 2.65. The New World monkeys gave indices ranging from 2.7 (*Aotus*) to 5.0 and the prosimians 8.6 to 18. Nonprimate mammals gave indices greater than 25. In summary, then, these data are in qualitative agreement with the more classic comparative data that place the apes, Old World monkeys, New World monkeys, and prosimians in taxa which form a series of decreasing genetic relationship to man.

The very close relationship existing among all hominoid albumins again brings sharply into focus the question posed in the beginning of this article— the nature of man's relationship to his primate relatives. The data are in agreement with other recent immunological work (Goodman 1961; 1962; 1963; 1967) as well as with the original work of Nuttall. It is now proper to ask, and to attempt to answer, the question: What does all this mean in evolutionary terms?

Table 6–1. Reactivity in the MC′F Procedure of Sera from Various Species with a Pool of Three Antisera Directed To HSA[a]

Species	Index of Dissimilarity
Hominoidea (man and apes)	
Homo sapiens [b]	1.0
Pan troglodytes	1.14
Gorilla gorilla	1.09
Pongo pygmaeus	1.22
Hylobates lar	1.28
Symphalangus syndactylus	1.30
Cercopithecoidea (Old World monkeys)	
Macaca mulatta	2.23
Papio papio	2.44
Cercocebus galeritus	2.30
Cercopithecus aethiops	2.59
Colobus polykomos	2.52
Presbytis entellus	2.65
Ceboidea (New World monkeys)	
Aotus trivirgatus	2.7
Pithecia monachus	3.9
Callimico goeldii	4.1
Callicebus cupreus	4.2
Ateles geoffroyi	4.2
Cacajao rubicundus	4.3
Lagothrix humboldti	4.5
Saguinus oedipus	4.5
Alouatta caraya	4.5
Saimiri sciurea	4.5
Cebus capucinus	5.0
Prosimii (Prosimians)	
Galago crassicaudatus	8.6
Nycticebus coucang	11.2
Tarsius spectrum	11.3
Tupaia glis [c]	11.0
Lemur fulvus	18
Nonprimates	
Bos taurus	32
Sus scrofa	>35

a. The antiserum mixture was made by mixing the three individual antisera in reciprocal proportion to their MC′F titers; that is, 8.8 parts of pool II (titer = 1/5000) plus 6.3 parts of 5₄ (titer = 1/7000) plus 4.0 parts of 6_F (titer = 1/11000). Pool II was generously donated by Hafleigh and Williams (1966).

b. G. Sensabaugh has tested serum samples from 20 individuals of diverse human groups and found no variation in I.D.

c. This index was given as 7.6 in a previous publication (Sarich and Wilson, 1966). A repeat of that experiment indicates that an error was made at that time and thus removes the only I.D. given by a pool that significantly deviated from a logarithmic mean of values given by the individual antisera. The reason for the original error is not clear at this time.

There has been a tendency to view the phylogenetic significance of comparative molecular data with a certain reserve (for example, Simpson 1964; Buettner-Janusch and Hill 1965). Indeed, these data are open to varying interpretations as the lack of other direct evidence makes possible at least three explanations for the close structural similarity of ape and human albumins:

(a) Albumin evolution has been slow in the various ape and human lineages, or both, since their separation. Both Goodman and Hafleigh and Williams have tended to favor this explanation.

(b) We and the other apes share a more recent common ancestry than is generally supposed. Albumin evolution has proceeded at a normal rate for primates and the immunological distances that separate them are an accurate reflection of the corresponding phyletic distances. This is the view favored here.

(c) Molecular parallelism in albumin evolution has occurred, independent albumin lineages evolving immunologically similar amino acid sequences, thus exaggerating their phyletic closeness. This possibility is at once the least likely and the most difficult to disprove of the three.

To effectively choose among these hypotheses requires first a consideration of evolutionary rates among primate albumins.

RATES OF ALBUMIN EVOLUTION

The approach that is used in this investigation to the question of rates may be illustrated with reference to Fig. 6–3. Let us suppose that the structure of a specific protein is compared in three species: man, chimpanzee, and rhesus monkey. Let us also suppose that man and the chimpanzee are known from nonmolecular evidence to have a more recent common ancestor (Y) than that which gave rise to all three species (X). Thus the evolutionary lineages leading to man and chimpanzee separated from the lineage leading to rhesus at the same time and shared a period of common ancestry (from X to Y) after this separation. We then ask whether the protein under consideration has changed as much in the human lineage as in the chimpanzee lineage.

Immunologically we answer this question by preparing antisera to the purified proteins of the three species and then performing cross-reaction experiments. First, antibodies to the rhesus protein are tested for reactivity with those of chimpanzee or man. Alternatively, antibodies to the chimpanzee protein and to the human protein are reacted with the corresponding rhesus protein. If the human-rhesus cross-reaction is weaker than the chimpanzee-rhesus cross-reaction, we infer that more evolutionary change has occurred in the human lineage than in the chimpanzee lineage since the time of separation of the two.

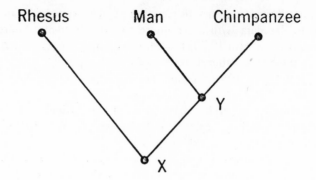

Fig. 6–3. A phylogeny for man, chimpanzee, and rhesus
monkey. The common ancestral forms are indicated by X
and Y.

Thus it is necessary to consider first the evolutionary history of the various primate albumin alineages. The phyletic framework upon which our approach is based follows a consensus based on the views of most of the workers who have studied primate relationships (Simpson 1962; Fieldler 1955) and is illustrated in Fig. 6–4. It is thought that certain groups of primate species stand in monophyletic relation to others; that is, they shared a period of common ancestry after the other groups had become separate lineages. For example, the Anthropoidea (apes, man, New and Old World monkeys) shared a period of common ancestry (from X to Y in Fig. 6–4) after the ancestors of the modern prosimians had become a separate group. Similarly, the Catarrhini (apes, man, Old World monkeys) shared a period of common ancestry (from Y to Z in Fig. 6–4) after the ancestors of the Ceboidea (New World monkeys) had become isolated, and the Hominoidea (apes and man) shared a period of common ancestry after the separation of the ancestral Cercopithecoidea (Old World monkeys). These cases of probable monophyly provide a basis for comparing the degrees of change shown along the various primate albumin lineages.

To begin the comparison of these degrees of change, three antiserum pools directed against the albumins of *Homo*, *Macaca*, and *Cebus* were used to measure the immunological distances to a set of prosimian albumins.

The monophyly of the Anthropoidea relative to the Prosimii means that the time of divergence of every anthropoid lineage from that leading to any specific modern prosimian is identical. The data in Table 6–2 show that the albumin of any specific prosimian is about as different from human albumin as it is from that of an Old World monkey (*Macaca*) or a New World monkey (*Cebus*). It would appear then that the three anthropoid lineages represented here have experienced comparable degrees of albumin evolution since their separation from the prosimians and from each other. It should also not be overlooked that all three prosimian lines tested give indices very similar to each

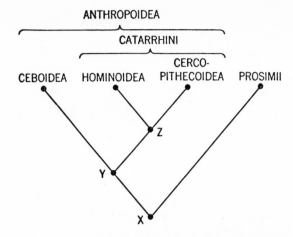

Fig. 6–4. A working model of primate phylogeny based on a general consensus of taxonomists who have used nonmolecular evidence. The distances between the indicated points of common ancestry are not meant to indicate a quantitative scale of relationships in either temporal or morphological terms.

other. This result suggests that the albumins of *Galago, Tarsius,* and *Nycticebus* have also undergone similar degrees of evolution since their separation from each other.

These conclusions were checked in greater detail by measuring the immunological distances between the albumins of more closely related species. Table 6–3 represents the results of experiments in which eleven ceboid species were reacted with antisera prepared against five catarrhine albumins. The mean

Table 6–2. Reactivity of Prosimian Albumins with Antisera Directed to Anthropoid Albumins

Species of Albumin	*Index of Dissimilarity*		
	Antiserum to *Homo*[a]	Antiserum to *Macaca*[b]	Antiserum to *Cebus*[c]
Galago crassicaudatus	8.6	8.7	10.9
Nycticebus coucang	11.2	11.5	11.2
Tarsius spectrum	11.3	9.8	13.1

a. As in Table 6–1, footnote a.
b. A pool of three antisera to *Macaca mulatta* albumin.
c. A pool of three antisera to *Cebus capucinus* albumin.

Table 6–3. Reactivity of Ceboid Albumins with Antisera Directed to Catarrhine
Albumins

Antiserum directed to albumin of	Mean I.D. for eleven ceboid[a] albumins
Homo sapiens[b]	4.2
Pan troglodytes[c]	3.9
Macaca mulatta[d]	3.8
Cercopithecus aethiops[e]	3.6
Presbytis entellus[f]	4.2

a. The eleven ceboid species are listed in Table 6–4. The serum albumin of each was reacted with each of the five antiserum pools.
b. As in Table 6–1, footnote a.
c. A pool of four antisera to *Pan* albumin.
d. As in Table 6–2, footnote b.
e. A pool of three antisera to *Cercopithecus* albumin.
f. A pool of three antisera to *Presbytis* albumin.

immunological distance (ID) for the eleven ceboid albumins is close to 4 for each antiserum, indicating that the albumins of the Hominoidea (here represented by *Homo* and *Pan*) have changed to much the same degree as those of the Cercopithecoidea (*Macaca, Cercopithecus, Presbytis*) since they last shared a common ancestor (Z in Fig. 6–4).

The eleven New World monkey species tested (representing all ceboid subfamilies) form another test case, the various lineages represented by these eleven species having probably been distinct for very long periods of time. This conclusion is supported by the evidence of the fossil record (Olson 1964); the taxonomy, which has seven subfamilies with only one to three genera per subfamily (Fiedler 1955); and the immunological data of Goodman (1967). In addition, my own data show that intergeneric I.D.'s among the various ceboids are in the range 2.3± 0.3 (except for *Ateles-Lagothrix* and *Cacajao-Pithecia*). Thus the various ceboid lineages are about as distinct from one another as are the Cercopithecoidea from the Hominoidea (see Tables 6–5 and 6–6).

Table 6–4 lists the mean I.D.'s for each ceboid albumin given by the five antisera to catarrhine albumins. These range from 2.7 to 5.0, with eight out of eleven values falling between 3.6 and 4.5. These data indicate, as will be discussed in detail later, that *Aotus* albumin has evolved about 40 percent less than the average ceboid albumin and *Cebus* some 15 percent more. The other nine species tested are within 15 percent of the mean. Thus the various ceboid lineages have undergone similar degrees of change in the evolution of their albumins.

Table 6–4. Reactivity of Ceboid Albumins with Antisera Directed to Catarrhine
Albumins

Species of albumin	Mean I.D. [a]
Aotus trivirgatus	2.7
Pithecia monachus	3.3
Callicebus cupreus	3.6
Ateles geoffroyi	3.6
Callimico goeldii	3.7
Saguinus oedipus	4.0
Lagothrix humboldti	4.1
Alouatta caraya	4.3
Cacajao rubicundus	4.3
Saimiri sciurea	4.6
Cebus capucinus	5.0

a. Mean given by the five antisera to catarrhine albumins listed in Table 6–3. The serum albumin
of each of the eleven ceboid species was reacted with each of the five antiserum pools.

The evolution of the various catarrhine albumins has also been investigated using antisera directed to the albumins of *Homo*, *Pan*, *Macaca*, and *Cercopithecus*. Tables 6–5 and 6–6 show that the albumins of the six cercopithecoid lineages tested have undergone very similar degrees of albumin change during their evolutionary history, as have the six hominoid lineages. The human lineage, for example, is seen to have undergone as much albumin evolution as have any of the five lineages leading to the apes (*Pan*, *Gorilla*, *Pongo*, *Hylobates*, *Symphalangus*).

The various anthropoid albumins are thus seen to have undergone similar degrees of change along their separate evolutionary paths. Since the various prosimian albumins give rather similar I.D.'s when tested with antisera to anthropoid albumins (see Table 6–2), it is probable that this conclusion can be extended to include all primate albumins. However, a direct test is not possible at this time to exclude the possibility that prosimian albumins have evolved to a degree that is different from that characteristic of the anthropoids. Such a test would be possible only if antisera directed to a nonprimate albumin prepared in a nonmammal were available for testing. Even without this conclusive evidence, it is extremely unlikely that a group as highly diversified and with as little evolutionary or morphological unity as the living prosimians should somehow show such distinct unity in the evolution of their albumins. In summary then, it would appear that the various primate albumins have undergone similar degrees of evolution throughout the whole of the Cenozoic era, a period approximating 65 million years (Kulp 1961).

Table 6–5. Reactivity of Old World Monkey Albumins with Antisera Directed to Hominoid Albumins

	Index of Dissimilarity		
Species of albumin	Antiserum to Homo [a]	Antiserum to Pan [b]	Mean
Macaca mulatta	2.23	2.0	2.11
Papio papio	2.44	2.02	2.24
Cercocebus galeritus	2.30	2.07	2.19
Cercopithecus aethiops	2.59	2.62	2.60
Colobus polykomos	2.52	2.16	2.34
Presbytis entellus	2.65	2.50	2.57
Mean	2.45	2.23	2.34

a. As in Table 6–1, footnote a.
b. As in Table 6–3, footnote c.

Table 6–6. Reactivity of Hominoid Albumins with Antisera Directed to Old World Monkey Albumins

	Antiserum to Macaca [a]	Antiserum to Cercopithecus [b]	Mean
Pan troglodytes	2.05	2.30	2.17
Gorilla gorilla	1.95	2.30	2.13
Pongo pygmaeus	2.13	2.20	2.17
Hylobates lar	2.22	1.92	2.07
Symphalangus syndactylus	2.18	1.92	2.05
Homo sapiens	1.94	2.25	2.09
Mean	2.08	2.16	2.12

a As in Table 6–3, footnote d.
b As in Table 6–3, footnote e.

This finding of regularity in the evolution of primate albumins does not stand in isolation. The evolution of the cytochromes *c* (Margoliash and Schejter 1965; Fitch and Margoliash 1967), hemoglobins (Zuckerkandl and Pauling 1962; 1965), and insulins (Smith 1966) seems to have followed a similar pattern. These findings, however, do stand in stark contrast to the usual views concerning the irregularities in rates of morphological evolution (Simpson 1953). The fact that molecular evolution can proceed with a remarkable and certainly totally unexpected regularity removes many of the objections that have been raised to the application of such data to the resolution of phyletic and taxonomic problems. More importantly it raises profound theoretical questions concerning the nature and coordination of the forces producing such regularity in genetically isolated lineages. These, however, are peripheral to the problem of primate relationships basic to this article.

The data cited above indicate no conservatism in the evolution of any particular hominoid albumin relative to any other, nor, indeed, in the evolution of hominoid albumins relative to those of any equivalent primate taxon.

The possibility must therefore be entertained that the living apes and man do indeed share a more recent common ancestor than is usually supposed. To convert this qualitative assessment into a realistic set of phyletic conclusions requires that some estimates concerning time relationships be made. The amounts of change shown by the various primate albumin lineages throughout the Cenozoic have been remarkably similar; I would now extend this to say that rates of change have also been similar along these lineages. Any alternative explanation couched in evolutionary terms would require that either the selection pressures on the various independently evolving primate albumin lineages have increased or decreased in some regular fashion among all these lineages or perhaps that very different and uneven evolutionary rates have somehow averaged out so as to give the illusion of constancy. Either possibility becomes increasingly untenable as the number of independent lineages studied increases and either is extremely difficult to support in terms of any reasonable model. Until otherwise demonstrated, then, I prefer to choose the simplest interpretation of these data: *The selection pressures on the primate albumin molecule have been relatively constant throughout the Tertiary, and the amount of change has been directly proportional to the amount of time elapsed.* In essence, then, the evolution of the albumin molecule serves as a biological clock— the irregularities within that clock being, as will be shown, statistical in nature, the major remaining problem being its calibration.

TIME SCALE DERIVATION

The calibration of any clock requires that a linear scale be established so that equal increments of time are reflected by equal motions of the clock. In terms of the immunological data, then, one asks: What is the function relating immunological distance to the absolute time that separates any two lineages? Two direct approaches to the solution of this problem exist at present. The first is to compare immunologically a series of proteins derived from forms whose temporal relationships are known from the fossil record. The MC'F data relevant for this approach are limited to those provided by Wilson and co-workers

(1964). Various enzymes (heart-type lactic dehydrogenase [H₄LDH], muscle-type lactic dehydrogenase [M₄LDH], aldolase, triosephosphate dehydrogenase [TPD], and glutamic dehydrogenase [GDH]) were compared immunologically among taxa whose time span covers much of the range of vertebrate history. These data suggest, as shown in Fig. 6–5, that the desired function is an exponential one; that is, log I.D. is approximately proportional to the absolute

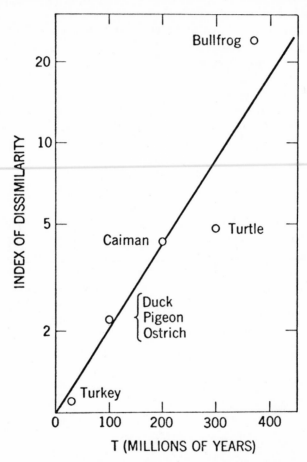

Fig. 6–5. The relationship between the mean MC'F indices given by antisera to five purified chicken enzymes with the indicated species and probable times of separation between them and the line leading to the chicken. The MC'F data are from Wilson *et al.* (1964:1264) and the estimated times are educated guesses based on a survey of appropriate literature. The semilog plot is empirical and is the best fit to the data. See also Salthe and Kaplan (1966).

times separating any two species. Salthe and Kaplan (1966) have shown that a more detailed study of the evolution of the lactic dehydrogenases leads to the same conclusion.

A second approach compares immunologically a series of homologous molecules whose primary sequences are known. The body of data on this point is limited to two molecules: hemoglobin (Wilson *et al*, 1964; Reichlin, personal communication) and cytochrome *c* (Margoliash 1966) but again an exponential relation is suggested (Fig. 6–6). Thus the basic relationship relevant to this study takes the form:

$$\log \text{I.D.} = kT$$

where I. D. is the MC′F immunological distance between any two species and T is the time of divergence between the two lineages which led to these species.

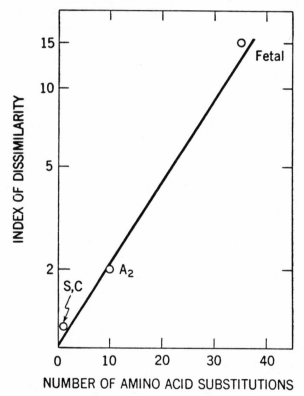

Fig. 6–6. The relationship between the immunological distance and number of amino acid differences among various human hemoglobins given by a rabbit antiserum to human hemoglobin A .

The proportionality constant k, however, describes the rate at which the particular set of molecules being studied evolves and certainly cannot be assumed to be the same for each set. Different molecules or parts thereof have been demonstrated to evolve at different rates. For example, cytochrome c in the pig, cow, and sheep is identical in its 104 amino acids whereas a peptide that can be cleaved from the fibrinogen molecule differs between the cow and pig in 10 of 20 residues (Doolittle, Schubert, and Schwartz 1967). Therefore this slope must be fixed by what is known from the mammalian fossil record and by such tests of internal consistency as we are able to make on the immunological data.

The requirement for fixing k is that a given I.D. refers to a known T. The problem lies in the fragmentary nature of the primate fossil record. However it is generally agreed that at least one of the living prosimians, *Tarsius*, represents a lineage already distinct in the early Eocene (see Simons 1963). As there is no reason to believe that any other prosimian group shows closer relationship to the higher primates, these suborders (Anthropoidea and Prosimii) must already have been distinct at this time (50 million years ago). On the other hand, it can logically be argued that all living primates derive from a common ancestral form living no earlier than later Cretaceous times (Simons 1963; Van Valen and Sloan 1965). Thus in the basic equation given above an I.D. of approximately 10 (mean anthropoid-prosimian distance) corresponds to a time of separation (T) between these suborders in the range of 50 to 70 million years. I have assumed a mean figure between these extremes as the most reasonable estimate that can be made at this point for a specific time relationship between living primates. If I.D. = 10 when T = 60, then k is 1/60 or 0.0167. All other relationships can then be placed in time relative to this one and any necessary adjustments in the assumed figure of 60 million years will be reflected by proportionate changes in the derived dates. It seems extremely unlikely that this figure could be in error to a sufficient degree to invalidate the general conclusions drawn below (Table 6–7 and Fig. 6–7).

Table 6–7. Indicated Times of Separation Between the Lineages Leading to the Modern Groups Listed

Groups	*Time (Millions of Years)*
Homo–Pan–Gorilla	3.5±1.5
Hylobatids–other Hominoids	7 ±1
Cercopithecoidea–Hominoidea	22 ±2
Catarrhini–Platyrrhini	36 ±3
Anthropoidea–Prosimii	60 (assumed)

a. The ranges given indicate the extent of antiserum variability.

b. These data are given in more detail and graphically in Fig. 6–6.

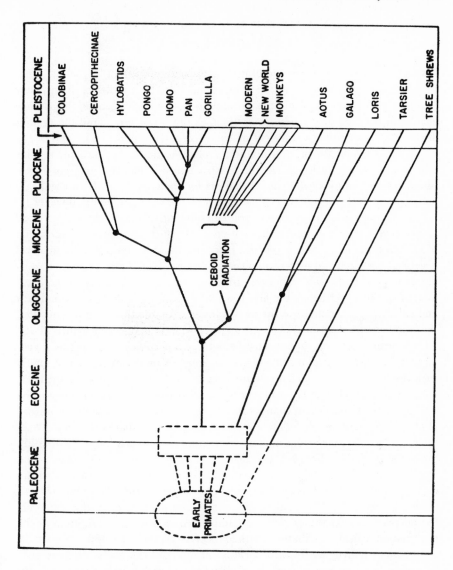

Fig. 6-7. Primate evolution as seen from the immunological study of primate albumins. The time axis is drawn to scale with the beginning of the Paleocene taken to be 65 million years ago. The points of divergence are given in this fashion for the sake of simplicity. The probable ranges indicated by the data are given in Table 6-7.

Though the dates derived in this fashion lead to considerable discussion this is deferred until the matter of the variations seen in the degrees of evolution shown by various primate albumins is discussed.

VARIATIONS IN EVOLUTIONARY RATES

The process of molecular evolution is discontinuous; that is, the minimum possible change is the substitution of one amino acid for another in the primary sequence of a particular molecule. In diploid organisms, of course, this change can be distributed over many generations as the "wild type" and the mutant alleles coexist in either a transient or balanced polymorphism. The process, as has been shown for the primate albumin molecule, can be a remarkably regular one. This very regularity allows the construction of a model of molecular evolution which, paradoxically enough, allows for such deviations from regularity as are found in the degrees of change shown by the various albumin lineages.

It appears that the process of primate albumin evolution can be described as one governed by a constant selection pressure which allows the incorporation of adaptive mutations to proceed at a rate which is very similar in a number of genetically isolated and extremely diverse lineages. The mechanics of such coordination over such wide ranges of time and space are of course completely unknown, but nevertheless the above would appear to be the most economical and satisfying explanation of the available data. In addition, it is obvious that the number of amino acid changes to which our indices correspond is finite, which means that each change must be separated from any precursor by a very large number of generations in any given lineage. A process which occurs under such restrictions; that is one involving change which proceeds at a specified rate and where each change is an independent event can be described statistically. The number of amino acid changes that have occurred in each albumin lineage of equal time length will follow a Poisson distribution; that is, there is a two-thirds chance that the actual number of changes in any such lineage will fall in the range $N \pm \sqrt{N}$, where N is the mean number of changes occurring over that length of time. If a set of albumins equally distant in time from each other are compared immunologically, corresponding variations in the I.D.'s obtained will occur. These variations are then not due to any differences in the actual selection pressures on the evolving albumin lineages but are a reflection of the expected statistical distribution in their degrees of evolution given the conditions of a specified rate of incorporation of adaptive mutations into the gene pool of an evolving species and the independence of each such incorporation.

Now the number of amino acid changes that have occurred in any albumin lineage is unknown and quite likely to remain so for an appreciable length of time. Nevertheless the immunological data do allow reasonable estimates to be made as to the number of amino acid differences corresponding to a given immunological distance. The primate data (Sarich 1967: 82–3) as well as comparative hemoglobin data (see Fig. 6–6) suggest that in the evolution of the primate albumin molecule, approximately one amino acid substitution per million years per lineage has occurred. This estimate allows an analysis of the variations seen in the degrees of albumin shown by the various New World monkey lineages.

The New World monkeys are a particularly good group for such an analysis, as the taxonomic (Simpson 1945; Fiedler 1955), paleontological (Olson 1964), and published immunological (Goodman 1967) data all agree that the various platyrrhine taxa, at least at the subfamily and often at the generic level, have been distinct for very long periods of time. This is fully confirmed by my own data which have been previously discussed.

If the average time of separation for the various New World genera is taken to be approximately 25 million years, the mean number of amino acid changes in each albumin lineage over that span of time is on the order of 25. We should expect that the actual amounts of change should be such that two-thirds of the lineages distinct for that period of time should fall in the range of 25 ±5 amino acid substitutions. Using the data from Table 6–4 and the time scale given in Fig. 6–7 one may calculate the apparent time separating any given New World monkey albumin from the catarrhines. These calculations indicate that *Aotus* albumin has evolved approximately 40 percent less than the average platyrrhine albumin and that of *Cebus* approximately 20 percent more. All other genera fall in the range of ±15 percent of the mean. Eight of nine relevant genera (*Lagothrix* and *Pithecia* are excepted as being relatively closely related to *Ateles* and *Cacajao* respectively) thus fall within ±20 percent of the mean, whereas only two-thirds might be expected to. This is, of course, not a significant deviation, and indicates that the above estimates are generally compatible with the statistical model presented. There is therefore no reason to suggest any mysterious forces or pressures as being involved in molecular evolution, though the coordination of the usual ones basic to evolutionary theory over such large ranges of time and space must still remain a mystery.

THE EVOLUTION OF THE HOMINOIDEA

Throughout the research effort discussed in this article the emphasis has been on the rigorous testing of the concept that comparative immunological data have their place in phylogenetic studies. It has been shown that a sensitive, economical, and reliable immunological technique is available for such work. The reservations often expressed concerning the variability and nonreciprocity of antisera are seen to be minor issues. Contrary to all expectations, it appears that molecular evolution can be a remarkably regular phenomenon and that deviations from regularity can be explained by a simple statistical model. Finally, a time scale can be constructed from these data and internal tests of its accuracy are possible. The question now is what does all this tell us about the evolution of the primates in general and man in particular?

The time scale evolved above suggests that a clear-cut choice can be made among the various conflicting hypotheses concerning ape and human origins. What is an extremely complex intellectual history in detail would seem to break down into a basic dichotomy, as succinctly stated by Heberer (1962:205):

One [view] sees the hominid ancestors as having the morphology of differentiated brachiators [that is, swinging and hanging tree climbers], a morphology for which the model is furnished by recent pongines and which is characterized, among other things, by relatively long arms and relatively short legs. The second view does not assume morphologically fully differentiated brachiators, especially forms possessing the typical brachiating limb proportions, but rather forms, essentially still pronograde, which possessed an intermembral index of 100. If one is a "brachiationist" one must set the subhuman phase of our phylogeny in the Pliocene, perhaps in the Middle or even Later Pliocene; if one is an "antibrachiationist," one allows oneself greater time limits for the dating of the process of isolation, or about from the Upper Miocene to the Upper Oligocene.

The dates suggested in this article would place the origin of all the living Hominoidea near the Mio-Pliocene boundary and give the African apes and man a common middle to late Pliocene ancestor, thus clearly favoring the "brachiationist" views.

This conclusion, of course, stands at considerable variance with the prevailing views concerning the evolution of the apes and man. Nevertheless it would, if valid, solve many of the problems that have long troubled the students of this group. The many common features of morphology and concomitantly of behavior, particularly those concerned with the thorax and upper limb, that man and the apes share in varying degrees (Washburn 1963) are not evidenced in the scanty Miocene ape postcranial material. The analyses of this material (Napier and Davis 1959; Zapfe 1960; Clark 1964; Ankel 1965) make it clear that these were basically quadrupedal and probably tailed forms. Their dentitions, however, often show remarkable similarities to those of modern forms, and this has led to the assignment of a number of them to lineages still represented today. Thus *Ramapithecus* has been viewed as a Miocene hominid (Simons and Pilbeam 1965), *Dryopithecus (Proconsul) major* as a Miocene gorilla (Leakey 1967) and the *Limnopithecus-Pliopithecus* group as Miocene hylobatids (Patterson 1954). This disparity between the dental morphology and the indicated locomotor pattern makes the appelation "dental apes" for these Miocene forms an appropriate one. The morphological similarities between the modern apes and man thus would seem to require either parallelism or a post-Miocene common ancestry as an explanation. The immunological evidence would suggest that the latter is true, but parallelism, as discussed previously, is a third possibility for explaining the close similarities among hominoid albumins.

Parallelism in molecular evolution can be considered a relatively rare phenomenon on purely probabilistic grounds once it is conceded that any specific evolutionary problem is unlikely to have an equivalent set of mutants available for its solution in genetically isolated lines. The relative infrequency of mutations and the finite nature of the real world would seem to make this the case. Nevertheless, it remains a possibility if a particular phyletic scheme drawn on the basis of molecular data shows certain relationships as unexpectedly close. *Hylobates* and *Homo* albumins are a case in point. Though the relatively clear hylobatid line of which Patterson speaks (1954:206): "Gibbons have rather distinctive molars and because of this it is possible to trace a phyletic thread back from the present that does not get lost in the dryopithecine tangle," is no longer so clear (Schultz 1966:20), the suggestion that *Homo* and *Hylobates* share a common ancestor near the Mio-Pliocene boundary is unlikely to find much support. To my knowledge, only a single passing reference in a general article on primate dentition by Butler (1964:2–3) suggests that the hylobatids might stand so close to man:

> In other cases resemblances may indicate relationship. *Proconsul* and *Pliopithecus* are very close in dental characters, even where they differ from modern anthropoid apes. *Pliopithecus* is usually regarded as a primitive gibbon, while *Proconsul* is supposed to be nearer the great-ape group. Yet the degree of similarity is such as to suggest that it is artificial to divide the Miocene Pongidae between the two sub-families, which probably diverged at a later date.

Accepting the time scale derived previously, for the sake of argument, the question of parallelism or convergence can be investigated. One could suggest, for example, that the similarities among hominoid albumins are the result of parallelism and not of recent common ancestry. That is, immunologically similar albumin structures have been evolved in genetically isolated lineages. Table 6–8 summarizes data relevant to this issue obtained with the three sets of

Table 6–8. Reactivity of Various Primate Albumins with Antisera Directed to Hominoid Albumins

Species of Albumin	Index of Dissimilarity		
	Anti-*Homo*[a]	Anti-*Pan*[b]	Anti-*Hylobates*[c]
H. sapiens	1.0	1.09	1.29
P. troglodytes	1.14	1.0	1.40
P. paniscus	1.14	1.0	1.40
G. gorilla	1.10	1.17	1.31
P. pygmaeus	1.22	1.24	1.29
S. syndactylus	1.27	1.25	1.07
H. lar	1.27	1.25	1.0
M. mulatta	2.23	2.0	2.30

a. As in Table 1, footnote a.
b. As in Table 3, footnote c.
c. A pool of three antisera to *Hylobates lar* albumin

antihominoid albumin sera thus far prepared. It should be noted that the I.D.'s of the other apes (with the obvious exception of the siamang) and man obtained with antisera to gibbon albumin are very nearly the same, indicating that these albumins have changed to much the same degree since their separation from the gibbon albumin lineage. Yet antisera to chimpanzee and human albumins demonstrate that human, chimpanzee, gorilla, and orang albumins are quite different from one another. To support the idea of parallelism and an ancient division between the hylobatids and the other apes and man, then, one would have to postulate that gibbon albumin evolved in parallel to those of the other apes until the radiation of these latter lineages began and then diverged from all of these (clearly, gibbon albumin cannot have evolved in parallel to all four nonhylobatid lineages at the same time). It is obvious that this is an extremely improbable set of circumstances to postulate when a much simpler explanation is available. In the same fashion those who would explain away the morphological similarities in the trunk and upper limbs among all the living apes and man as due to parallelism must make a similar appeal to coincidence.

The data already presented allow a picture to be drawn of the recent course of pongid and hominid evolution that is elegant in its simplicity. The numerous branches of the widespread group of Miocene dryopithecines must have left but a single survivor. A small form of this surviving lineage became uniquely successful through the development of the locomotor-feeding adaptation termed brachiation and the subsequent radiation of the group possessing this adaptation thus made it the only surviving lineage of the many apes present throughout the tropical and subtropical Miocene forests of the Old World. The degree of common ancestry shared by the living apes and man after the initial success of this development seems, on the basis of the immunological and paleontological data, to have been relatively limited. This is as might be expected, for rapid development of a new structural-behavioral complex or grade and its subsequent adaptive radiation is the common evolutionary pattern (Simpson, 1966:235).

The products of such an adaptive radiation show similarities in basic pattern, reflecting the attainment of a new grade of organization, but differences in detail, representing the various lines comprising the adaptive radiation. The unity of the modern Hominoidea, then, is based on the relatively short period of time during which a major adaptation was being evolved, their diversity on the relatively long periods of time that each line has been evolving independently of the others.

The immunological evidence indicates that we and the African apes still shared a common ancestor in the Middle Pliocene and that the lines leading to the chimpanzee, gorilla, and man diverged at approximately the same time. The chimpanzee therefore stands no closer to the gorilla than either does to man (a similar conclusion was reached by Goodman, 1963, on the basis of his more qualitative data using antisera to a number of hominoid serum proteins).

On the other hand, the earliest fossil hominids yet found are the South African australopithecines, probably dating to more than 2 million years ago (Howell 1965:369;1967:103). Thus there are approximately 1 to 3 million years available to progress from a form ancestral to the African apes and man (and presumably not particularly unlike a small chimpanzee) to one in which the bipedal adaptation is well advanced. In view of what has already been said concerning the rapid nature of major adaptive shifts, this would seem to be more than enough time.

Thomas Henry Huxley wrote in 1863:123

> every bone of a Gorilla bears marks by which it might be distinguished from the corresponding bone of a man; and that, in the present creation, at any rate, no intermediate link bridges over the gap between *Homo* and *Troglodytes*.
>
> It would be not less wrong than absurd to deny the existence of this chasm; but it is at least equally wrong and absurd to exaggerate its magnitude, and, resting on the admitted fact of its existence, to refuse to inquire whether it is wide or narrow.

This study has had as one of its foci an inquiry into the breadth of that chasm. To give an answer 105 years later, it may be said that the chasm is indeed narrow, but very deep.

REFERENCES

Ankel, F., 1965, Der canalis sacralis als indikator fur die Lange der caudal-region der primaten. *Folia. Primat.* **3**:263–276.

Boyden, A., 1951, A half-century of systematic serology. *The Serological Museum,* Bull. No. 6:1–3.

———, 1958, Comparative serology:aims, methods, and results. *Serological and Biochemical Comparisons of Proteins.* W.H. Cole, ed., 3–24 (Rutgers University Press, New Brunswick).

Buettner-Janusch, J., and R.L. Hill, 1965, Molecules and monkeys. *Science,* **147**:836–842.

Butler, P.M., 1965, Tooth morphology and primate evolution. *Dental Anthropology,* D.R. Brothwell, ed., 1–14 (Crowell-Collier and Macmillon, Inc., New York).

Clark, W. E. Le Gros, 1964, *Fossil Evidence for Human Evolution,* 2d ed., 174–197 (University of Chicago Press, Chicago).

Doolittle, R.F., D. Schubert, and S.A. Schwartz, 1967, Amino acid sequence studies on artiodactyl fibrinopeptides. I. Dromedary camel, mule deer, and Cape buffalo. *Arch. Biochem. Biophys.* **118**:456–467.

Fiedler, W., 1955, Ubersicht uber das system der primates. *Primatologia,* **1**:267 (Karger, Basel).

Fitch, W. M., and E. Margoliash, 1967, Construction of phylogenetic trees. *Science,* **155**:276–284.

Goodman, M., 1961, The role of immunochemical differences in the phyletic development of human behavior. *Human Biology,* **33**:131–162.

————, 1962, Evolution of the immunologic species specificity of human serum proteins. *Human Biology,* **34**:104–150.

————, 1963, Serological analysis of the systematics of recent hominoids. *Human Biology,* **35**:377–436.

————, 1963*b*, Man's place in the phylogeny of the primates as reflected in serum proteins. *Classification and Human Evolution.* S.L. Washburn, ed. (Aldine Publishing Co., Chicago).

————, 1967, Deciphering primate phylogeny from macromolecular specificities. *Am. J. Phys. Anthrop.* **26**:255–276.

HAFLEIGH, A. S. and C. A. WILLIAMS, JR., 1966, Antigenic correspondence of serum albumins among the primates. *Science,* **151**:1530–1535.

HEBERER, G., 1962, The subhuman evolutionary history of man. *Ideas on Human Evolution.* W. W. Howells, ed., 203–241 (Harvard University Press, Cambridge).

HOWELL, F. C., 1965, *Current Anthropology,* **6**:368–373.

————, 1967, *American Journal of Physical Anthropology,* **27**:95–101.

HUXLEY, T. H., 1863, *Evidence as to Man's Place in Nature* (Williams & Northgate, Ltd., London).

KITCHIN, F. D., N. A. BARNICOT, and C. J. JOLLY, 1967, Variations in the group-specific (Gc) component and other blood protiens of baboons, in *The Baboon in Medical Research,* Vol. II. H. Vagtborg, ed. (University of Texas Press, Austin).

KLOTZ, I. M., 1967, Protein subunits: a table. *Science,* **155**:697–698.

KULP, J. L., 1961, Geologic time scale. *Science,* **133**:1105–1114.

LEAKEY, L. S. B., 1967, An early Miocene member of the Hominidae. *Nature,* **213**:115–123.

MARABLE, I. W. and W. G. GLENN, 1964, Quantitative serological correspondence of ungulates by gel diffusion. *Taxonomic Biochemistry and Serology.* C. A. Leone, ed., 75–99, (Roland, New York).

MARGOLIASH, E., 1966, Informal seminar reporting on immunological comparisons of various cytochromes *c* by M. Reichlin (given at the University of California, Berkeley).

————, and A. SCHEJTER, 1966, Cytochrome *c. Advances in Protein Chemistry.* **21**:113–386.

MELARTIN, L. and B. S. BLUMBERG, 1966, Albumin Naskapi: a new variant of serum albumin. *Science,* **153**:1664–1666.

NAPIER, J. R. and P. R. DAVIS, 1959, The fore-limb skeleton and associated remains of *Proconsul africanus. Fossil Mammals of Africa,* No. 16 [British Museum (Natural History), London].

OLSON, E. C., 1964, The geology and mammalian faunas of the Tertiary and Pleistocene of South America. *American Journal of Physical Anthropology,* **22**:217–226.

PATTERSON, B., 1954, The geologic history of non-hominoid primates in the Old World. *Human Biology,* **26**:191–209.

PUTNAM, F. W., 1965, Structure and function of the plasma proteins. *The Proteins,* H. Neurath, ed. (Academic Press Inc., New York). 2nd ed. v. 111, 154–269.

SALTHE, S. N., and N. O. KAPLAN, 1966, Immunology and rates of enzyme evolution in the amphibia in relation to the origins of certain taxa. *Evolution,* **20**:617–633.

SARICH, V. M., 1967, A Quantitative Immunochemical Study of the Evolution of Primate Albumins. Unpublished Ph.D. thesis (University of California, Berkeley).

————, and A. C. WILSON, 1966, Quantitative immunochemistry and the evolution of the primate albumins. *Science,* **154**:1563–1566.

————, 1967, Rates of albumin evolution in primates. *Proc. Nat. Acad. Sci.* 58: 142–148.

————, 1968, Immunological time scale for hominid evolution. *Science,* 158:1200.

SCHULTZ, A. H., 1966, Changing views on the nature and interrelations of the higher primates. *Yerkes Newsletter,* **3**:1:15–29.

SIMONS, E. L., 1963, A critical reappraisal of Tertiary primates. *Evolutionary and Genetic Biology of Primates.* J. Buettner-Janusch, ed., **1**:65–129 (Academic Press, Inc., New York).

————, 1965, New fossil apes from Egypt and the initial differentiation of the Hominoidea. *Nature,* **205**:135–139.

SIMONS, E. L. and D. R. PILBEAM, 1965, Preliminary revision of the Dryopithecinae (Pongidae, Anthropoidea). *Folia Primat.* 3:81–152.

SIMPSON, G. G., 1945, The principles of classification and a classification of the mammals. *Bull. Am. Mus. Nat. Hist.* **85**:1.

————, 1953, *The major features of evolution* (Columbia University Press, New York)

————, 1962, Primate taxonomy and recent studies of nonhuman primates. Ann. *New York Acad. Sci.* **102**:497.

————, 1964, Organisms and molecules in evolution. *Science,* **146**:1535–1538.

————, 1966, *The Meaning of Evolution,* rev. ed. *(Yale University Press, New Haven).*

SMITH, L.F., 1966, Species variation in the amino acid sequence of insulin. *Am. J. Med.* **40**:662–666.

VAN VALEN, L., and R. E. SLOAN, 1965, The earliest primates. *Science,* **150**:743–745.

WASHBURN, S. L., 1963, Behavior and human evolution. *Classification and Human Evolution.* S. L. Washburn, ed., 190–203 (Aldine Publishing Co., Chicago).

————, and D. A. HAMBURG, 1965, The study of primate behavior. *Primate Behavior.* I. De Vore, ed. (Holt, Rinehart and Winston, Inc., New York). 1–15

WILLIAMS, C. A., JR., 1964, Immunochemical analysis of serum proteins in primates: a study in molecular evolution. *Evolutionary and Genetic Biology of Primates,* J. Buettner-Janusch, ed. (Academic Press, Inc., New York). **2**:25–74.

WILSON, A. C., N. O. KAPLAN, L. LEVINE, A. PESCE, M. REICHLIN, and W. S. ALLISON, 1964, Evolution of lactic dehydrogenases, *Fed. Proc.* **23**:1258–1266.

ZAPFE, H., 1960, Die primatenfunde aus der miozanen spaltenfullung von Neudorf an der March, Tschechoslowakei. *Schweiz. Palaeontol. Abhdl.* **78**:1–293.

ZUCKERKANDL, E., and E. PAULING, 1962, Molecular disease, evolution and genic heterogeneity. *Horizons in Biochemistry,* M. Kasha and B. Pullman eds. (Academic Press, Inc., New York). 189–225.

————, 1965, Evolutionary divergence and convergence in proteins. *Evolving Genes and Proteins.* V. Bryson and H. J. Vogel, eds. (Academic Press, Inc., New York). 97–166.

7 · The Recent Hominoid Primates

Adolph H. Schultz
Anthropologisches Institut der Universität Zurich

PREFACE

During the hundred years following Huxley's (1863) epochal publication of "Evidence as to man's place in nature" the comparative-anatomical and palae-ontological study of the primates most similar to men progressed at a rapidly increasing rate. In an attempt to survey the great mass of accumulated new evidence for man's evolutionary history Prof. Heberer had in 1962 invited some of his colleagues to contribute reviews of their respective fields of research for a volume centered upon our present views on man's place among the primates, entitled *Menschliche Abstammungslehre, 1863–1964.* The writer had been assigned the chapter on the living anthropoid apes, with special emphasis on their morphology and with the understanding that the fossils, dentition, skull, brain, and historical aspects are to be dealt with in separate chapters by other authors. With this general orientation, including the condition that the book is intended for the "educated layman" and should go into print very quickly, the writer had assembled and turned in his manuscript in 1962, but eventually it did not appear until three years later. For the latter reason the writer was glad to have been asked to translate and revise his chapter in German for a new publication in English. The necessary consent of the editor of the original German edition was readily and generously given by Prof. Heberer when Prof. Washburn and the writer discussed this matter with him during the international congress of primatology in Frankfurt a. M. in 1966. It was also agreed

Author's translation and revised version of "Die Rezenten Hominoidea" in *Menschliche Abstammungslehre*, edited by Gerhard Heberer, Stuttgart, Gustav Fischer Verlag, 1965. By permission of the editor and publisher.

that the writer would be free to make alterations in his text according to his latest views and to change or add such illustrations as seem desirable.

A brief description of the distinguishing characters of the recent man-like apes gains most of its interest through comparisons between these specializations and the corresponding conditions of lower primates on one side and of man on the other. The enormous amount of relevant information which has become available in widely scattered publications can no longer be surveyed completely in a review of limited size. It seems justified, therefore, to deal here chiefly with such topics which have received comparatively little attention in most of the many summarizing accounts of the higher primates by other authors and to select some of the subjects which have been of particular interest to the writer. With these selections it will be possible to demonstrate not only the outstanding evolutionary trends, common to all hominoids, but also some of the more significant specializations characterizing the different families and genera. The particular conditions in the latter often represent simply different stages of perfection along the same general trends or reveal the comparatively late diverging innovations acquired by single genera or species. To include in addition a critical discussion of our latest knowledge of the brain, teeth, chromosomes, hemoglobins, parasites, and so on of the living higher primates would require today the cooperation of many specialists, without as yet leading to general and close agreement in phylogenetic conclusions regarding the precise interrelations of the hominoids.

The detailed classification of primates and parts of its nomenclature are being continually changed in numerous more or less significant respects and hence are not used in the literature in a uniform and generally understood manner. It will be necessary, therefore, to begin with some brief introductory explanations of the system and names preferred by the writer. These follow mainly the scholarly taxonomic chapter by Fiedler (1956) in the first volume of the well-known handbook of primatology, which can be consulted for a full discussion of this matter and, incidentally, also for a great deal of further information and literature on hominoids, contributed by many other specialists.

INTRODUCTION

The suborder Simiae of the primates is clearly divided in two ancient groups according to some of their anatomical characters, which differ consistently. One of these main groups is found exclusively in America and the other ranges through Africa and the southern part of Asia and in times past also Europe. The simian primates of the Old World, the so-called catarrhines, can be subdivided quite sharply into the superfamilies of Cercopithecoidea, or catarrhine monkeys, and of Hominoidea. To the latter are assigned all man-like apes as well as man and his close forerunners, which are often and rightly referred to as the higher primates. Of this formerly larger superfamily of Hominoidea survive only three families of which the Hylobatidae contain the gibbons and siamangs, the Pongidae the three types of great apes and the Hominidae recent man. Only the last-named has gained world-wide distribution and by far the largest population of all primate species.

The smallest of the recent hominoids, the hylobatids, are still more numerous and more widely ranging than the great apes of today and have developed two generically distinct types (*Hylobates* and *Symphalangus*) and a total of six or possibly seven good species. In contrast to this the orang-utans (*Pongo*) and gorillas (*Gorilla*) are each represented by only one species and the chimpanzees (*Pan*) by two. A great many additional species of recent apes had been proposed and described under a confusing variety of names during the first few decades of our century, but all of these are today regarded as at most mere local races, if not as manifestation of the exceptionally great variability of the pongids in particular.

In the single species of siamangs[1] the Sumatran animals are generally somewhat larger than the Malayan ones and in the also single species of orang-utans the hair color is as a rule slightly darker in Bornean individuals than in those from their last refuge area in Sumatra, where they still survive. With such very limited differences one can merely justify expected geographic races, but not separate species. The best-known chimpanzee species (*Pan troglodytes*) seems to have become more or less clearly differentiated into three subspecies, of which two live in West-Africa, *P. t. verus* occurring toward the north and *P. t. troglodytes* farther south, while *P. t. schweinfurthi* ranges through parts of Central Africa. A second and much later discovered species of chimpanzees (*Pan paniscus*) is isolated on the left side of the Congo river and tends to be slightly smaller and to have certain other distinctive features, but the commonly used name of "pygmy chimpanzee" is hardly warranted in view of the fact that the individual variations in body size of both species overlap extensively (Schultz 1954). Among gorillas one can also distinguish different types on the basis of a number of minor features (Schultz 1934), particularly the two subspecies of the so-called "lowland" and "mountain" gorillas, which should be more appropriately named western and eastern gorillas, since their respective ranges, though smaller than those of chimpanzees, are not at all restricted to low coastal zones or else mountainous ones.

In this review of the recent hominoids it can merely be mentioned that the great variety of fossil ones provides very tempting evidence for a provisional

---

[1]The gibbons which are isolated in the Mentawi Islands, west of Sumatra, had formerly been regarded as a separate species of "dwarf siamangs," but for numerous reasons are more properly assigned to the genus *Hylobates* in which they have been placed in a subgenus *Brachitanytes* (Schultz 1932; 1933).

reconstruction of the general phylogenetic relationships within this entire superfamily. These fossils, however, are still inadequate for plotting the exact places and ages of divergence in the evolutionary pathways leading to the living types. From fossil finds we have learned that from a common ancestral stock of all later higher primates there have evolved more families than survive, such as the Oreopithecidae and Pliopithecidae, which seem to have died out in Pliocene time. We have no fossils, however, to trace any of the modern apes far back into the past. Of the African apes not a single tooth has ever been found to indicate their appearance and distribution during the Pleistocene period, and of gibbons and orang-utans we can merely demonstrate their much wider distribution during the same brief period, but all preceding lines of connection with earlier forms remain hypothetical. These remarks are inserted here to point out that the determination of the phylogenetic interrelations of the modern hominoids and, particularly, of man's place among them still rests mainly on comparative studies of the living forms which offer endless possibilities for obtaining morphological, biochemical, behavioral and still further evidence.

Body Size and Proportions

The body size of the living hominoids differs at least as widely as did that of the fossil ones. Gibbons are mere dwarfs alongside gorillas, among which some old males can attain a weight of over 200 kg., representing the extreme of all recent primates and one reached by only few of the past, such as *Gigantopithecus* or *Megaladapis*. Intraspecifically body size can also vary to a remarkably high degree not only in man, but in the man-like apes as well. For instance, in a series of 80 adult gibbons from a small area the fresh body weight was found to range from 3.8 to 7.3 kg. (Schultz 1944). That longitudinal dimensions have an equally high variability can here be indicated only by the following data: The length of the humerus varies among 145 perfectly normal, adult, male, western gorillas between 389 and 500 mm. according to measurements by Schultz (1937) and by Randall (1943–1944) (32 of the 84 specimens of the latter author had already been used by the former author and have naturally been counted only once).

The average sex difference in body weight is negligible in some hominoid genera, but extremely great in others, as shown by the data in Table 7–1. In orang-utans and gorillas this sex difference is fully as marked as, for example, in baboons or proboscis monkeys, whereas in gibbons it is barely recognizable with many individual females equalling or even surpassing males in size, as is so often the case also among platyrrhines.

The body proportions of all higher primates are in various respects very distinct from those of monkeys, and this not only in consequence of their different modes of locomotion but also due to common specializations, shared by

Table 7–1. Average body weights (kg.) of adult female and male hominoids according to data by the author and those collected by him from the literature. Since reliable weights of adult gorillas have rarely been recorded the present averages are merely approximate ones. The figures for man represent rough general averages of data for different races.

		Females	Males	Female Aver. in Percent Male Aver.
Gibbon	*(H. lar)*	5.3	5.7	93
"	*(H. concolor)*	5.8	5.6	103
"	*(H. hoolock)*	6.6	6.9	96
"	*(H. klossii)*	6.5	6.2	105
Siamang		10.2	11.1	92
Orang-utan		37	75	49
Chimpanzee		42	48	88
Gorilla		85	175	48
Man		58	65	89

all recent hominoids. Table 7–2 lists the averages of some of the most significant proportions, based on the author's measurements of the outer bodies of numerous fully adult apes and men. The corresponding averages for adult macaques (*Macaca mulatta*) must suffice here for representing these conditions in Old World monkeys, among which most of these relative measurements are comparatively uniform (Schultz 1956). From the first four indices of the table it is evident that the trunk of higher primates is without exception very much stouter and particularly broader than that of macaques and all the many other Cerocopithecoidea whose proportions have been determined so far. This striking and consistent difference between the higher and the lower catarrhines manifests itself also in the relative width of the hipbones and of the sternum, as well as in the shape of the thorax, the curvature of the ribs, and so on, as will be shown in the discussion of the skeleton. With the widening of the chest in all hominoids the shoulderblades have been shifted to the broad back from their lateral position, typical for all quadrupedal monkeys, prosimians and most other mammals (Fig. 7–1). The shoulderjoints of the apes and man have come to lie in one frontal plane with the spinal column and no longer in one plane with the sternum, and they face laterally instead of ventrally, as in monkeys.

From the data in Table 7–2 it is seen also that this important and general increase in the relative girth and breadth of the trunk in all hominoids has advanced more in siamangs than in gibbons and has become much more extreme in gorillas than in man. The latter difference is clearly apparent in Fig. 7–2, where it should also be noticed that the height of the trunk of the man-like

Table 7–2. Averages of some body proportions of adult hominoids and macaques based upon strictly corresponding measurements by the author (for further data on more proportions and in additional primates see Schultz 1956). Number of specimens in parentheses. Relative Head Size = (Length + Breadth + Height of Brain Part): 3 in percent of Trunk Length. Relative Ear Size = Height × Breadth of Outer Ear in percent of Head Length times Total Head Height. For all other details of the absolute and relative measurements see Schultz 1929.

Proportion	Macaque (28)	Gibbon (80)	Siamang (9)	Orang (13)	Chimp. (30)	Gorilla (5)	Man (25)
Chest Girth:Trunk Length	104	152	170	187	165	217	160
Shoulder Breadth:Trunk Length	34	53	52	62	57	70	65
Hip Breadth:Trunk Length	34	43	47	50	52	66	61
Chest Breadth:Chest Depth	88	117	125	126	127	138	128
Lower Limb Length:Trunk Length	100	148	131	116	127	124	169
Upper Limb Length:Trunk Length	113	243	233	200	172	172	148
Upper Limb Length:Lower Limb Length	112	165	178	172	136	138	88
Foot Length:Trunk Length	44	52	52	62	50	47	48
Hand Length:Trunk Length	29	59	51	53	49	40	37
Thumb Length:Trunk Length	16	31	28	23	23	22	25
Head Size:Trunk Length	21	26	26	26	26	29	30
Total Face Height:Trunk Length	21	19	23	30	27	28	24
Upper Face Height:Head Size	74	52	62	86	77	72	50
Relative Ear Size	14	13	8	3	17	4	5

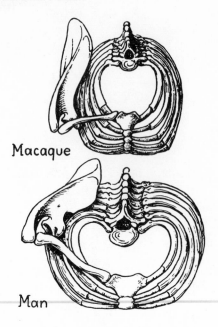

Macaque

Man

Fig. 7–1. Cephalic view of thorax and
right shoulder girdle of adult macaque
and man. (*From Schultz 1957*)

apes is accentuated by the high position of their shoulders. Even with the arms
hanging down freely the clavicles of the apes diverge steeply toward the high
shoulders, whereas those of man are directed almost horizontally, except in
early fetal life, when the shoulders still lie well above the sterno-clavicular
joints (Schultz, 1926). Externally man is the only hominoid with a clearly-
formed neck, deserving that name, because in the full-grown apes the anatomical neck is hidden laterally behind the high shoulders, in front by the large
face and dorsally by the powerful nuchal musculature, reaching to the high
shoulders, as also shown in Fig. 7–2.

The proportionate lengths of the limbs surpass in all recent hominoids
those of catarrhine monkeys according to the relevant indices in Table 7–2.
The total lower limb length (from great trochanter to sole of foot) in its percentage relation to the trunk length (suprasternal notch to upper edge of pubic
symphysis) varies but little around 100 in adult Old World monkeys, and
among the apes it has increased least in orang-utans with their exceptionally
weak legs and most in gibbons. The variations of this proportion range in 80
adults of *Hylobates lar* from 132 to 166 and in 30 adult chimpanzees from 114
to 150, with the highest values of both series clearly surpassing the lowest ones
among normal human beings. For instance, in a series of only 25 adult bodies
from several human races the author obtained a corresponding range of 141 to

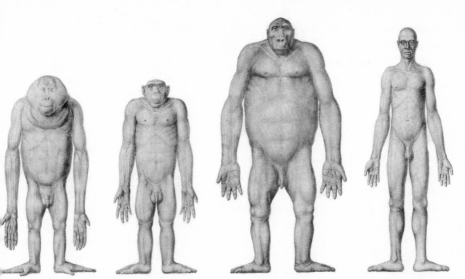

Fig. 7–2. The body proportions of an adult orang-utan, chimpanzee, gorilla, and man, reduced to the same scale and drawn without hair and with straightened lower limbs and feet turned laterally to facilitate comparisons. (*From Schultz 1933*)

179. It can be stated, therefore, that it is merely on an average that man has acquired the relatively longest lower extremities and that some gibbons and even chimpanzees can have proportionatley longer legs than have some men at the completion of growth. Incidentally, the highest of all values for this same index are found in certain prosimians, particularly those specialized for leaping, such as tarsiers, sifakas, and so on. It should also be mentioned that the great average relative leg length of man is ontogenetically a remarkably late acquisition, since at birth it still averages only about 110, a value which is not at all outstanding among newborns of other primates.

The relative total length of the upper limb (from acromion to the tip of the longest finger in percentage of trunk length) surpasses even in man all the corresponding values for Old World monkeys, reaching in some races maximum figures of 188. The latter fall well within the ranges of variations of adult chimpanzees (157 to 200) and gorillas (148 to 187). Among all primates this relative arm length has increased by far the most in the Asiatic apes, particularly in the gibbons, whose arms measure individually up to 274 percent of their trunk length and in upright posture reach clear to the ground in spite of the high shoulders and comparatively long legs. This specialization in the length of the arms of the best brachiators is far more extreme than the increase in the length of the legs of bipedal man. It is specially the forearm which has become so extraordinarily lengthened in the Asiatic apes, as shown by the following averages of the brachial index (radius length in percent of humerus length): Gibbons = 113, siamangs = 111, orang-utans = 100, chimpanzees = 93, gorillas = 80, man = ca. 76 (Schultz 1937). The increased length of the lower limb of man, however, has not affected one segment more than the other, because the analogous crural indices (tibia length in percent of femur length) differ but little among the hominoids, averaging 87 in gibbons and siamangs, 92 in orang-utans, 83 in chimpanzees, 80 in gorillas, and 83 to 89 in the various races of man (Schultz 1937).

The intermembral index, which expresses the total length of the upper limb in percentage of that of the lower one, is one of the few proportions of adults which distinguishes man from the apes even if the ranges of individual variations are taken into consideration. In all adult catarrhines the upper limbs surpass the lower ones in length, except in man, in whom the legs become post-natally longer than the arms, as they do also in many prosimians (Schultz 1954; 1956). The distinction of this important and intraspecifically quite constant proportion is in man not nearly as marked as it is in siamangs, whose average intermembral index of 178 has changed much more from the corresponding average of 112 for macaques, which represents roughly an unspecialized condition. An intermembral index without the inclusion of hand and foot, which has been obtained from measurements of the long limb bones of many very large series of adult skeletons, also separates man from the apes, but not from all other primates, as shown by the following few data: The length of humerus+radius in percentage of the length of femur+tibia varies in a total of 753 skeletons of different human races between 64 and 79 and averages 128 in gibbons, 148 in siamangs, 144 in orang-utans, 107 in chimpanzees, and 117 in gorillas. The same index varies among catarrhine monkeys between 75 and 100, thus reaching occasionally just below the highest figures of man. The lowest of all these intermembral indices are found in the prosimian genera of *Tarsius, Propithecus* and *Galago* with values very near 50 (Schultz 1937; 1954).

The hand-like grasping ability of the feet of most monkeys and apes, in contrast to the lack thereof in our feet, had led Schreber (1775) to propose a radical separation between man and the nonhuman primates known at that time. Blumenbach (1791) followed this with the formal division of Linné's preceding single order of Primates in the two orders of Bimana and Quadrumana, the former being reserved exclusively for man. This naive classification according to one highly overrated distinction persisted in some quarters for a surprisingly long time. Nevertheless the feet and hands of primates are of outstanding interest because they have generally retained original pentadactyl conditions with much more limited modifications than they have in so many other mammals.

In early stages of fetal development the feet of man are far more similar to those of monkeys than they are to their own, final condition in adult life. As shown in Fig. 7–3, the human fetal foot still has a relatively short, abduced first toe and relatively long phalangeal parts of the other toes among which the

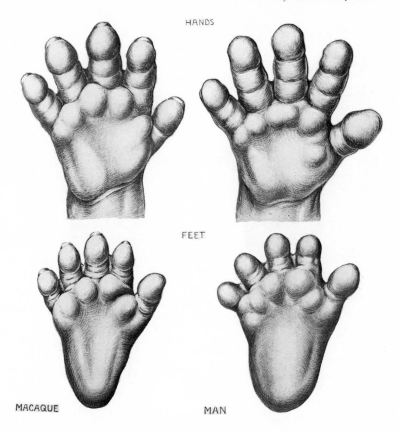

HANDS

FEET

MACAQUE   MAN

Fig. 7–3. (*Above*) hands and (*Below*) feet of (*Left*) a fetus of a macaque and (*Right*) of a man with sitting heights of 24 mm. (*From Schultz 1957*)

middle one is the longest. The primitive touch pads are well formed and so are the cutaneous interdigital webs, particularly between the second and third toes, where they are retained throughout life in some chimpanzees, occasional men and gibbons, and nearly all siamangs, the last having gained their name of *Symphalangus syndactylus* from that feature. Such ontogenetic findings leave no doubt that the foot of adult man with all its specializations for bipedal walking has been transformed from the prevailing type of primate feet, adapted chiefly to grasping and climbing. That such transformations have primarily resulted from modifications in the rates of growth of different parts of the feet, has been shown by detailed studies of the individual development of different primates (Schultz 1956).

The eastern gorilla, discovered only at the beginning of our century and hence unknown when all apes had been assigned to the "Quadrumana," resembles man most closely in regard to the outer form of its foot (Fig. 7–4). The

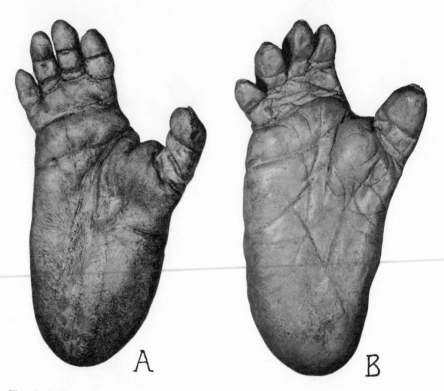

Fig. 7–4. Feet of adult male gorillas: (*A*) western, (*B*) eastern subspecies. (*From Schultz 1931*)

grasping ability of the first toe is decidedly more limited than in typical western gorillas and the other toes appear to be remarkably short and better suited for terrestrial than aboreal life.[2] In the gibbons, siamangs, and orang-utans the toes II to V are exceptionally long and together serve as a perfect climbing-hook for their life in the trees. The opposite extreme exists in the foot of terrestrial man, whose lateral toes have become shortened not only externally, but also in their entire phalangeal portions, to a much more marked degree than in any other primate (Fig. 7–5). The first toe, which is so uniform and thumb-like in all adult monkeys, has become specialized in widely different ways among the hominoids. In the Hylobatidae this digit is remarkably long and nearly to its base free of the sole, giving it a great mobility, but only moderate strength. This unique condition corresponds to that of the thumb in the same apes,

[2]In walking on flat ground the first toe is abduced, but not rotated. The separate, distal parts of the other toes are extremely short on account of thick plantar padding which extends far distally, but the total length of the phalanges is only moderately shortened as indicated in the foot of an eastern gorilla in Fig. 7–5.

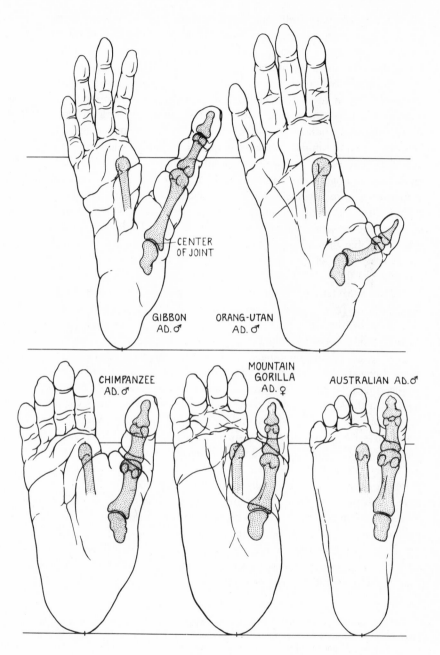

Fig. 7–5. Feet of adult hominoids showing the exact relation between the outer form and some skeletal parts of the same specimens, all reduced to equal length from heel to second metatarso-phalangeal joint. (*From Schultz 1950*)

which is also comparatively long and free of the palm for most of its metacarpal segment. In eastern gorillas and in man only the distal part of the phalangeal portion of the great toe really reaches beyond the plantar pillow. In all orangutans the permanently abduced first toes have clearly degenerated as in no other primate. Not only is this digit relatively short and exceptionally far proximal, but in more than half of all orang-utans it also contains only one phalanx instead of the normal two[3], as shown by the example in Fig. 7–5. This elimination of a phalanx is analogous to the reduction of the short fifth toe of man, in which the middle phalanx is quite commonly lacking, or to the nearly universal suppression of the outer thumbs of *Ateles* and of *Colobus*, or of the outer second fingers of *Arctocebus* and *Perodicticus*. That the entire feet of orang-utans have become one-sidedly specialized as extremely long hooks is evident also from their enormous proportionate length, which surpasses that of all other higher primates according to the data in Table 7–2. When standing upright on flat ground orang-utans have to support themselves awkwardly on the lateral edges of their outwardly twisted feet with the long and curved phalanges of the digits II to V tightly flexed as in a fist.

The total length of the hand in relation to the trunk length has its maximum average among all hominoids in gibbons and its minimum in man, as shown by the data in Table 7–2. The hand is also most slender in the former, though broadest not in man, but in gorillas (Fig. 7–6). The proportionate length of the phalangeal and metacarpal parts of the fingers has remained remarkably uniform in all higher primates. In the middle digit, for example, this relation equals approximately 3:2 in the long-handed gibbons as well as in the great apes and even in man with his short hands (Schultz 1930). In contrast to this, the corresponding proportion of the hominoid feet shows very marked generic differences, since the lengths of the phalangeal and metatarsal parts of the toes have evidently changed independently of each other.

The thumb is of particular interest as a vital aid for most arboreal primates in securing good holds on branches and on account of its gradually perfected usefulness for many additional purposes. The thumb of all hominoids is longer in relation to their size, as represented by trunk length, than it is in any monkeys and reaches its maximum relative length in gibbons, while man and the great apes have very similar, smaller averages, according to Table 7–2. Only in its relation to the greatest hand length is the thumb of man longer than that of the apes and thereby reaches beyond the palm, as shown in Fig. 7–6.

---

[3]Tuttle and Rogers (1966) have recently reported this congenital bilateral lack of a terminal phalanx in the first toes of orang-utans in 60 percent of 30 animals from the Yerkes Primate Center with a surprisingly unequal distribution in both sexes, namely in 87 percent of females, whereas in only 33 percent of males. According to the writer's former (1941; 1956) and latest records on a total of 121 other orang-utans of known sex, the same condition existed in 62 percent of all specimens, females alone showing it in 73 percent, but males in only 49 percent of the cases. In a few additional orang-utans this reduction was present on one side only.

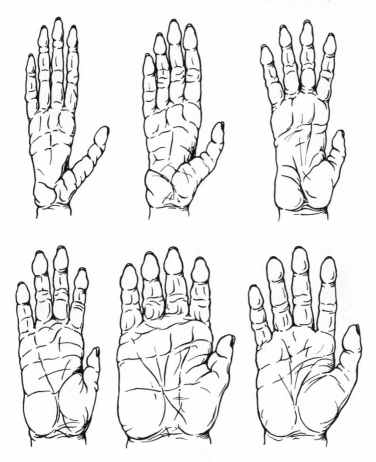

Fig. 7–6. Hands of adult hominoids, reduced to same total length. (From top left to bottom right) Gibbon, siamang, orang-utan, chimpanzee, gorilla, and man. (*From Schultz 1965*)

This, however, does not support the frequent claim that the human thumb has become longer, because it is the length of the other fingers of man and even the size of his entire hand which are comparatively small and may possibly have become reduced only after man's hands had become freed from their former functions of support and locomotion. The free part of the thumb branches from the palm much nearer the wrist in all catarrhines than in any New World monkeys and at the same time it has become very much rotated to face the other digits for effective opposability. As shown by the examples in Fig. 7–3. these conditions are not yet present in early fetal life when the thumb still branches from near the base of the second finger and is as yet not the least rotated. This stage of development remains practically unchanged in platy-rrhines, whereas in all catarrhines the thumb shifts and rotates during later fetal development as it did in its evolutionary specialization (for details see Schultz 1926; 1949; 1956).

As a unique specialization of chimpanzees and gorillas is to be mentioned that they support themselves in quadrupedal posture on the knuckles of their fingers II to V, since these digits become automatically flexed with the slightest dorsal extension of the hand on account of the relatively short flexor muscles of the fingers. Undoubtedly in closest connection therewith the skin on the dorsal side of the middle segments of these fingers has developed regular dermato-glyphics, which are not present in any other primates (Biegert 1961). This support on the knuckles in standing quadrupedally raises the level of vision and the mechanical finger flexion is of advantage in hanging under branches as well

Fig. 7–7. Different positions of the hands in quadrupedal posture in some catarrhines. (*Drawn from photographs*)

as in carrying objects during bipedal walk. These specializations are not clearly developed in orang-utans and totally lacking in man, gibbons and all other catarrhines (Fig. 7–7).

The last four indices in Table 7–2 express some proportions of the head in an exact numerical manner. The percentage relation between the mean head diameter and the trunk length is significantly greater in all hominoids than in macaques and other monkeys. This, however, shows the corresponding difference in relative brain size in only a very approximate, general way, because the outer dimensions of the brain part of the head are much influenced by the development of the supraorbital arch and the thickness of the temporal muscles as well as the existence of cranial crests. In gorillas the head height can furthermore be greatly increased by the frequent thick subcutaneous pad of connective tissue near the vertex (Straus 1942) (see Fig. 7–12).

The size of the face in its relation to that of the trunk is much larger in the pongids than in the other hominoids and surpasses even in man that of gibbons. According to the relation between the upper face height and the mean head diameter the three great apes are again distinguished by the largest averages and man and the gibbon by the smallest ones, with the siamang bridging the gap. From these and various other relative measurements, representing the proportionate size of the face, it has become very evident that it is not the face of man which has become exceptionally small, but the faces of the great apes and most of all those of male orang-utans and gorillas, which have evolved to an enormous size. Not only gibbons, but a variety of monkeys have proportionately just as small, or even smaller, faces than man, and this not for allometric reasons alone (see Figs. 7–8, 7–30, 7–31).

CHARACTERS OF THE OUTER BODY

The pigmentation of skin and hair can vary very extensively not only in man, but also in all man-like apes and, furthermore, can change with age at least as much in the latter as in the former. For instance, many chimpanzees have as light a skin color as Europeans, while others acquire regionally brown or black skin sooner or later, often extending even to the palms and soles. As in some colored human beings, the epithelial lining of the gums and palate of apes often show dark pigment in irregular distribution. The hair color of *Hylobates lar* varies even within local populations to a surprising degree between nearly white, brown, and black, except for the always white hands, feet, and brows (Fig. 7–9). Among chimpanzees rare individuals also can have very light or reddish hair, and in some young gorillas the hair is gray or chestnut-brown instead of nearly black. The hair on the back of old male gorillas turns very light so that they well deserve their name of "silver-back." Full-grown orang-utans often develop hair of record length, measuring at times more than 70 cm. on the back and shoulders. The density of hair is another variable feature of

Fig. 7–8. Female white-handed gibbon with its young of 2
months. (*Photograph by J. Klages, from Schultz 1965*)

hominoids, as shown by the data in Table 7–3. As a rule this density is most
marked on the head and much smaller on the ventral than on the dorsal side of
the trunk. In male gorillas the entire wide chest becomes practically bare with
advancing age. Gibbons have by far the densest hair of all catarrhines and the
difference between their extreme hair density and the very moderate density of
the great apes is much more pronounced than the difference between the latter
and that of man. It is of interest also that the siamang resembles the pongids
more nearly than the gibbons in regard to its hair density, as in many other
features. Many adult orang-utans develop remarkably conspicuous moustaches
and/or beards which usually are of lighter color than their other hair. They
occur only in occasional females and can be totally absent in a minority of even
fully-grown males. Similarly striking individual variations without close sex-
linkage exist also in the unique cheekpads of adult orang-utans (Fig. 7–9 and

Fig. 7–9. An old male orang-utan in the London Zoo.

7–10). These puzzling formations are never exactly alike in any two specimens, they can be lacking in some few males and fairly well formed in rare females. They are already indicated in fetuses by perpendicular skin folds and in newborns by faint ridges of converging hairs, but any further development appears only after puberty (Schultz 1941; 1956).

All catarrhine monkeys and all gibbons and siamangs have in common sharply bordered horny callosities, covering directly the ischial tuberosities and thus serving as hard pads in sitting. Ontogenetically, however, these structures differ significantly in the Cercopithecoidea and Hylobatidae since they appear

Table 7–3. The average numbers of hairs per square centimeter of skin on the vertex, back, and chest of adult primates (from Schultz 1931, and some later data).

	Vertex	Back	Chest
Macaques	650	480	70
Gibbons	2100	1720	600
Siamangs	715	430	260
Orang-utans	158	175	105
Chimpanzees	185	100	70
Gorillas	410	145	4
Europeans	330	0	3
Negroes	305	0	0
Mongolians	128	0	0

early in the prenatal development of the former, whereas not until the time of birth or even later in the latter, when they replace the preceding lanugo hair of the corresponding region (Schultz 1933; 1937; 1956). Many individuals of the great apes can also acquire such cornified callosities of considerable size and thickness, but only gradually during postnatal growth. In man alone has nothing like it ever been recorded, evidently because the gluteal musculature is interposed between skin and bone.

The volar sides of the hands and feet of all primates are covered by highly specialized, tactile skin, bearing complicated ridge patterns of so-called dermatoglyphics which appear already on the embryonic touchpads and retain their detailed arrangement throughout life. The systematic and very comprehensive investigation of these structures by Biegert (1961) supports convincingly the assumption of a common origin of all recent hominoids and the conclusion that the three families must have evolved in diverging directions, because their differently specialized ridge patterns can all be derived from generally more primitive conditions of lower catarrhines, from which man has not deviated the most in all respects.

All simian primates have normally only two mammary glands left which develop near the second or third ribs where they usually remain permanently. In man alone do they migrate caudally during growth, to become centered at about the fourth intercostal space. In orang-utans and some species of monkeys the nipples lie far laterally near the axillae, but in the hylobatids and African great apes they have come practically as close together as in man. The glandular tissue of the breasts is widely spread out over the chest with little difference in its thickness in typical monkeys, but among the hominoids it is much more limited in extent while increasing in depth during lactation until many female apes develop similarly protruding or even hanging breasts as exist in women.

Fig. 7–10. Head of another old male orang-utan with strong moustache and beard and differently formed cheek pads. (*Drawn from a photograph*)

Among external features may here also be mentioned the throat pouches which are most conspicuous in adult siamangs and orang-utans. In old males of the latter species these pouches can reach all the way to the axillae and hold more than 6 liters of air when fully extended. The laryngeal pouches of gorillas can extend equally far, but are usually less voluminous. Among chimpanzees the corresponding sacs are as a rule of very modest size, but some remarkably large ones have been described, including a record one of an old female, which appeared like a huge goitre (Yerkes 1943). The exact function of these laryngeal formations, which have been thoroughly reviewed by Starck and Schneider (1960), cannot yet be satisfactorily explained. They are not simply secondary sex characters, even though they are usually best developed in old males. Their supposed role as a resonating apparatus is also unconvincing in view of the fact that gibbons and siamangs can call equally loud, but only the latter have and make use of pouches with an effective volume.

The external genital organs of the hominoids have been dealt with in a voluminous literature, which has recently been reviewed by Hill (1958). For the purposes of this paper it must suffice to discuss briefly the most interesting generic differences in these structures. The male genitalia and, particularly, the testes are exceptionally small in gorillas, whereas comparatively large in chimpanzees, as shown by the following data: The testicular weight in percentage of body weight averages among adults 0.27 in chimpanzees, 0.08 in man and gibbons, 0.05 in orang-utans (Schultz 1938) and only about 0.02 or even less in gorillas (Wislocki 1942, Hall-Cragg 1962). The permanent descent of the testes takes place some time before birth in man, whereas usually not until during infancy in the apes. The scrotum of all pongids lies behind the penis, as in man, but in the Hylobatidae the paired scrotal sacs are situated on both sides or even toward the front of the penis. A so-called baculum or penis bone occurs in all male hominoids, except man, but is proportionatley much smaller in the apes than in many monkeys. Of the external female genitalia it is specially noteworthy that those of the gibbons resemble the human condition more closely than do those of the great apes, whose labia majora tend to disappear during early growth. Important generic differences exist also in regard to the cyclic swelling of the female pudendal region which reaches an enormous size in mature chimpanzees during each menstrual period, is barely indicated in gorillas, occurs only toward the end of pregnancy in orang-utans, and is totally lacking in gibbons and man. An excellent and detailed discussion of these sex swellings, which are found also in a great variety of Old World monkeys, has been published by Harms (1956).

Among the external features of the head one may mention the remarkable existence of deep wrinkles in the skin of chimpanzees and gorillas, present already in older fetuses and becoming most marked on and below the eyelids, the cheeks and the region of the mouth. The numerous oral wrinkles are undoubtedly connected with the great mobility of the large lips (Figs. 7–11 and 7–12). The shape and size of the outer nose differs enormously among hominoids, even though the noses of all are supported by the same few cartilages, as shown by the examples in Fig. 7–13. The septum cartilage of the apes projects very little beyond the bony aperture, corresponding to their flat outer noses, and the roof cartilage forms only a small continuation of the nasal bones, especially in gorillas. The wing cartilages are also not nearly as large in the apes as they are in man, not even those in the excessively broad and thick nasal wings of gorillas. In the captive adult male gorilla "Gargantua" the author found a roof cartilage of less than 1 cm² and paper-thin alar cartilages, limited to the nasal center and not extending into the huge wings, which were mere pads of fat. In contrast to this, the prominent nose of man is far more extensively supported by cartilage,

Fig. 7–11. Heads of a female and a male chimpanzee at different ages. (*From Schultz 1940*)

Fig. 7–12. Head of an adult male gorilla. (*Drawn from a photograph*)

which closely determines its shape. While the nearly immobile nasal wings of the apes consist of little more than skin and fat, the thin and mobile wings of human noses are extensively stiffened by cartilage to keep them from being sucked shut with every inhalation.

The outer ears of the hominoids differ widely in their relative size, as shown by the last index in Table 7–2. Orang-utans are distinguished by the proportionately smallest ears of all primates, whereas chimpanzees by nearly the largest ones among the Simiae. No functional reasons can be given for this extreme difference between these pongids, of which one has its ears atrophied and the other excessively overdeveloped in individually variable degrees. Ontogenetically this is a direct result of very different rates of growth, since small ears simply increase their size far less than large ones, particularly postnatally,

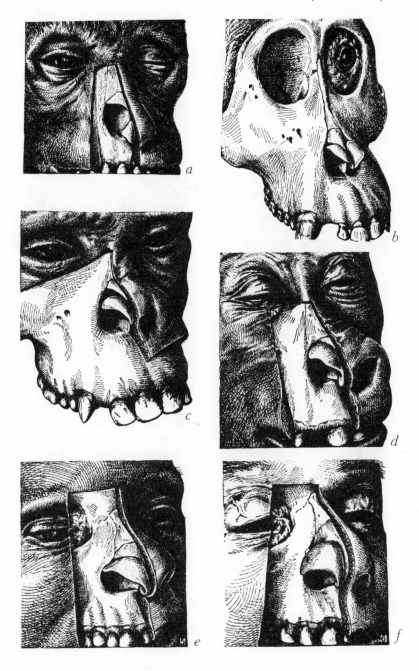

Fig. 7–13. Noses and nasal cartilages of (*a*), a siamang, (*b*), orang-utan, (*c*), chimpanzee, (*d*), gorilla, (*e*), negro, and (*f*), European. (*From Schultz 1935*)

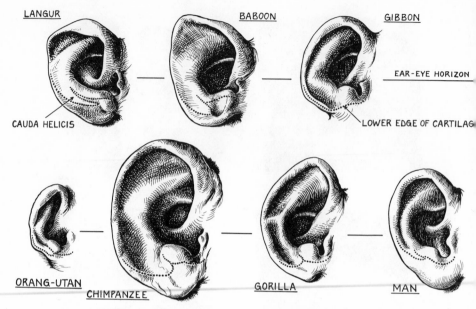

LANGUR   BABOON   GIBBON

EAR-EYE HORIZON

CAUDA HELICIS   LOWER EDGE OF CARTILAGE

ORANG-UTAN   GORILLA   MAN
CHIMPANZEE

Fig. 7–14. The outer ears of some adult catarrhines with the lower border of the cartilage shown by the dotted lines. (*From Schultz 1950*)

inasmuch as newborn orang-utans still have relatively larger ears than adults. The edge of the helix shows in hominoids a strong tendency to become rolled-in not only on top, but also posteriorly, where this occurs rarely and then as a mere indication among the lower catarrhines (Fig. 7–14). Clearly pointed ears, commonly called "satyr ears," are among monkeys typical for only macaques and baboons and do not occur in any hominoids, not even in early stages of development.[4] There is no justification, therefore, to interpret the occasional "Darwinian tubercles" on human ears as an atavistic manifestation of ancestral, pointed ears (Lasinski 1960). True ear lobules, free of cartilage, exist not only in most human beings, but also in the African apes and some monkeys, while they are absent in gibbons and nearly all orang-utans (Fig. 7–14). The extrinsic ear musculature of the hominoids is poorly developed in comparison with that of monkeys, whose ears are correspondingly more mobile.

Among the superficial characters there are finally to be mentioned the interesting palatine ridges, or rugae, which have been retained even by man as utterly useless remnants. These transverse folds of the lining of the hard palate exist in nearly all mammals and appear already at early stages of intrauterine development. As a rule they aid the newborn in firmly holding the maternal nipple and later in life they not only lead food to the grinding teeth, but, when

[4]The pointed form of the ear of the fetus of supposedly an orang-utan, pictured by Darwin (1874), is clearly due to accidental distortion through having been preserved in a tight container. Furthermore this specimen is certainly not an orang-utan, but in the writer's opinion a gibbon.

cornified, are also helpful in crunching food. Many mammals have their entire hard palates covered with dense rows of parallel rugae of considerable and very effective height. In all prosimians they are also well developed, though not as numerous as in most ungulates. The great majority of monkeys still possess from 6 to 10 of these transverse folds, extending mostly back to the last molars, as shown by the example of the macaque in Fig. 7–15. In the higher primates one can recognize a clear trend to limit these ridges to the anterior part of the palate and to interrupt and ramify these, now low, folds into more or less irregular and asymmetrical patterns. According to the numerous data, collected by the writer (1958), gibbons, siamangs, and orang-utans have as rough averages 8 pair of rugae, which often still reach as far back as the second molars. A quite complicated pattern is characteristic for chimpanzees, among which the highest numbers of rugae have been found. These numbers varied between 5 and 15 in 46 chimpanzees, between 3 and 10 in 16 gorillas, and between 2 and 8 in 519 human beings. These folds, which retain their number throughout life, extend only to the first molars in the African apes and often to merely the posterior premolars in man. It is of interest to note that with advancing degeneration of these structures they have become specially variable in most their details.

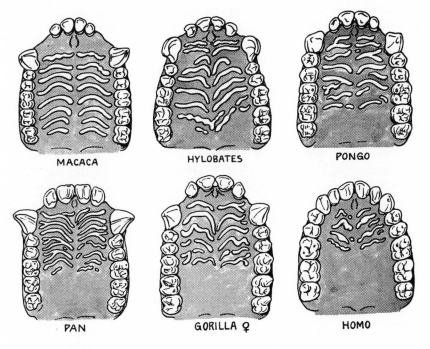

MACACA   HYLOBATES   PONGO

PAN   GORILLA ♀   HOMO

Fig. 7–15. Typical palatine ridges of adult hominoids and of a macaque. (*From Schultz 1958*)

SKELETON

Of all bodily parts of the recent man-like apes the skeleton has become best known because it is available in our collections in numbers adequate for a full consideration of its important intraspecific variability. That the latter is of great interest in the study of phylogenetic problems can here be shown by the example of the numerical variations of the vertebrae. With only few highly specialized exceptions all mammals possess normally 7 cervical vertebrae. For primates it can also be confidently assumed that this same number has remained unchanged, because 6 or 8 of these vertebrae have been found in only very rare cases. In striking contrast to this high stability of the phylogenetically constant number of cervical vertebrae, there have occurred extremely great changes, accompanied by very marked variability, in the number of vertebrae in the tails of primates, which ranges from 0 to 35! In all recent hominoids the tail has become extremely reduced, except for its brief appearance in embryonic life before it is overgrown by adjoining tissues and its more numerous segments have been resorbed or fused. In adults the rudimentary coccygeal vertebrae have been found to vary between 3 and 5 and to average 4.2 in a total of 745 human skeletons. In the man-like apes this reduction has generally progressed even farther, namely to averages between only 2.2 in siamangs and 3.3 in chimpanzees, with a total range of individual variations for apes from 0 to 6 (Schultz 1930; 1961).

The combined number of thoracic and lumbar vertebrae is a clear expression for the important segmental position of the pelvic ring on the vertebral column. This number fluctuates among primates between 15 and 24, with values above 20 occurring only in certain prosimians and a few exceptional platyrrhines. Among all Old World monkeys these vertebrae number as a rule 19 and vary merely between 18 and 20. The recent hominoids are the only primates showing a pronounced reduction in this number and hence a clear trend to shift the pelvis in a cranial direction. As is evident from the data in Table 7–4, this specialization has progressed most in orang-utans and also more in the other pongids than it has in man. The relevant marked difference between gibbons and siamangs is of interest as showing again a closer approach to the great apes in the latter than in the former, which are the only hominoids which still have occasionally 19 thoracic + lumbar vertebrae. This reduction of the number of presacral segments took place mainly at the expense of the lumbar region. The great majority of catarrhine monkeys has retained the original number of 7 lumbar vertebrae, combined with 12 thoracic ones, but in all recent hominoids the lumbar region has been shortened by at least one segment and usually by several. On an average gibbons and man possess 5 lumbar vertebrae, siamangs 4.4, orang-utans 4.0, and both the African apes 3.6 with only 3 existing in more than a third of the cases (for details see Schultz 1961). Due to the extremely short lumbar region of the great apes and the fact

Table 7-4. Percentage distribution of variations in the number of thoracic + lumbar vertebrae and of sacral vertebrae and average numbers of these vertebrae in hominoids and macaques (from Schultz 1961). To limit this table to the most significant data, all cases of transitional vertebrae have here been included with the nearest lower variations. Numbers of skeletons examined are listed in parentheses.

	Number of Vertebrae	Macaque (216)	Gibbon (319)	Siamang (29)	Orang (127)	Chimp. (162)	Gorilla (81)	Man (125)
Thoracic + Lumbar	15	—	—	4	19	—	—	—
	16	—	—	10	74	29	43	7
	17	5	5	48	7	68	56	91
	18	91	72	38	—	3	1	2
	19	4	23	—	—	—	—	—
	20	—	—	—	—	—	—	—
	Average	19.0	18.2	17.3	15.9	16.8	16.6	17.0
Sacral	2	3	—	—	—	—	—	—
	3	93	3	—	—	—	—	—
	4	4	42	38	3	1	1	3
	5	—	51	55	59	36	36	72
	6	—	4	7	36	55	56	24
	7	—	—	—	2	8	6	1
	8	—	—	—	—	1	1	—
	Average	3.0	4.6	4.7	5.4	5.7	5.7	5.2

that also their extremely long iliac blades can reach high above the lumbo-
sacral border, the iliac crests approach the last pair of ribs so exceptionally
closely that the lateral flexibility of the trunk has become far more restricted in
the pongids than in man, the Hylobatidae and, of course, the lower catarrhines.
This is very evident from the examples in the Figs. 7–16, 7–17, and 7–18, and
explains the necessarily close correspondence in the transverse direction and
curvature of the ilia and the lower part of the thorax in the great apes.

The original number of vertebrae, fused in the sacrum, was most likely
only 3 and this has been retained practically unchanged by the great majority
of lower primates. A significant increase in this number of sacral vertebrae has
taken place quite independently in two groups, namely in the lorisoid prosimians, which have as many as 9 such segments, and in all the hominoids, as
shown in Table 7–4. This phylogenetic trend to enlarge the solid sacral wedge
between the hipbones has progressed least among the higher primates in
gibbons and most in the great apes, agreeing thereby with the degrees of specialization in the reduction of presacral vertebrae. That the addition of vertebrae to the hominoid sacrum has not yet become stabilized, is shown by the
remarkable range of numerical variations of the sacral segments in gorillas and
chimpanzees, which extends over 5 figures, whereas in monkeys at most over
only 3. "Unilateral variations," represented by asymmetrical transition-ver-
tebrae, with typical lumbar characters on one side and sacral ones on the other,

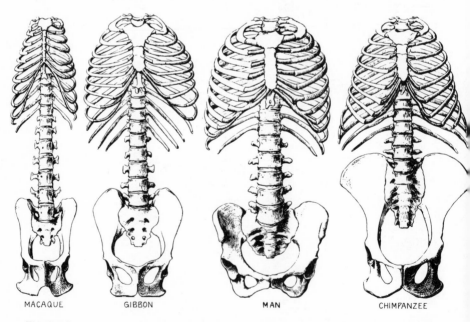

MACAQUE   GIBBON   MAN   CHIMPANZEE

Fig. 7–16. Exact drawings of ligamentous trunk skeletons of four adult female primates,
reduced to same total length. (*From Schultz 1950*)

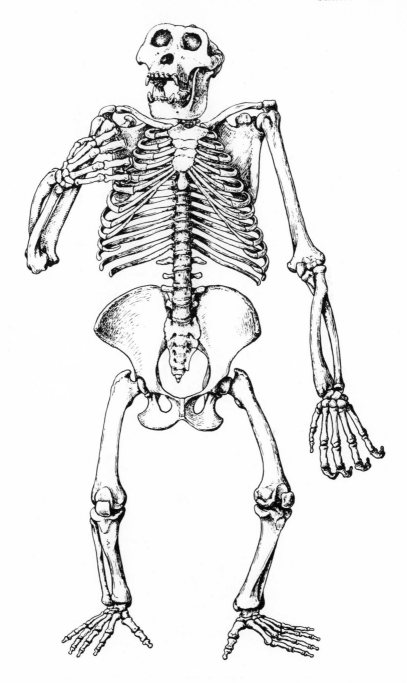

Fig. 7–17. Skeleton of an adult male western gorilla. (*Mounted and drawn by the author*)

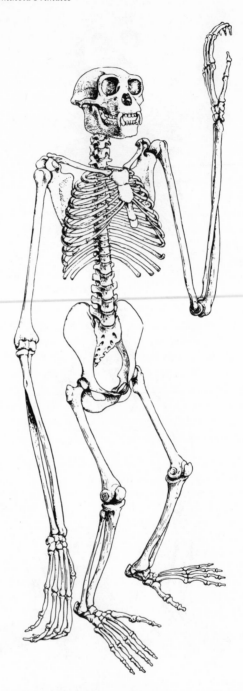

Fig. 7–18. Skeleton of an adult siamang. (*Mounted and drawn by the author*)

are also exceptionally frequent in all apes, as has been demonstrated in a special publication by the author (1961).

The proportional length of the different regions of the vertebral column depends not only on the number of segments but often also on other factors, as is very evident, for example by the extremely different lengths of the neck in giraffes and in elephants in spite of both containing 7 cervical vertebrae. In primates the relatively longest necks belong to the hominoids whose cervical regions equal always more than 20 percent of the entire length of the presacral spine in contrast to the considerably shorter neck length of all lower catarrhines. Man and the man-like apes are distinguished from all other catarrhines by their relatively longer thoracic and much shorter lumbar regions, as shown in Table 7–5 and by many more data in a former publication by the author (1961). As a rule the lumbar region is actually longer than the thoracic one in the Old World monkeys, whereas much shorter in all higher primates and this even more so in the apes than in man.

The thickness and, particularly, the breadth of the bodies of the thoracic and lumbar vertebrae is relatively much greater in hominoids than in monkeys (Schultz 1953). This difference can only in part be due to the different body weights, carried by the spinal column, because the small gibbons as well as the large gorillas surpass the cercopithecoids in this respect. The largest relative breadth of the lumbar vertebrae exists in man, most likely as a result of his erect posture which has changed the vertebral column from what is functionally a carrying beam in quadrupeds into the only true upright *column* with a thickness gradually increasing toward the base, as in the trunk of a tree.

Among the many other characteristics of the hominoid vertebrae there are some of particular interest because they have become most highly specialized in

Table 7–5. Average length of the cervical region of the vertebral column in percentage of the trunk length and average lengths of the cervical, thoracic, and lumbar regions in percentage of the total presacral spine length (with the wet intervertebral discs) in adult hominoids and macaques (after Schultz 1961).

	Cervical R.	Cervical R.	Thoracic R.	Lumbar R.
	Trunk Length	Presacral Spine Length		
Macaque	17.2	16.6	40.8	42.6
Gibbon	21.7	21.0	48.7	30.3
Siamang	23.5	20.8	50.1	29.1
Orang-utan.........	24.2	24.5	50.9	24.6
Chimpanzee........	22.5	23.5	53.5	23.0
Gorilla	24.2	24.2	51.2	24.6
Man...................	25.3	22.0	45.1	32.9

man, or else decidedly less so than in the apes. For instance, the dorsal spines of the cervical vertebrae of all great apes have acquired an exceptional length to support their powerful nuchal musculature, needed in carrying the heavy and very poorly balanced head (Fig. 7–19). Cervical spines of such great length occur among all other primates only in the prosimian pottos in which they protrude on the surface and serve for protection when the head and neck are much flexed. In other mammals one often finds similarly overdeveloped vertebral spines, but only in the anterior part of the thoracic region and in a few ungulates also on the seventh cervical vertebra. Since recent and fossil man have as short dorsal spines on the vertebrae of their necks as have gibbons and all monkeys, it can be concluded that only the pongids have become highly specialized in this respect. Especially in full-grown male orang-utans and gorillas, these spines attain such an excessive length that the movability of their necks is very restricted. In the lateral processes of the cervical vertebrae exist also marked differences among the hominoids, especially in the formation of the foramina transversalia, through most of which pass the vertebral arteries. These openings between the true transverse processes and the vestigeal costal elements are very rarely missing in even the seventh vertebra of man, but in the other primates it is rare to find corresponding foramina in this segment. In gibbons, for example, real foramina are lacking in the seventh vertebra in two thirds of the cases and in orang-utans even in all cases. The latter are distinguished by the frequent absence of transverse foramina in also the sixth and fifth vertebrae of the neck, which bear at best mere notches in place of holes (Schultz 1961).

The longitudinal axis of the vertebral column in a position of rest deviates from a straight line much more in man than in the nonhuman primates. The regionally alternating curves of the human spine, shown in Fig. 7–20, increase the springiness of the perpendicular presacral column. The most marked change from a straight continuation of the row of vertebrae exists in man at the

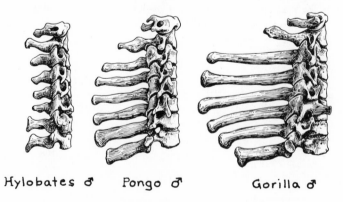

Hylobates ♂   Pongo ♂   Gorilla ♂

Fig. 7–19. Side views of the first eight vertebrae of adult male gibbon, orang-utan, and gorilla. (*From Schultz 1961*)

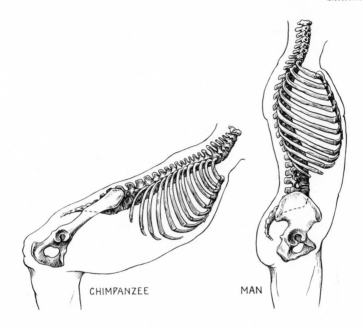

CHIMPANZEE   MAN

Fig. 7–20. The curvature of the vertebral column and the position and size of the hip bone in an adult ape and man. (*From Schultz 1957*)

lumbo-sacral border, where the sacrum is so abruptly bent back that it forms a striking promontory with the lumbar region. Man, however, is not the only primate possessing such a promontory, as has often been claimed, but he is the one whose sacrum has become dorso-flexed most extremely in connection with other unique specializations in his entire pelvis. As shown by the examples in Fig. 7–21, all man-like apes have also acquired unmistakable promontories as adults, though not nearly as marked ones as that of man. The angle between the ventral profiles of the lumbar and of the sacral region increases during growth in all higher primates; in man it is as yet barely indicated in the middle of fetal life, reaches about 20° at birth and somewhere between 60° and as much as 80° in adults. In apes the same angle appears later and increases more slowly to values between 22° and 38° of adults according to the author's data for great many specimens. In most monkeys the sacrum deviates but little from the general direction of the spinal column even in adults, but in baboons the caudal end of the sacrum tends to be bent far dorsally to provide a sufficiently wide pelvic passage-way for the unusually large heads of their full-term fetuses (Schultz, 1961, Fig. 17). With the erect presacral part of the human spinal column transmitting its load onto only the anterior end of the sharply tilted sacrum, man has acquired a mechanically precarious articulation at his promontory. It is at this place that the last lumbar vertebra is apt to slip forward and produce a condition known as spondylolisthesis of varying severity, which

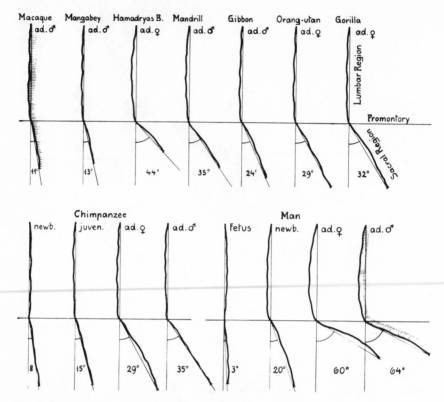

Fig. 7–21. Exact ventral profiles of the lumbar and sacral vertebral regions and angles between their different directions in some catarrhine primates. (*From Schultz 1961*)

is not at all rare in man (Taillard 1957), but has never been found in other primates.

As has already been mentioned, the trunk of all hominoids has become extremely broad. In consequence the transverse diameter of the thorax has also come to surpass the sagittal one in length (Fig. 7–22). At the same time the vertebral column of the higher primates has migrated ventrally in contrast to the condition typical for all quadrupedal monkeys whose vertebrae hardly protrude into the chest cavity. As shown by the outlines of chest cavities in Fig. 7–22, this hominoid distinction appears only gradually during growth and becomes most pronounced in adult man. The latter extreme represents undoubtedly an adaptation for the advantageous distribution of the load around the upright column which has closely approached the center of gravity. It is of great interest, therefore, that this condition has also developed in all the apes, though not as an equally marked departure from the dorsal position of the vertebrae in monkeys. In direct connection with this specialization of hominoids the ribs had to become much more strongly bent at their dorsal ends than in

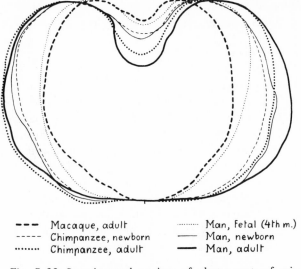

- - - Macaque, adult	········ Man, fetal (4th m.)
- - - - - Chimpanzee, newborn	——— Man, newborn
········· Chimpanzee, adult	▬▬▬ Man, adult

Fig. 7–22. Superimposed tracings of plaster casts of eviscerated thoracic cavities, cut perpendicular to thoracic spine at level of ventral ends of sixth ribs, reduced to same sagittal diameter. (*From Schultz 1956*)

monkeys, as is shown by the examples in Fig. 7–23. The transverse diameters of the thorax increase steadily in a cranio-caudal direction in all the great apes, which possess a funnel-shaped thorax, while in gibbons and man it is normally

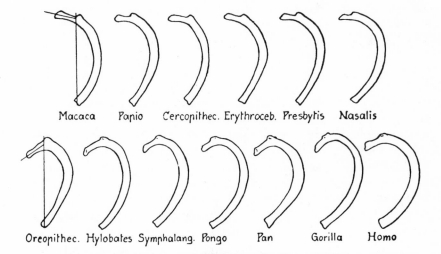

Macaca   Papio   Cercopithec.   Erythroceb.   Presbytis   Nasalis

Oreopithec.   Hylobates   Symphalang.   Pongo   Pan   Gorilla   Homo

Fig. 7–23. Tracings of second ribs of some adult catarrhines, reduced to same straight length of corpus. (*From Schultz 1960*)

more barrel-shaped, as shown in the Figs. 7–16, 7–17, and 7–18, and most clearly in the X-ray photograph of the trunk of an orang-utan, published by the author in 1961.

Together with the entire trunk the sternum of all higher primates has also become much broader than that of the Cercopithecoidea, so that the former had sometimes been referred to as *Latisternalia*. The data for the length–breadth relation of the corpus sterni in Table 7–6 show this striking difference between lower and higher primates and also that in this respect chimpanzees have become least specialized, whereas siamangs and orang-utans most specialized. Intraspecifically this proportion is characterized by an enormous variability in the higher primates, as are so many of their other distinguishing features. The uppermost part of the sternum—the manubrium—is unusual in the Hylobatidae inasmuch as it extends as one single bone to the third ribs in nearly all specimens (Fig. 7–16 and 7–18), a condition only occasionally seen in orangutans and gorillas and as very rare exceptions in man. The longest part of the sternum—the corpus—consists in all monkeys of a row of bony segments which normally never fuse, in contrast to the conditions in all apes and man, whose sternebrae tend to become united with advancing age and this in a caudocranial sequence. This typically hominoid specialization of fusing the segmental ossification centers for the corpus sterni into one single bone occurs ontogenetically earlier in man than in the apes in which this process is usually not completed until old age. Detailed findings of this sort, which can be explained only as resulting from shared evolutionary trends, are convincing proofs of the common origin of all hominoids.

The shoulder girdle of the higher primates has also been greatly influenced by the general broadening of the trunk which has led to a lengthening of the collar bones and to the already mentioned shifting of the shoulder blades

Table 7–6. Breadth of corpus sterni in percentage of its length in a total of 300 adult catarrhines (Schultz 1930; 1961, and 11 new data). The length was always measured from the level of attachment of the second ribs, even if the manubrium extended to the third ribs.

	Range of Variations	*Average*
Cercopithecus....................	9—14	10.6
Macaca............................	8—14	12.2
Hylobates........................	25—56	35.1
Symphalangus..................	49—58	53.3
Pongo	43—92	56.8
Pan.................................	16—37	23.9
Gorilla............................	31—62	45.0
Homo	25—49	35.8

from the sides to the back. The clavicles of monkeys measure only about 15 or 16 percent of their trunk lengths, but those of all hominoids from anywhere between 26 and 35 percent, having to reach from the ventral manubrium to the dorsal and often far cranially situated acromion (see Fig. 7–1 and Table 7–7). As is to be expected, this relative clavicular length has attained its extreme in the expert brachiators—the Asiatic apes—but it is surprisingly larger in man than in the African apes, even though the human clavicles are horizontally directed instead of steeply diverging upward as in the apes.

The shoulder blades are built quite uniformly in the Old World monkeys, roughly as in the macaque in Fig. 7–24, but among the hominoids they have developed remarkably different shapes, as shown by the examples in the same figure. The bony plates above and below the scapular spine serve exclusively for the attachment of muscles and as levers for muscular actions and hence have highly variable and often even asymmetrical forms and proportional sizes, conditioned by corresponding differences in muscular development. Orang-utans and gorillas represent opposite extremes in the relation in size between the fossae supraspinata and infraspinata. As is also indicated in Fig. 7–24, the acromial process is much longer and broader in all higher primates than in monkeys according to exact measurements on many specimens (Schultz 1930).

In the pelvic girdle of the hominoids one can again recognize the influence of the general widening of the entire trunk and this most clearly in the significantly broader iliac blades than in any of the other primates (Figs. 7–16, 7–25, and 7–26). To be more precise, it is the fossa iliaca which has become so much enlarged and this even more in the gorilla than in man, while the great total width of the human ilium is largely due to the uniquely increased sacral surface, that is, its dorsal part which had to become strengthened with the acquisition of the erect posture with which a larger share of the body weight is

Table 7–7. Averages of the length of the clavicle in percentage of the trunk length in adult catarrhines. As a rule these averages are slightly larger in males than in females, but in chimpanzees and gorillas they are alike in both sexes.

Genus	*Specimens*	*Average*
Cercopithecus	10	15.1
Macaca	20	16.2
Hylobates	20	32.4
Symphalangus	3	34.5
Pongo	8	35.3
Pan	15	26.8
Gorilla	10	26.0
Homo	20	29.9

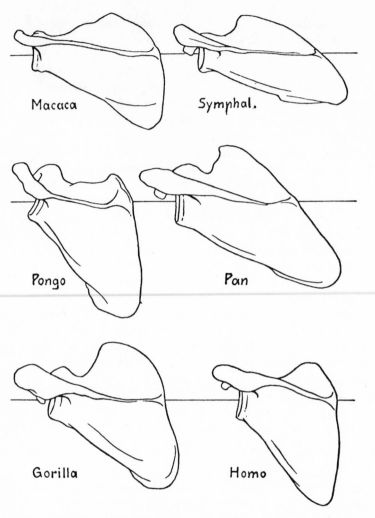

Fig. 7–24. Scapulae of adult macaque and hominoids, oriented according to their morphological lengths. (*From Schultz 1965*)

transmitted from the spinal column to the hip bones than in quadrupeds or brachiators. By exact measurments it was found that the area of the sacro-iliac joint is just twice as large per kilogram of body weight in man than in the great apes (Schultz 1961). For the same reason the hip joint has also become exceptionally large in bipedal man. The ilia of the pongids have not only increased their width, but also their length. Individually the greatest iliac length amounts to as much as 42 percent of the trunk length in some apes, whereas never more than 25 percent in man. In the cercopithecoids this index is not much larger than in man, with averages fluctuating between only 23 and 28, but in gibbons

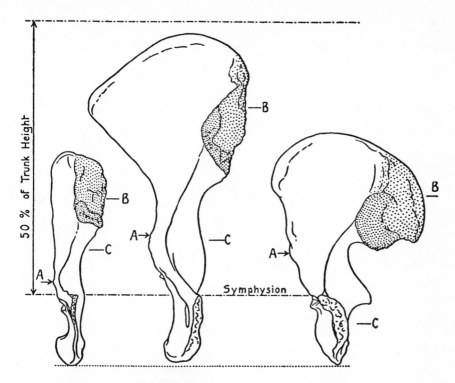

Fig. 7–25. Medial views of right hip bones of adult macaque, gorilla and man, reduced to same trunk length and with symphysion at same level: (*A*) highest point of acetabulum, (*B*) highest ventral midsagittal point of sacrum, (*C*) lowest midsagittal point of sacrum. (*From Schultz 1936*)

the average has increased to about 33, in orang-utans to 36 and in the African great apes to 38 (Schultz 1950).

As is shown most clearly in Fig. 7–20, the weight of the trunk is transfered in apes from the sacro-iliac joints by the long iliac levers to the far caudally situated hip joints, whereas in upright man these joints lie in one perpendicular plane and also much nearer together on account of the shortness of the human ilium which has telescoped the sacrum into the pelvic outlet (Fig. 7–26). The pelvis of man has become distinguished in many further respects. In nonhuman primates the sacrum lies always high above the pubic symphysis, but in man it has sunk down to a position practically opposite the symphysis, to which it has to remain parallel to keep the birth canal open all the way (Fig. 7–20). The transverse diameter of the latter vital passage is in man fully as wide as the sagittal diameter (Fig. 7–37). This is due not only to the low position of the promontory, but also to the fact that the human sacrum is extraordinarily wide and thus wedges the hipbones far apart Fig. 7–26. The greatest breadth of the sacrum equals well over 90 percent of the pelvic inlet breadth in

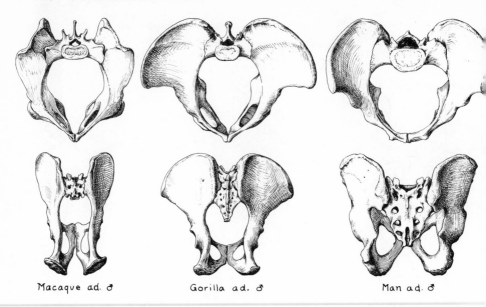

Macaque ad. ♂   Gorilla ad. ♂   Man ad. ♂

Fig. 7–26. Cephalic and dorsal views of pelves of adult macaque, gorilla and man, reduced to comparable sizes. (*From Schultz 1961*)

man, whereas only somewhere between 70 and 85 percent in the apes (Schultz 1961). The already mentioned, extreme tilting of the pelvic axis, the rotation of the ventral part of the ilium from a frontal to a sagittal direction and the comparative shortness of the ischium, together with the shifting of its tuberosity toward the enlarged acetabulum, are additional specializations of the human pelvis which represent functional adaptations for the altered muscular requirements of perfected bipedal locomotion. That most of these numerous, unique features of man's pelvis are already quite clearly established during fetal development (Rickenmann 1957; Olivier 1962) tends to support the view of an early acquisition of the erect posture in hominids.

The most significant proportions in the length of the limb bones correspond very closely to those obtained with measurements on the outer body, which have already been discussed. Not only the relative length but also the relative thickness of the long bones shows enormous differences among the hominoids, the latter depending chiefly on body size and relative limb length. As is to be expected, the heavy gorillas have extremely plump bones and the small gibbons very slender ones. The great elongation of the arm bones of the latter required no additional thickness so that they appear especially gracile alongside the robust and relatively short arm bones of gorillas[5]. The middle girth of the

[5]For instance, the middle circumference of the humerus in percentage of its length averages in male gorillas 26, whereas in gibbons only 13 and in macaques of very similar body weight as the gibbons, but with far shorter humeri, 25.

ulna surpasses that of the radius in all hominoids, but in the cercopithecoids this relation is reversed with the radius being thicker than the ulna. The long bones of the higher primates are furthermore distinguished by the comparatively great thickness of the fibulae, especially in relation to their trunk length. Among the recent hominoids man is characterized by remarkably thin arm bones, combined with thick leg bones, and the orang-utan by unusually slender leg bones considering the large body size of these primates. These particular distinctions in regard to the degrees of robusticity of the long limb bones are in close agreement with the relative weights of these bones, which have also been determined in large series of primate skeletons (Schultz 1953; 1962) and are undoubtedly due to the very different and highly specialized use of the limbs in man and in orang-utan.

The foot skeleton of the higher primates is of great interest on account of its widely diverging specializations for different usage. As has already been mentioned in a preceding chapter and as is shown in Fig. 7–5, there exist remarkably great differences in the relative lengths of the toes among the adult hominoids. For instance, the total length of the phalanges of the middle toe in percentage of the combined length of tarsus and metatarsus III averages only 24 in man, whereas 77 in orang-utans and even up to 90 in some prosimians (see also Fig. 7–28). The extremely low index of man appears only gradually during growth, equalling 54 at the beginning of fetal life and still 30 at birth. The tarsus has become greatly enlarged not only in bipedal man, but also in the heavy gorilla, being in both of practically equal size in relation to their trunk lengths (Fig. 7–27). The tarsal length forms 50 percent of the total length of the foot skeleton in man, 40 in gorilla, 34 in chimpanzee, and only between 26 and 28 in orang-utan and hylobatids. The metatarsus and tarsus together constitute the two-armed lever with which the body can be lifted at the ankle joint. The mechanically decisive proportion between the proximal power arm and the distal load arm of this lever differs very widely among primates, as shown by the examples in Fig. 7–28. The power arm amounts to only 18 percent of the load arm in gibbons, 19 in orang-utans, 27 in chimpanzees, 39 in man, and even 44 in gorillas. In all Old World monkeys these percentage relations are remarkably constant, fluctuating only little around 23 (Schultz 1963). The strength required of the calf muscles when lifting the body naturally diminishes with an elongation of the power arm, but a relatively great length of the latter, with a consequently distal fulcrum, is disadvantageous for jumping because the correspondingly short load arm gives only a limited lift to the body.

The first toes of chimpanzees, gorillas and man have become much thicker and stronger than the other toes in contrast to this condition in all monkeys. Only in man does the "great toe" reach about as far as his much shortened other toes. However, the total length of the first digit (with its metatarsus) is not specially great, because it equals roughly half of the total length of the entire foot skeleton in not only man, but also in chimpanzees and gibbons, and

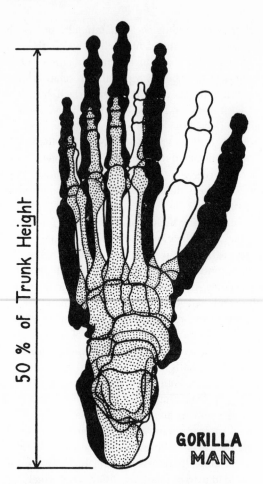

Fig. 7–27. Superimposed foot skeletons of an adult
gorilla and a man, both reduced to same trunk
length. (*From Schultz 1936*)

in relation to the length of the foot lever the first ray is even much shorter in
man than in the hylobatids, as shown by Fig. 7–28. The first toe of man has
become adapted to terrestrial locomotion through the lack of ontogenetic rotation, typical for most other primates, and the loss of metatarsal, but not
phalangeal, movability. That the great toe of man developed from an opposable
first digit, typical for other primates, is evident from the shape of the joint
between the hallux and the first cuneiform bone, which is still not entirely flat,
but slightly convex, and not directed transversely, but somewhat medially, in
spite of the loss of abductability (Fig. 7–27). The difference in the exact formation of this joint between man and particularly the eastern gorilla is insignificant in comparison with the corresponding difference between the latter and

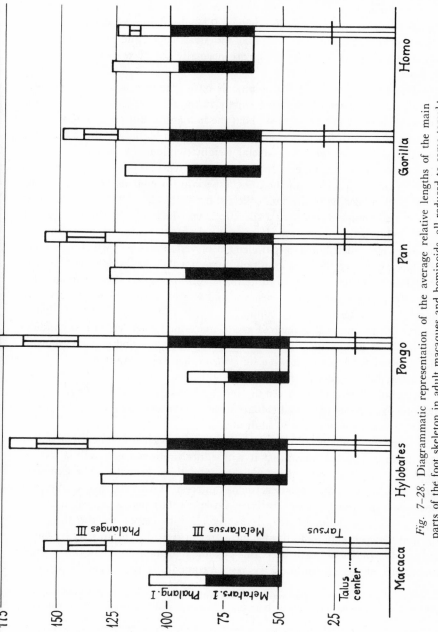

Fig. 7–28. Diagrammatic representation of the average relative lengths of the main parts of the foot skeleton in adult macaques and hominoids, all reduced to same tarsal+ metatarsal length (=100). *(From Schultz 1963)*

the chimpanzee (Schultz 1930). The typical simian foot skeleton, designed for climbing and grasping, has in man become altered also through the development of marked sagittal and transverse arches, which act as shock-absorbing springs in his unique mode of locomotion. The distribution of the load over the whole foot corresponds closely to that of the African apes, and even man's degenerated phalanges of the lateral toes are normally still flexed as in most other primates.

The hand skeletons of the hominoids have remained much more uniform than their foot skeletons, differing chiefly in the relative length of the fingers, which has already been discussed. That the human hand is surprisingly gracile in comparison with the hands of apes is best shown by the weight of the hand bones in percent of the total skeletal weight (without the caudal vertebrae). These percentages average only 2.7 in man, whereas consistently more in monkeys and much more in the apes, especially in gibbons (6.1) and orangutans (6.0), according to the data collected by the author (1962). The carpus of some of the hominoids contains a specialization which has often been overrated in its phylogenetic significance. It concerns the small central bone which is an old and widely distributed carpal element of vertebrates and which is supposedly lacking among the Simiae in only man, gorilla and chimpanzee. Early in development, however, a separate *centrale* still appears in these primates, but normally it fuses with the *naviculare* and this in man already in the third month of intrauterine life, in chimpanzees about at the time of birth and in gorillas during infantile growth. Exactly the same fusion has also been found repeatedly in some evidently old orang-utans, siamangs, and gibbons, showing that a trend to eliminate a separate *centrale* has been acquired by all hominoids, but differs widely in regard to the ontogenetic stage at which it manifests itself (Schultz 1936; 1956). Even the very early disappearance of the *centrale* of man does not occur in all individuals since in rare instances it still can persist as a separate carpal element to adult life.

Since the skulls of all recent hominoids have been so frequently described and illustrated in the literature,[6] it will suffice to discuss here only a few examples of the many cranial specializations of these primates. The extremely large human brain had aroused intense interest also in the size of the skull cavity for the brain, especially after Owen (1868) had assigned man to a separate class of animals—the *Archencephala*—to emphasize the sharp distinction between man and all other primates in regard to brain size. By means of later discoveries of fossils it became possible to demonstrate that this extraordinary size of the human brain has been a comparatively late development. At

[6]Among the innumerable publications dealing with the skulls of the recent Pongidae the following may be specially mentioned as being based on exceptionally large series: The old but still exemplary monographs by Selenka (1898; 1899) on the skulls of all three great apes, the well-illustrated study by Coolidge (1929) on subspecific differences in the skulls of gorillas and the report by Allen (1925) on cranial variability in chimpanzees. Large series of hylobatid skulls have been used by the writer in two detailed papers (1933; 1944).

the same time it has also been recognized that brain size is primarily dependent upon its allometric relation to body size. Thus it can be readily understood why the cranial capacity of, for example, the small *Saimiri* monkeys is larger in relation to body weight than is the corresponding relation in man(Schultz 1941).

Table 7–8 lists first of all the absolute sizes of the cranial capacities in adult higher primates and the surprisingly great ranges of individual variations of these measurements. The recently found maximum capacity of 752 cm³ among all apes (Schultz, 1962) stands much nearer to the minimum value of *Homo erectus* than to that of adult gorillas, which equals only 340 cm³ in females and 420 cm³ in males. The last column in Table 7–8 shows the important, but only approximate, relative cranial capacity. In this respect the small gibbons come nearest to man, as is to be expected for reasons of allometry, which also explain the sex differences in this index. The latter are most marked in orang-utans and gorillas simply because the sexes of these apes differ also most in regard to their general body size. The relative cranial capacity undergoes very marked changes during growth on account of the precocious development of the brain, which increases in size more rapidly than the body in general during early stages and more slowly during postnatal life. As shown by the growth curves for the *relative* capacity in Fig. 7–29, this index drops with increasing body weight from way above 10 in the smaller fetuses to less than 2 in large adult men and to less than 1 in all great apes of more than 45 kg. weight. It is of interest also that the curve for man flattens out more gradually than do those for the apes, indicating a longer continued postnatal brain growth in the former. At birth the cranial capacity equals in man only about 25 percent of its final size in adults, whereas in the apes anywhere between 35 and 61 percent, according to the writer's latest study (1965). From Fig. 7–29 it is also evident that this hominoid trend to enlarge the cranial capacity and brain beyond what might be expected from body size is already apparent in gibbons (as among platyrrhines in spider monkeys), has farther progressed with equal intensity in all great apes, and has reached its extreme in recent man. These different steps in the evolution of brain size appear remarkably early in ontogeny.

The size of the eye and of the orbit is, like that of the brain, allometrically dependent upon body size, and in its relation to the latter it decreases with advancing age more evenly than does brain size. For instance, the orbital volume in percent of body weight equals among adults 0.21 in a small marmoset, weighing 0.7 kg., 0.15 in a gibbon of 5.4 kg., 0.06 in a chimpanzee of 44 kg., 0.04 in a man of 66 kg., and 0.03 in a gorilla of 142 kg. (Schultz 1940, and new figure for gorilla). In newborns of the great apes and man the orbital volume has reached already one fifth of its final size in adults, whereas the total body size not nearly that much (Schultz 1965). On an average adult male chimpanzees surpass adult male gibbons 7.9 times in body weight, but only 2.6

Table 7-8. The cranial capacities (cm³) of adult hominoids according to data from the literature and those of the author (1933; 1940; 1941; 1944; 1962; 1965). The figures in the last column express the average capacities in percentage of the corresponding body weights (g.) as listed in Table 7-1. For the gibbons the weights and capacities could be determined by the author in 82 of the same specimens, but the weights of siamangs and great apes are based on much smaller series than their capacities, so that the *relative* capacities for these apes are only approximate. All data for man are merely rough, general averages, gained from published reports on many different races.

	Sex	Skulls	Range of Variations	Average	Range in Percent of Average	Capacity in Percent of Weight
Gibbon (H. lar)	Female	85	82–116	101	34	2.0
	Male	95	89–125	104	35	1.9
Siamang	Female and Male	40	100–152	125	42	1.2
Orang-utan	Female	111	276–494	366	60	1.0
	Male	96	320–540	424	52	0.6
Chimpanzee	Female	63	275–455	355	51	0.9
	Male	70	322–500	396	45	0.9
Gorilla	Female	173	340–595	458	56	0.5
	Male	400	420–752	535	62	0.3
Man	Female	hundreds	1000–1600	1300	46	2.2
	Male	”	1100–1700	1400	43	2.1

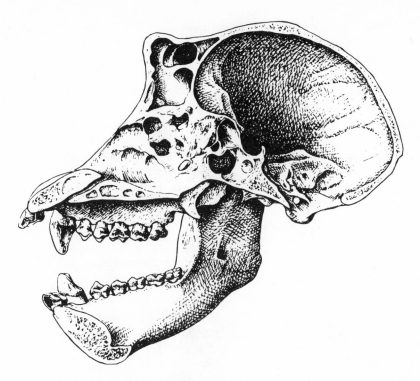

Fig. 7–33. Midsagittally cut skull of an adult chimpanzee showing some of the large sinuses and the proportionate size of the jaws and teeth.

orang-utans and least, if at all, in man. This striking difference is due to the fact that in the apes the postinfantile cranial growth in length takes place almost entirely in the precondylar parts, as is clearly evident from Fig. 7–32. In man, on the other hand, the fetal position of the condyles, only a little behind the center of gravity of the head, persists practically unchanged throughout growth and thus permits man's greatly reduced nuchal musculature to balance the head in his erect posture. The mechanically disadvantageous location of the occipital joint of adult apes requires such powerful nuchal muscles that their area of cranial attachment has usually to be enlarged with the addition of occi-pital crests. If the entire heads of adult apes are placed in the ear-eye horizon and supported on the occipital condyles, it has been determined experimentally that to balance the head in that position takes a weight, attached at the inion, which greatly surpasses the weight of the head itself, whereas in adult man such a weight averages only about one fifth of the head weight (Schultz 1942). Incidentally, in its relation to the entire body weight the head weighs more in most adult apes than it does in man in spite of the marked difference in brain weight.

Besides the above mentioned occipital crests apes often develop also sagittal ones to provide an enlarged surface for the attachment of the temporal muscles (Fig. 7–34). The height of these sagittal crests is directly influenced by the size of the jaws in relation to the surface area of the cranial vault. The crests start their development only with the fully completed eruption of the permanent dentition and can continue to grow for a long time thereafter. They are always present in old male gorillas, though very variable in size. Sagittal crests develop also in the majority of adult male orang-utans, rarely in male chimpanzees and least frequently in male gibbons. Since females have on an average the smaller dentitions and temporal muscles they do not acquire these crests nearly as often as do males, but small crests have been found in some females of all apes.

AGE CHANGES

That the phylogenetic specializations of the hominoids can frequently be traced back to modifications in their ontogenetic processes has already been

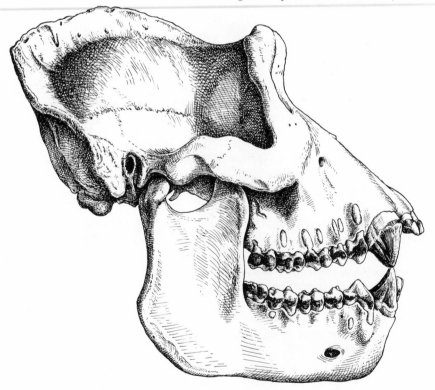

Fig. 7–34. Skull of an adult male western gorilla with exceptionally large teeth and powerful zygomatic arches, but moderate sagittal crest. (*From Schultz 1964*)

shown by various examples. Some features, typical for the higher primates, reach their distinct condition only with the completion of growth. Besides these there exist many other important age changes which influence the finished bodily form very little, if at all, and which hence have not yet been discussed. Among the latter none are of greater interest than the prolongation of the various life periods which represents a general hominoid trend, clearly recognized through comparisons with lower primates (Schultz 1949; 1956). Prenatal life lasts only about 6 weeks in the most primitive primates—the treeshrews—, 18 weeks in lemurs, 24 weeks in the intensely studied macaques and most likely not significantly longer in other monkeys. In gibbons this period has become prolonged to 30 weeks, in chimpanzees to nearly 34 weeks, and in orang-utans as well as gorillas, according to the few reliable records available so far, to about 38 weeks, that is, to as much as on an average in man. The postnatal life periods show this trend of prolongation to an even more pronounced degree with man representing the extreme of this specialization. All three great apes have practically the same tempo of development which forms a stage between that of gibbons on one side and that of man on the other, as seen in Fig. 7-35. Even the Hylobatidae differ from the lower primates by having acquired a longer period of growth and a later onset of sexual maturity. This general slowing down of development, which has begun in monkeys, as compared with prosimians, has become greatly accentuated in all apes and has progressed most in man regarding postnatal life, has had undoubtedly many profound consequences which can here be merely indicated in a few sentences. The prolongation of infantile dependency and of sexual immaturity has necessitated various adaptations in social behavior, has increased the time for learning and has brought about longer intervals between succeeding generations. The latter implies a reduction of the potential rate of population growth as well as of the tempo of possible evolutionary change in a given time-span. The also greatly increased average longevity of the hominoids has not been accompanied by a corresponding improvement of the durability of all organs. For instance, since the dental tissues have not become strengthened to endure more years of usage, not only man but also the apes commonly experience the extensive break-down of their misnamed "permanent" teeth during the final stages of their alloted life-spans (Schultz 1956).

The diagram in Fig. 7-35 shows also the approximate duration of fertility in females which, like the other main life periods, has not only increased in the hominoids, but begins and ends much later than in any of the lower primates. It is in regard to the upper limit of the reproductive period in its relation to the total life-span that modern man has come to differ strikingly from the nonhuman primates, inasmuch as a relatively early menopause seems to be a human distinction. This conclusion is supported by a growing number of recent reports on surprisingly long continued ovulatory cycles and even pregnancies of captive monkeys and apes of known old age, which can now be kept in much

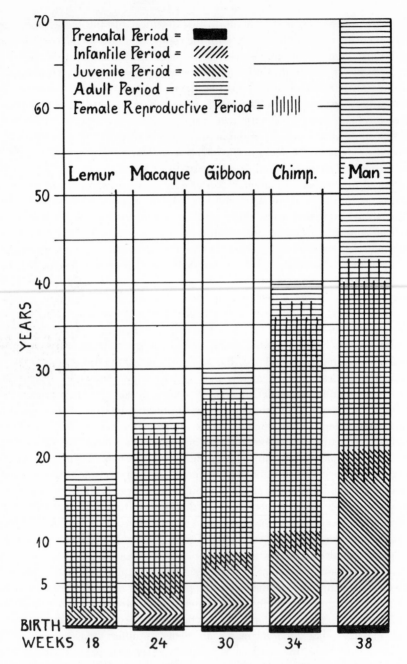

Fig. 7–35. The approximate average duration of the main periods of life in some lower and higher primates. The limits of the infantile and juvenile periods are based upon comparable stages of dental development. (*From Schultz 1966*)

better health than formerly. The unique lengthening of recent man's life-span beyond the age of female reproduction appears in this light more than ever as a result of our cultural advances.

In spite of the prolonged gestation periods of the higher primates their maturity at birth has not progressed nearly as much as it has in all monkeys. This is very evident from the different state of ossification in newborns, of which typical examples are shown in Fig. 7–36. It will be noted that the full-term fetuses of hominoids have as yet not nearly as many ossification centers in the carpal elements and in the epiphyses of the other limb bones as have newly born macaques and baboons. The closure of the fontanelles and the development of the teeth and hair have also advanced far more in viable newborn monkeys than in newborns of the higher primates. While macaques and guenons can usually sit and even stand up quite readily within a few days after birth, all hominoids remain very helpless for many weeks and develop far more slowly than any normal Cercopithecoidea. The detailed report on the physiological maturation of infant chimpanzees by Riesen and Kinder (1952) and the recent opportunities to follow the development of captive-born gorillas leave no doubt that the differences in this respect between these apes and man are insignificant in comparison with the far greater differences between monkeys and apes.

With an average birth weight of nearly 3.5 kg. man surpasses all other primates, since newborns of even the great apes usually weigh hardly 2 kg. In percentage of the maternal body weight that of the newborn equals anywhere between at least 5 and more than 10 in monkeys, 7.5 in gibbons, usually 5.5 in man, but only between 2.4 and 4.1 in the great apes (Schultz 1960). The full-term fetuses of the latter, therefore, are extraordinarily small[7], a fact which shows itself also in their relation in size to the pelvic birth canal of the mother. This remarkable peculiarity of the pongids is illustrated in Fig. 7–37 where it is very evident that the head of the newborn has ample room to pass through the wide pelvic inlets of great apes in contrast to the shockingly crowded conditions for the delivery of monkeys, gibbons and man. This explains the usually easy and rapid birth of the pongids and the often very prolonged and difficult labor in other simian primates, including man (Harms 1956).

Of all the manifold postnatal developmental changes those of the dentition have been studied in particularly large series of primates, because they are well suited for determining the relative ages of specimens. The eruption of the deciduous teeth begins in monkeys as a rule at or very soon after birth with the middle incisors. These teeth are also the first to appear in the higher primates, but not until about the age of three months in the pongids and even later in

---

[7]The curves of the intrauterine growth in length and in weight of chimpanzees fall below those of man for only the last few weeks (Schultz 1956). In the writer's experience all newborn pongids have far less subcutaneous fat than develops during the last stage of fetal life in man to become a distinguishing character of the great majority of human newborns.

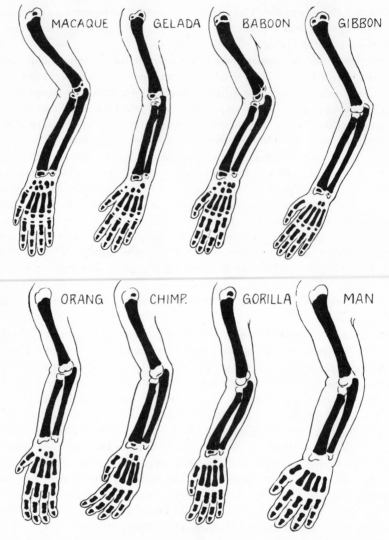

Fig. 7–36. Ossification of the upper extremities of some newborn catarrhines, as shown by X-ray photographs. (*From Schultz 1966*)

man. The central incisors are followed by the lateral ones, then by the anterior milk molars and somewhat later by the canines and last of all by the posterior milk molars in all Old World monkeys, gibbons, and man. The pongids alone form an exception to this rule inasmuch as their deciduous canines erupt after all milk molars have appeared. The first permanent molars are added to the deciduous dentition only after a considerable resting period in the process of eruption, namely in the middle of the second year in macaques, toward the end

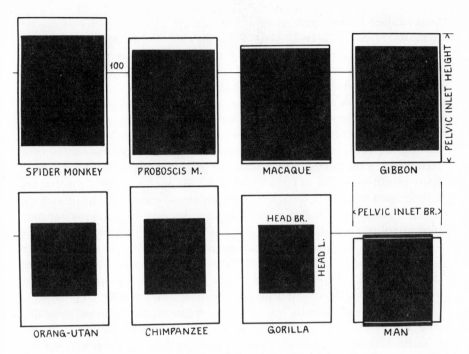

Fig. 7-37. Diagrammatic representation of the relation in size between the average diameters of the pelvic inlet in adult females and the average head length and breadth of newborns of the same species. (*From Schultz 1949*)

of the third year in the great apes, and not until after the completed sixth year in Europeans. Shortly after these ages there usually follows the first replacement of deciduous teeth with the eruption of the permanent middle incisors. The next replacement is that of the lateral incisors, which is succeeded by the addition of the second permanent molars and then by the replacement of the milk molars through premolars. The canines are not exchanged until about the time the last permanent molars are added, the exact sequence varying somewhat according to species and to sex. This order of eruption of the second dentition, expressed by the formula M1–I1–I2–M2–(P P)–(C M3), represents the general rule for all catarrhines, except recent man. In the latter there has appeared a trend to replace the milk teeth before the addition of all permanent molars, so that the following altered formula is now commonly found at least in Europeans: (I1 M1)–I2–(P C P)–M2–M3, with the teeth enclosed in parentheses erupting often in rapid and variable sequence. Due to the greatly prolonged growth of recent man it has obviously become a selective advantage to replace the delicate milk teeth as soon as possible in preference to the addition of all permanent molars which are no longer indispensable for masticating the prepared food of civilization. The primitive order of dental eruption, which has been retained by some prosimians and at least one platyrrhine (*Aotus*), has the formula M1–M2–M3–I1–I2–C–(P P P), showing that the addition of all permanent molars precedes the process of replacement and quickly gives these rapidly maturing primates long rows of grinding teeth for their early start in chewing solid food (Schultz 1935; 1956; 1960).

In Europeans the dentition is not fully erupted until all the epiphyseal lines of the long limb bones have become obliterated and growth in length has ceased in these bones. As shown by the comparisons in Fig. 7–38, this particular relation between dental and skeletal development represents an extreme retardation in the former in contrast to the process of epiphyseal closure. In all lower primates, studied so far, and in the Asiatic apes even the last molars are fully erupted when only the epiphyses of the elbow region have fused with the adjoining diaphyses. In chimpanzees and gorillas dental eruption is not completed until epiphyseal closure has progressed much farther at the approximate age of 11 years, but not nearly as far as in any of the races of man for which the relevant data have been collected. From Fig. 7–38 it can also be concluded that the sequence of epiphyseal obliteration is remarkably uniform among these different primates and certainly far more so than the order of dental eruption.

The closure of the main cranial sutures occurs among the recent great apes much sooner and more rapidly than in man and can even begin before the termination of dental eruption. In most platyrrhines these sutures remain open to old age, and in catarrhine monkeys and the hylobatids they disappear generally at earlier relative ages than in typical platyrrhines and in man, but much later than in the great apes. As a rule the occipito-sphenoid suture becomes closed before the sutures of the vault except in the great apes in which the latter sutures often begin to obliterate before even the basal one does. A supposed lack of intermaxillary bones had long ago been regarded as a clear morphological distinction of man. This widely held view was abandoned only after Goethe's famous demonstration of its fallaciousness.[8] The very minor specialization in man's intermaxillaries actually consists merely in their early prenatal fusion with the maxillaries on the facial side, preventing the appearance of corresponding sutures, which exist in all other primates. These sutures tend to become closed in particularly their alveolar parts much sooner in the great apes than in monkeys, in which they are often even among the very last sutures to disappear. Such great differences in the relative ages, at which one or another suture closes, are not at all uncommon in primates. For instance, the internasal suture usually becomes obliterated well before birth in macaques and many

---

[8]Even slightly before that time there had also appeared a little-known, but very noteworthy book on the skeleton of primates by Josephi (1787) which contains a detailed chapter on the intermaxillary, including the following historically interesting statement: "Man nimmt diese *ossa intermaxillaria* mit als ein Hauptunterscheidungszeichen der Affen vom Menschen an; indess, meinen Beobachtungen nach, hat der Mensch ebenfalls solche *ossa intermaxillaria*, wenigstens in den ersten Monaten seines Seyns, welche aber gewöhnlich schon früh, und zwar schon im Mutterleibe mit den wirklichen Oberkiefern vorzüglich nach aussen verwachsen. . . ."

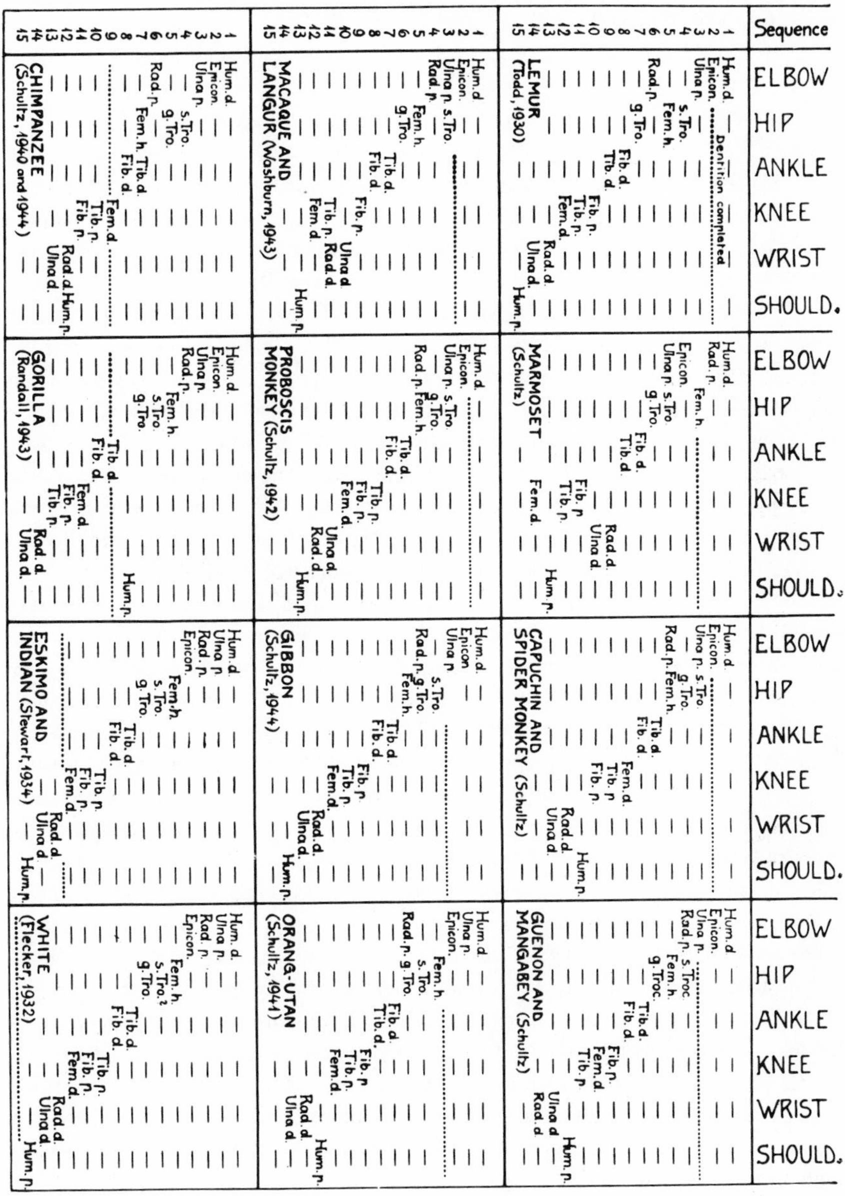

Fig. 7–38. Sequence of epiphyseal union in the long bones of the limbs according to the literature and the author's data. The stage at which the permanent dentition becomes completed is shown by horizontal dotted lines. (*p*) proximal, (*d*) distal, (*s*) small, (*g*) great. (*From Schultz 1956*)

chimpanzees, whereas in man it never closes, except in rare old individuals (Schultz 1956; Chopra 1957).

Secondary Sex Differences and Variability

More or less striking sex differences in the color, pattern or length of hair and in other superficial features of most often the face are very common in primates and seem to serve mainly for recognizing, impressing or threatening purposes. Really great differences in size and strength of the body and of the canine teeth, by which males become effective defenders, are comparatively rare and almost entirely limited to catarrhines, such as baboons, most macaques, some species of langurs, proboscis monkeys, orang-utans, and gorillas. This minority is by no means composed of only terrestrial or large-bodied forms, as has been claimed, but embraces a wide variety of small and large species with very different modes of life. Species characterized by moderate sex differences in body build also include arboreal as well as terrestrial ones, namely man, chimpanzee, and a great many monkeys of the Old and New World. The least body differentiation according to sex exists in the majority of prosimians and of platyrrhines, besides the Hylobatidae. Among the recent hominoids sex differences in the body size of adults are on an average exceedingly small in gibbons and extremely large in orang-utans and gorillas, as has already been shown in Table 7-1. Such sex differences do become much more marked with advancing growth, being as yet barely indicated at birth, if recognizable at all by wellfounded averages. It can be concluded, therefore, that either the rates of postnatal growth of its duration can differ in the two sexes. That both these factors can also act in combination has been demonstrated for macaques, chimpanzees and man, whose curves of growth for females fall below those for males during late juvenile life and cease to rise at a somewhat earlier age (Schultz 1956). The sexes can differ also in regard to some of their body proportions. The relative circumference of the chest, for example, averages 203 in adult male orang-utans and only 171 in adult females, but in gibbons both sexes are practically alike in this respect. The relative hip breadth is the only index which surpasses in females that of males in consequence of the marked widening of the female pelvis after puberty (Schultz 1949; 1956). A pronounced sexual dimorphism frequently develops also in the face part of the skull, which becomes higher and more protruding in adult males of particularly orang-utans and gorillas in connection with the corresponding difference in the size of the entire dental apparatus (Schultz 1962). It is well known that in the majority of primates the canines of males are strikingly large in comparison with those of females of the same species. This rule, however, has exceptions among widely different primates, lacking a noteworthy sex difference in this respect, such as man, all Hylobatidae and various Callithricidae. Among the recent Pongidae a sexual difference in the size of the canines is not nearly as great and constant in chimpanzees as it is in the two other genera.

Further secondary sex characters of the hominoids have already been mentioned in preceding chapters as representing purely quantitative differences. In orang-utans, for example, beards and cranial crests are merely more frequent in males and their crests and throat pouches become larger than in females. In adult gorillas there are fewer and shorter hairs on the chests of males than of females, and the supraorbital torus of the former becomes more strongly developed in adults. The typical amount and kind of sex differentiation in man varies considerably according to race, but always remains exceedingly moderate in comparison with the great differences in some other catarrhine primates.

It has already been pointed out repeatedly above that the man-like apes are distinguished by a remarkably great intraspecific variability in regard to most of their characters. This often not duly appreciated fact can here be demonstrated by a few more examples. Man is supposed to have 12 thoracic, 5 lumbar, and 5 sacral vertebrae according to all textbooks, but actually this combination of the numbers of segments in these spinal regions exists in only 71 percent of human beings and in the remaining 29 percent there occur several other less frequent combinations of numerical variations. As shown by Table 7–9, the most frequent vertebral formula is found in from 72 to 86 percent of catarrhine monkeys, that is, their constancy in this respect is only a little more marked than it is in man. Contrasting with this the statistical norms of all the man-like apes occur in far smaller percentages of specimens, the great majority having different vertebral formulae with frequencies below that of the norm. It is of interest that the already discussed extreme specializations of the apes in their regional numbers of vertebrae are accompanied by this extraordinary lack of intraspecific stability.

Table 7–9. Most frequent combination of variations in the number of precaudal vertebrae (= statistical norm) in some catarrhine genera. The number of cervical vertebrae is not included because it is 7 with extremely rare exceptions (from Schultz 1957 and 1961 with a few additions).

Genus	Skeletons	Norm			Percentage Occurrence
		Thor.	Lumb.	Sacr.	
Macaca	216	12	7	3	73
Cercopithecus	59	12	7	3	72
Presbytis	122	12	7	3	86
Hylobates	319	13	5	5	36
Pongo	127	12	4	5	43
Pan	162	13	4	6	27
Gorilla	84	13	4	6	28
Homo	493	12	5	5	71

In a formerly much discussed book on the "Hallmarks of Mankind" Wood Jones (1948) had supported his theory of a separate human descent from tarsier-like ancestors with various claims regarding the topographic relations between the ethmoid bone and its adjoining cranial elements, but evidently without having investigated the variability of these features in adequate series of primate skulls. According to the just-named author a junction of the right and left frontals behind the ethmoid, with the formation of a fronto-basilar suture, is a "catarrhine specialization" which is missing only in man (besides the orang-utan). From the writer's extensive data, shown in Table 7–10, however, it is evident that one is dealing here with merely a quantitative distinction since the fronto-basilar suture is found only in about one fourth of chimpanzees and half of all gorillas, as well as in 3 percent of human beings (Fig. 7–39). That these are hereditary variations appears very probable in view of the fact that this suture existed in 10 percent of negro skulls, whereas in only

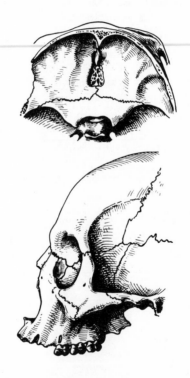

Fig. 7–39. Skulls of two adult Papuas, (Above) floor of cranial cavity with a fronto-basilar suture; (below) medial orbital wall with a fronto-maxillary suture. (*From Schultz 1952*)

Table 7–10. Percentage frequencies of variations in the relations between the ethmoid and sphenoid in the cranial base and between the ethmoid and lacrimal or the frontal and maxillary in the medial orbital wall of simian primates (from Schultz 1950; 1965).

	Skulls	Spheno-Ethmoid Suture	Fronto-Basilar Suture	Orbits	Lacrimo-Ethmoid Suture*	Fronto-Maxillary Suture
Platyrrhina	63	23	77	250	100	0
Cercopithecoidea	341	0.3	99.7	1050	100	0
Hylobatidae	48	0	100	144	100	0
Pongo	94	99	1	310	100	0
Pan	86	77	23	374	63	37
Gorilla	62	50	50	262	49	51
Homo	1016	97	3	1470	99	1.2

*Includes the few cases in which all four bones meet in a point.

0.4 percent of European skulls. Here it is of special interest that this is a feature in regard to which chimpanzees and gorillas are much more variable than all the other catarrhines.

The exact formation of the medial orbital wall had also been used by Wood Jones in support of his denial of any close relationship between man and the apes in the belief that the ethmoid and lacrimal meet in the former, while in the latter they are separated by the interposition of the frontal and maxillary. As is shown by the data on very extensive series in the right half of Table 7–10, a contact between the ethmoid and lacrimal bones actually exists not only in all hylobatids and orang-utans but also in nearly half of the gorillas and in even almost two thirds of the chimpanzees. The ethmoid and lacrimal bones are wedged apart through processes, extending from the frontal and maxillary bones, exclusively in 37 percent of chimpanzees, 51 percent of gorillas, and 1.2 percent of human orbits (Fig. 7–39), but not in any of the other hominoids nor in any monkeys. Even though this feature is 100 percent constant in the great majority of simian primates, it evidently can change easily since the fronto-maxillary suture behind the lacrimal was found in 13 out of 14 *Pan paniscus* examined by the writer and hence far more frequently than in *Pan troglodytes*.

The extraordinary variability of the man-like apes in their cranial proportions can here be indicated by only the following few examples: The length-breadth index of the brain-case (without crests) was found to range from 68 to 86 in a series of 248 adult *Hylobates lar* (Schultz 1944), from 70 to 92 in a series of 105 adult orang-utans (Schultz 1941), from 57 to 79 in a series of 80 adult western gorillas (Schultz 1962), and even from 69 to 98 in another series of 311 fully grown western gorillas, measured with a somewhat different technique by Randall (1943–1944). These remarkably large ranges of variations surpass those of most comparable series of human skulls. For instance, the same index fluctuated only between 61 and 78 among 328 skulls of adult Greenland Eskimos (Fürst and Hansen 1915). The variability of the face-part of the skull is as a rule even more marked than that of the brain-part, a distinction which is particularly pronounced in the great apes, as clearly shown by the skulls of chimpanzees in Fig. 7–40. These three examples of perfectly normal apes differ in so many details that formerly they might have been described as separate species, but today they can readily be fitted within the ranges of variations of large collections of chimpanzee skulls from limited regions. The teeth of the apes are also distinguished by an astonishingly great variability in their absolute and relative size, et cetera, as has been clearly demonstrated with very many and careful data by chiefly Remane (1954; 1961). This quite unusual lack of intraspecific stability in so many different characters of the recent man-like apes has unfortunately not always been taken into consideration in the interpretation and classification of fossil hominoid fragments.

It may finally be mentioned also that asymmetries, which in a sense represent bilateral variations, are by no means limited to man. It has been found,

Fig. 7–40. Skulls of wild adult male chimpanzees from West Africa. (*From Schultz 1963*)

however, that in man the long bones of the upper limbs are roughly twice as asymmetrical as are those of the lower limbs, whereas in monkeys and all apes there exist no significant differences in the degrees of asymmetry of the upper and the lower limb bones, as is shown by the condensed data in Table 7–11. It seems most probable that the liberation of man's arms from participating in locomotion has somehow favored an exceptionally marked degree of asymmetry in his arm bones.

SUMMARY AND CONCLUSIONS

Among the manifold conditions of the recent Hominoidea, which have been dealt with in this survey, nearly all have been found to differ significantly from the corresponding conditions of the lower catarrhines and to represent distinguishing characters, acquired from a common origin and adapted to often diverging modes of life. The most noteworthy and consequential of these hominoid specializations are the reductions in the number of presacral and caudal segments combined with the greater number of vertebrae fused in the sacrum, the striking widening of the entire trunk with its many correlated alterations, the increased relative length of the upper limbs, the great enlargement of the brain in its allometric relation to body size, and the prolongation of the various main periods of life together with the numerous changes in relative age, speed or duration of developmental processes, especially the reduced state of maturity at birth. An endless variety of further anatomical, physiological, and onto-genetic conditions, which have here not been mentioned at all, could be enumerated in support of the today generally accepted conclusion that man and all of the man-like apes belong into one and the same natural group of primates.

Table 7-11. Averages of the relative asymmetries of the humerus, radius, femur, and tibia of adult catarrhines (length of larger bone minus length of smaller bone in percentage of the latter, including symmetrical cases) (from Schultz 1937; 1944; 1965).

	Skeletons	Average Relative Asymmetry	
		Upper Limb	Lower Limb
Macaques............................	118	0.61	0.60
Gibbons	212	0.57	0.59
Orang-utans	69	0.69	0.63
Chimpanzees	88	0.69	0.65
Gorillas...............................	127	0.69	0.73
Different Races of Man.........	735	1.20	0.63

That the recent hominoids can readily be divided into three clearly differentiated and roughly equivalent subgroups has also been demonstrated with the evidence derived from a great variety of features.

The Hylobatidae have in general remained less specialized than have the great apes and man and represent in some ways transitional stages between Cercopithecoidea and the Pongidae, with the siamang having approached the latter more closely than have the gibbons. The differences between the gibbons and the larger siamang are not merely allometric ones, as has been rashly concluded by some students with very inadequate material, but consist also of numerous conditions which have nothing to do with body size, such as vertebral variations, density of hair, et cetera. Furthermore, the diploid number of chromosomes equals 44 in gibbons of all species studied so far, whereas 50 in the siamang, besides certain additional chromosomal peculiarities distinguishing the latter from the former (Hamerton et al. 1963; Chiarelli 1966). Even though the hylobatids still possess regularly well-formed ischial callosities and have made only modest progress in the enlargement of the brain, the changes in regional numbers of vertebrae, the widening of the iliac bones, and the retardation of growth and development, they have nevertheless gained some extreme and even unique specializations, such as the long canines of females, the greatest relative length of the arms and many distinguishing features of their hands, feet, sternum, hair, et cetera. In considering all of these conditions of the recent Hylobatidae it seems well justified to assume that they had followed their own course of evolution ever since they had begun to diverge from the same early ancestral stock of catarrhines which had also given rise to the other hominoids.[9]

[9]Recent investigations have at least cast serious doubts on the formerly widely held theory that the fossil Pliopithecus represents an early form of hylobatids (for further comments see Schultz 1966).

The numerous, closely corresponding, phylogenetic trends of specialization, which have been shared by all recent great apes, force us to conclude that they must have had one common origin and that they still fit well into the same subfamily of Ponginae. The modern proposals of radical changes in this classification on the basis of similarities in certain details of chromosome morphology or of blood chemistry seem premature and remain unconvincing as long as no thorough attempt is made to correlate such isolated findings with the vast mass of other pertinent evidence. The close relationship between all three types of the recent great apes is demonstrated beyond doubt by the remarkable agreement in all their significant developmental processes as well as in the great majority of their anatomical characters. Exceptions can readily be explained as limited specializations, acquired after the phylogenetic division of the three genera. Considering the great spatial and, most likely, chronological separation between the Asiatic and African pongids, it is to be expected that corresponding differences in the degrees of similarity had developed, particularly that chimpanzees and gorillas stand much closer to one another than either does to the orang-utan. Regardless, however, of what importance we may choose to assign to the many different bodily adaptations, which have resulted from the various modes of life of the great apes, there still remains the only justifiable conclusion that even the Asiatic and African ones have not become nearly as much separated as all three types are removed from recent man. Accordingly it seems far more likely that a separate hominid branch had appeared on the hominoid family tree before any of the branches leading to the recent pongids had clearly diverged from each other and not later, from only the lines ending in *Gorilla* and *Pan*, as has been assumed by Gregory (1934), Vallois (1955) and other authors.

While the Asiatic apes had evolved into the most highly perfected brachiators, the hominids had become extreme cruriators, as Keith (1934) had called them. The many profound specializations of man are chiefly those which had appeared as direct adaptations for, or as indirect consequences of erect posture, which was the first and most decisive change. To these first acquisitions was added the later great development of the brain with the correlated cranial transformations. The undoubtedly much more recent, extreme prolongation of the postnatal life periods also belongs to the outstanding innovations of human evolution.

As has been repeatedly emphasized here, great many specializations of all hominoids are very closely correlated with their posture and locomotion. In this connection it is to be mentioned first of all that the man-like apes can and do stand and walk bipedally much more easily than can the lower catarrhines. This ability had been prepared by the typically hominoid cranial migration of the pelvis, the ventral shift of the spinal column, the dorsal translocation of the shoulder blades, as well as the manifold and mechanically advantageous modifications in the pelvis and the feet. Upright walking and running has thus become easily possible for gibbons and even more so for siamangs. Chimpanzees and gorillas can also walk erect on the ground without difficulty, whereby they naturally carry the center of gravity of the body perpendicularly above the feet. Orang-utans in captivity are frequently seen to stand and sometimes to walk bipedally, but in an awkward fashion on account of their long feet, specialized for grasping limbs and unsuited for flat ground. The change from the occasional erect locomotion of apes to a permanent one in early man was far more readily accomplished with a hominoid bodily construction than with that of Old World monkeys.

The extreme specializations for two-armed locomotion seem not to have appeared until rather late in evolution according to what can be learned from fossil finds (Zapfe 1960 a. o.). Among all catarrhines the ability to brachiate has become most highly perfected in the recent Hylobatidae which can move by their arms alone with such amazing agility and speed that they can propel themselves through space for incredible distances without using their legs at all. The heavy orang-utans do not use brachiation nearly as often nor as gracefully, being by comparison slow and cautious in most their movements, though otherwise as well adapted to an almost exclusively arboreal life as their small cousins, the gibbons. Chimpanzees can brachiate as easily as and more speedily than orang-utans, but in general they spend much more daytime on the ground than in the trees and prefer quadrupedal locomotion if they do not carry food or newborns in their hands. The heavy adult gorillas can also move by their arms underneath branches, but hardly any better than well-trained boys are able to do, and usually they live on the ground rather than in trees (Schaller 1963). As is very evident from Fig. 7–41, the plump body build of full-grown gorillas is not at all suited for nimble quadrupedal locomotion, such as distinguishes the slender guenons. With its broad trunk, concave back, high shoulders, and stout legs the gorilla cannot rely for protection on speed, but rather on the strength of its powerful arms, which are freed for defense with the easily possible assumption of the upright posture.

It may be mentioned here also that the extremely arboreal existence of the Asiatic apes entails dangers which play not nearly as prominent a role in the terrestrial life of the African apes and man. This claim is based on the fact that repaired fractures, occurring in all parts of the skeleton, have been found among the former in up to 50 percent of old animals and as being more common at all ages than in the latter (Schultz 1956; 1961). It is quite certain that fatal accidents, which in tropical jungles rarely become known, are also specially frequent in the most arboreal and most commonly brachiating hominoids.

The preferred use of the upper limbs in the locomotion of brachiators could not transfer new functions to their lower limbs, but remained a limited specialization in comparison with the adaptations and consequences of bipedalism. With the latter the arms and specially the hands, freed from serving in

Fig. 7–41. Adult male gorilla of the middle Congo. Note face hanging far below the high shoulders, the "saddle back" and the broad hips. (*From Schultz 1965. After a film, courtesy of 20th Century-Fox*)

locomotion, were enabled to take over new tasks, beginning with the carrying of objects and leading to the manufacture of tools.

Among nature's exceptionally diverse experiments with the original stock of the hominoids the hylobatids were assigned the one-sided and restricted path to an extreme arboreal existence, the pongids had followed a very similar direction in Asia, while in Africa they had hesitated between life on the ground and in the trees, preferring the one or the other in varying degrees. By abandoning the forest and specializing in bipedal walk the hominids had been selected for the most successful experiment and could even remain more conservative in some ways than the great apes while acquiring other unique and decisive specilizations.

REFERENCES

ALLEN, J. A., 1925, Primates collected by the American Museum Congo Expedition. *Bull. Amer. Mus. Nat. Hist.*, **47**:283–499.

BIEGERT, J., 1961, Volarhaut der Hände und Füsse, *Primatologia*, **2**, Liefer. 3:1–326 (Karger, Basel).

BLUMENBACH, J. F., 1791, *Handbuch der Naturgeschichte*. 4te Aufl. (Göttingen).

CAVE, A. J. E., and R. WHEELER HAINES, 1940., The paranasal sinuses of the anthropoid apes. *J. Anat.*, **74**:493–523.

———, 1961, The frontal sinus of the gorilla. *Proc. Zool. Soc. London*, **136**:359–373.

CHIARELLI, B., 1966, Marked chromosome in catarrhine monkeys. *Folia primatologica*, **4**:74–80.

CHOPRA, S. R. K., 1957, The cranial suture closure in monkeys. *Proc. Zoolog. Soc. London*, **128**:67–112.

COOLIDGE, H. J., JR., 1929, A review of the genus *Gorilla, Memoirs Mus. Comp. Zool.* Harvard College, **50**:291–381.

DARWIN, C., 1874, *The descent of man, and selection in relation to sex.* 2nd ed. (London).

FIEDLER, W., 1956, Uebersicht über das System der Primates. *Primatologia*, **1**:1–266 (Karger, Basel).

FÜRST, C. M, and F. C. C. HANSEN, 1915, Crania Groenlandica. (Höst & Son, Copenhagen).

GREGORY, W. K., 1934, *Man's place among the anthropoids.* (Clarendon Press, Oxford).

HALL-CRAGG, E. C. B., 1962, The testis of *Gorilla gorilla beringei. Proc. Zoolog. Soc. London*, **139**:511–514.

HAMERTON, J. P., KLINGER, H. P., MUTTON, D. E., and LANG, E. M., 1963, The somatic chromosomes of Hominoidea. *Citogenetics*, **2**:240–263.

HARMS, J. W., 1956, Fortpflanzungsbiologie. *Primatologia*, **1**:561–660 (Karger, Basel).

———, 1956, Schwangerschaft und Geburt. *Primatologia*, **1**:661–722 (Karger, Basel).

HILL, W. C. O., 1958, External genitalia. *Primatologia*, **3**. T. 1:630–704 (Karger, Basel).

JOSEPHI, W., 1787, *Anatomie der Säugethiere.* 1. Band (Knochenlehre der Affen). (J. C. Dieterich, Göttingen).

KEITH, A., 1934, *The construction of man's family tree.* Forum Series No. 18 (Watts & C., London).

LASINSKI, W., 1960, Aeusseres Ohr. *Primatologia*, **2**, T. 1, Liefer. **5**:41–74 (Karger, Basel).

OLIVIER, G., 1962, *Formation du squelette des memberes chez 1' homme* (Vigot Frères, Paris).

OWEN, R., 1868, On the anatomy of vertebrates. Vol. III, *Mammals (Longmans, Green & Co., London).*

RANDALL, F. E., 1943–1944, The skeletal and dental development and variability of the gorilla. *Human Biol.*, **15**:236–254, 307–337, **16**:23–76.

REMANE, A., 1954., Methodische Probleme der Hominoiden-Phylogenie, II. *Z. f. Morphol. u. Anthropol.*, **46**:225–268.

———, 1961. Probleme der Systematik der Primaten. *Z. f. wissensch. Zool.*, **165**:1–34.

RICKENMANN, E., 1957, *Beiträge zur vergleichenden Anatomie insbesondere des Beckens bei Catarrhinen.* Diss. Univ. Freiburg (Switzerland).

RIESEN, A. H. and E. F. KINDER., 1952, *Postural development of infant chimpanzees.* (Yale Univ. Press, New Haven).

SCHREBER, J. C. D., 1775, *Die Säugethiere in Abbildungen nach der Natur mit Beschreibungen.* (Walther, Erlangen).

SCHULTZ, A. H., 1926, Fetal growth of man and other primates. *Quart. Rev. Biol.,* **1**:465–521.

——, 1929, The technique of measuring the outer body of human fetuses and of primates in general. Carnegie Inst. Wash. Publ. 394, *Contrib. to Embryol.,* **20**:213–257.

——, 1930, The skeleton of the trunk and limbs of higher primates. *Human Biol.,* **2**:303–438.

——, 1931, Man as a primate. *Scientific Monthly,* **1931**:385–412.

——, 1931. The density of hair in primates. *Human Biol.,* **3**:303–321.

——, 1932, The generic position of *Symphalangus klossii. J. Mammal.,* **13**:368–369.

——, 1933, Observations on the growth, classification and evolutionary specialization of gibbons and siamangs. *Human Biol.,* **5**:212–255, 385–428.

——, 1933, Die Körperproportionen der erwachsenen catarrhinen Primaten, mit spezieller Berücksichtigung der Menschenaffen. *Anthropol. Anz.,* **10**:154–185.

——, 1934, Some distinguishing characters of the mountain gorilla. *J. Mamm.,* **15**:51–61.

——, 1935, Eruption and decay of the permanent teeth in primates. *Amer. J. Phys. Anthropol.,* **19**:489–581.

——, 1935, The nasal cartilages in higher primates. *Amer. J. Phys. Anthropol.,* **20**:205–212.

——, 1936, Characters common to higher primates and characters specific for man. *Quart. Rev. Biol.,* **11**:259–283, 425–455.

——, 1937, Proportions, variability and asymmetries of the long bones of the limbs and the clavicles in man and apes. *Human Biol.,* **9**:281–328.

——, 1938, The relative weight of the testes in primates. *Anat. Rec.,* **72**:387–394.

——, 1940, The size of the orbit and of the eye in primates. *Amer. J. Phys. Anthropol.,* **26**:389–408.

——, 1941, The relative size of the cranial capacity in primates. *Amer. J. Phys. Anthropol.,* **28**:273–287.

——, 1941, Growth and development of the orang-utan. Carnegie Inst. Wash. Publ. 525, *Contrib. to Embryol.,* **29**:57–110.

——, 1942, Conditions for balancing the head in primates. *Amer. J. Phys. Anthropol.,* **29**:483–497.

——, 1944, Age changes and variability in gibbons. *Amer. J. Phys. Anthropol.,* n. s. **2**:1–129.

——, 1949, Ontogenetic specializations of man. *Arch. Julius Klaus-Stift.,* **24**:197–216.

——, 1949, Sex differences in the pelves of primates. *Amer. J. Phys. Anthropol.,* n. s. **7**:401–424.

——, 1950, Morphological observations on gorillas. Henry Cushier Raven Memorial Vol.: *The Anatomy of the Gorilla,* 227–253 (Columbia Univ. Press, New York).

——, 1950, The physical distinctions of man. *Proc. Amer. Philos. Soc.,* **94**:428–449.

——, 1952, Ueber das Wachstum der Warzenfortsätze beim Menschen und den Menschenaffen. *Homo,* **3**:105–109.

——, 1952, Vergleichende Untersuchungen an einigen menschlichen Spezialisationen,

Bull. Schweiz. Ges. f. Anthrop. u. Ethnol., **28**:25–37.

————, 1953, The relative thickness of the long bones and the vertebrae in primates. *Amer. J. Phys. Anthropol.*, n. s. **11**:277–311.

————, 1954, Bemerkungen zur Variabilität und Systematik der Schimpansen. *Säugetierkundl. Mitteil.*, **2**:159–163.

————, 1954, Studien über die Wirbelzahlen und die Körperproportionen von Halbaffen. Vierteljahrsschr. Naturfor. Ges. Zürich, **99**:39–75.

————, 1955, The position of the occipital condyles and of the face relative to the skull base in primates. *Amer. J. Phys. Anthropol.*, n. s. **13**:97–120.

————, 1956, Postembryonic age changes. *Primatologia*, **1**:887–964 (Karger, Basel).

————, 1956, The occurrence and frequency of pathological and teratological conditions and of twinning among nonhuman primates. *Primatologia*, **1**:965–1014 (Karger, Basel).

————, 1957, *Die Bedeutung der Primatenkunde für das Verständnis der Anthropogenese.* Ber. 5te Tagung D. Ges. f. Anthropol., 13–28.

————, 1957, Past and present views of man's specializations. *Irish J. Med. Science*, **1957**:341–356.

————, 1958, Palatine ridges. *Primatologia*, 3, T. **1**:127–138. (Karger, Basel).

————, 1960, Einige Beobachtungen und Masse am Skelett von *Oreopithecus*. *Z. Morphol. u. Anthropol.*, **50**:136–149.

————, 1960, Age changes and variability in the skulls and teeth of the Central American monkeys *Alouatta*, *Cebus* and *Ateles*. *Proc. Zool. Soc. London*, **133**:337–390.

————, 1960, Age changes in primates and their modifications in man. *Human Growth*, 1–20 (Pergamon Press, London).

————, 1961, Some factors influencing the social life of primates in general and of early man in particular. *Viking Fund Publ. in Anthropol.*, **31**:58–90.

————, 1961, Vertebral column and thorax. *Primatologia*, 4, Liefer, **5**:1–66.

————, 1962, The relative weights of the skeletal parts in adult primates. *Amer. J. Phys. Anthropol.*, n. s. **20**:1–10.

————, 1962, Die Schädelkapazität männlicher Gorillas und ihr Höchstwert. *Anthropol. Anz.*, **25**:197–203.

————, 1962, Metric age changes and sex differences in primate skulls. *Z. Morphol. u. Anthropol.*, **52**:239–255.

————, 1963, Relations between the lengths of the main parts of the foot skeleton in primates. *Folia primatoligica*, **1**:150–171.

————, 1963, Age changes, sex differences, and variability as factors in the classification of primates. *Classification and Human Evolution* (S. L. Washburn, ed.) 85-115. Chicago.

————, 1964, A gorilla with exceptionally large teeth and supernumerary premolars. *Folia primatologica*, **2**:149–160.

————, 1965, Die rezenten Hominoidea. *Menschliche Abstammungslehre* (G. Heberer, ed.), 56–102. Stuttgart.

————, 1965, The cranial capacity and the orbital volume of hominoids according to age and sex. Homenaje a Juan Comas, **II**:337–357. Mexico.

————, 1966, Changing views on the nature and interrelations of the higher primates. Yerkes Newsletter (Emory University), **3**: 15–29.

SELENKA, E., 1898, Rassen, Schädel und Bezahnung des Orangutan. *Studien über Entwickelungsgesch.*, Heft 6, Menschenaffen. (Wiesbaden).

——, 1899, Schädel des Gorilla und Schimpanse. *Studien über Entwickelungsgesch.*, Heft 7, Menschenaffen. (Wiesbaden).

STARCK, D., and R. SCHNEIDER., 1960, Larynx. *Primatologia*, 3. T. **2**:423–587 (Karger, Basel).

STRAUS, W. L., JR., 1942, The structure of the crown-pad of the gorilla and of the cheek-pad of the orang-utan. *J. Mammal.*, **23**:276–281.

TAILLARD, W., 1957, *Les Spondylolisthesis.* (Masson et Cie., Paris).

TUTTLE, R. H. and ROGERS, C. M., 1966, Genetic and selective factors in reduction of the hallux in *Pongo pygmaeus. Amer. J. Phys. Anthropol.*, **24**:191–198.

VALLOIS, H., 1955, Ordre des Primates. *Traité de Zoologie*, **17**:1854–2206. (Paris).

WEGNER, R. N., 1956, *Studien über Nebenhöhlen des Schädels*, Wissensch. Z. Univ. Greifswald, **5**, Mathem.-naturwiss. Reihe, 1.

WISLOCKI, G. B., 1942, Size, weight and histology of the testes in the gorilla. *J. Mammal.*, **23**:281–287.

WOOD JONES, F., 1948, *Hallmarks of mankind.* (Williams & Wilkins, Baltimore).

YERKES, R. M., 1943, *Chimpanzees: A laboratory colony.* (Yale Univ. Press, New Haven).

ZAPFE, H., 1960, Die Primatenfunde aus der miozänen Spaltenfüllung von Neudorf an der March, Tschechoslowakei. *Schweiz. Palaeontol. Abhdl.*, **78**:1–293.

8·Field Studies of Old World Monkeys and Apes

S. L. Washburn,
Phyllis C. Jay,
and Jane B. Lancaster
University of California, Berkeley

For many years there has been interest in the evolutionary roots of human behavior, and discussions of human evolution frequently include theories on the
origin of human customs. In view of the old and widespread interest in the
behavior of our nearest relatives, it is surprising how little systematic information was collected until very recently. At the time (1929) Yerkes and Yerkes
collected data for their book on the great apes (1), no one had devoted even one
continuous month to the systematic study of the behavior of an undisturbed,
free-ranging nonhuman primate. Apparently scientists believed that the behavior of monkeys and apes was so stereotyped and simple that travelers' tales
or the casual observations of hunters formed a reliable basis for scientific conclusions and social theorizing. As a part of the program of the Yale Labora-
tories of Comparative Psychology, Yerkes encouraged a series of field studies of
the chimpanzee (2), the mountain gorilla (3), and the howling monkey (4).
These first studies proved so difficult that Yerkes could write, in the intro-

Reprinted from *Science*, December 17, 1965, Vol. 150, No. 3703, pp. 1541–1547. Copyright
© 1965 by the American Association for the Advancement of Science. By permission of the authors
and the publisher.

duction to Carpenter's study, "His is the first reasonably reliable working analysis of the constitution of social groups in the infrahuman primates, and of the relations between the sexes and between mature and immature individuals for monkey or ape" (4, p. 4). Zuckerman, quite independently, had realized the importance of field observations and had combined some field work with physiology and the older literature to produce two very influential volumes (5). From this beginning, only Carpenter continued to make field studies of behavior, and his study of the gibbon (6) is the first successful study of the naturalistic behavior of a member of the family Pongidae. Hooton summarized (7) what was then known about the primates, particularly stressing the importance of behavior and the work of Carpenter and Zuckerman.

The war stopped field work, and no major studies were undertaken for some 15 years. Then, in the 1950's, investigators in Japan, England, France, Switzerland, and the United States independently started studies on the behavior of a wide variety of free-ranging primates. For the history of science it would be interesting to examine the reasons for this burst of parallel activity. Field studies were undertaken at more or less the same time, and publications start in the late 1950's and accelerate rapidly in the 1960's. This trend is still continuing and is well shown by the pattern of frequency of citations in a recent review by Hall (8). The review cites the papers of Bingham, Carpenter, Köhler (9), Nissen, Yerkes, and Zuckerman, but there are no references to additional field studies in the period 1941–1951, and most of the references are to papers appearing in 1960 or later.

The increased interest in primates, and particularly in the behavior of free-ranging primates, has given rise to several symposiums, and results of the new studies have been published almost as soon as they have been completed. Data from the recent field studies are included in volumes edited by Buettner-Janusch (10), Washburn (11), Napier and Barnicot (12), and, especially, DeVore (13). The volume edited by DeVore is devoted entirely to recent field studies and their evaluation. It includes accounts of the behavior of five kinds of monkeys, of chimpanzees, and of gorillas. Each chapter is by the person who did the field work, and in addition there are eight general chapters. Two new journals also are devoted to primates. *Primates*, published by the Japan Monkey Centre, is now in its 5th year, and *Folia Primatologica* has completed volume 3. Carpenter's field studies and general papers have been reprinted so that they are now easily available (14). Southwick has published a collection of readings in primate social behavior (15), and Eimerl and DeVore contributed a volume on the primates to the Life Nature Library (16). Field studies have recently been reviewed by Jay (17), and proceedings of a symposium organized and edited by Altmann should appear shortly (18). This abundance of published material makes it hard to believe that only 2 years ago a course on primate social behavior was difficult to teach because of the lack of easily available, suitable reading material.

THE NEW FIELD STUDIES

Obviously, with so much new data a complete review is impossible, and readers wishing more information and bibliography are referred to Jay (17) and to the symposiums previously noted. Here we wish to direct attention to the nature of the recent field studies and to a few of their major contributions. Perhaps their greatest contribution is a demonstration that close, accurate observation for hundreds of hours is possible. Prior to Schaller's field work, reported in 1963 (19), it was by no means clear that this kind of observation of gorillas would be possible; previous investigators had conducted very fragmentary observations, and Emlen and Schaller deserve great credit for the planning and execution of their study. A field study of the chimpanzee that seemed adequate in the 1930's now seem totally inadequate, when compared to Goodall's results (20). Today a field study is planned to yield something of the order of 1000 hours of observations, and the observer is expected to be close to the animals and to recognize individuals. A few years ago observations of this length and quality were thought unnecessary, if not impossible.

The importance of studies in which groups are visited repeatedly and animals are recognized individually may be illustrated by the problems they make it possible to study. For example, during one season of the year chimpanzees "fish" for termites by breaking off sticks or stiff grasses and sticking the prepared implement into a termite hole (21), and this whole complex of nest examination, tool preparation, and fishing is learned by the young chimpanzee. It can be seen at only one time of the year and can be appreciated only by an observer whose presence no longer disturbs the animals. Habituation to the observer is a slow and difficult process. Goodall reports (20) that after 8 months of observations she could approach to no closer than 50 meters of the chimpanzees and then only when they were in thick cover or up a tree; by 14 months she was able to get within 10 to 15 meters of them. The problem of tool use in nonhuman primates has been reviewed by Hall (22), but the essential point here is that the amount of throwing and object manipulation in the monkeys (Cercopithecidae) was greatly exaggerated in travelers' tales, which were uncritically accepted, and it took years of observation in a favorable locality to reveal the complexity of this kind of behavior in the chimpanzee (23).

Another example of the value of continued observations is in the study of deliberate hunting by baboons. In three seasons of field work and more than 1500 hours of observation DeVore had seen baboons catch and eat small mammals, but apparently almost by chance, when the baboon virtually stepped on something like a newborn antelope and then killed it (24, 25). But in 1965 DeVore saw repeated incidents of baboons surrounding, hunting, and killing small mammals (26).

The whole matter of predation on primates has been difficult to study. Rare events, such as an attack by an eagle (27) may be very important in the survival of primates, but such attacks are seldom observed, because the presence of the human observer disturbs either the predator or the prey. We think that the present deemphasis of the importance of predation on primates arises from these difficulties of observation and from the fact that even today most studies of free-ranging primates are made in areas where predators have been reduced or eliminated by man. Most predators are active at night, and there is still no adequate study of the nocturnal behavior of any monkey or ape. Predation probably can best be measured by studying the predators rather than the prey.

Recognition of individual animals is necessary for the study of many problems, from the first stages of the analysis of a social system to observations of social continuity or constancy of group membership; such observations are exceedingly difficult under most field conditions. For example, understanding of the dominance system implies repeated recognition of a number of animals under sufficiently various conditions so that the patterns of interaction become clear. Again, to be sure that a group has lost or gained a member, the observer must know the whole composition of the group.

Long-continued observations have proved to be important in many unexpected ways. For example, rhesus monkeys have been observed in several of their many very different habitats, and it has been found that young rhesus play more in cities than in some kinds of forest and play in the forest more at some seasons than at others. These differences are due in part to the amount of time which must be spent in getting food; the same forest troop may play more when fruits are available and hunger may be rapidly satisfied than at times of the year when the diet is composed of tiny seeds which take a long time to pick. Extracting the small seeds of sheesham pods during the months when rhesus troops spend most of their time in the sheesham trees takes many hours of the day (28). What might easily have been described in a short-term study as a species-specific difference of considerable magnitude turns out to be the result of seasonal and local variations in food source. It is essential to sample behavior in several habitats to gain an understanding of the flexibility of the built-in behavior patterns of a species, flexibility which precludes the need for development of new forms of genetically determined behavior to cope successfully with different habitats.

The long-term study in which many groups of a species are observed in different, contrasting localities, and in which at least some groups are known so well that most of the individuals can be recognized, will correct many false notions and will make valid generalizations possible. Although so far there have been only a few major investigations of this sort, some important generalizations seem possible.

Environment and Social Behavior

Nowhere is the extent to which the behavior of a species is adaptable and reponsive to local conditions more apparent than among groups of rhesus living in India. Rhesus occur naturally in such diverse environments as cities, villages, roadsides, cultivated fields, and many types of forest ranging to altitudes of over 2400 meters. Contact with man varies in these habitats from constant and close to rare and incidental.

Where rhesus groups are subjected to pressures of trapping, harassment, and high incidence of infectious disease, groups are tense and aggression is high. These pressures are found in areas where there is most contact and interaction with man, such as in cities and at places of pilgrimage. The animals are in generally poor physical condition, and numerous old and new wounds are evidence of a high rate of intragroup fighting. Tension among groups occupying adjacent areas of land is similarly high where there is insufficient space for normal movement and behavior, and where there may be intense competition for a limited supply of food and water. This is in sharp contrast to those groups living away from man where normal spacing among groups can be effected by the means evolved by the species. In the latter environments, such as forests, the rhesus are in excellent physical condition and what aggressive behavior occurs functions to maintain stable social groups and relationships among the members of the group; wounds are substantially fewer, and disease appears to be rare.

There has been considerable controversy in discussions of the relationships among social groups of the same species as to whether or not the geographical area occupied by a group should be called a territory or a home range. The point we wish to emphasize is that, within one species, populations living in different habitats may act quite differently toward neighboring groups. Populations may be capable of a wide variety of behavior patterns ranging from exclusive occupation of an area which may be defended against neighboring groups to a peaceful coexistence with conspecifics in which wide overlap in home ranges is tolerated. Because local populations of a species may maintain their ranges in different ways it is necessary to investigate all variations in group spacing in diverse habitats before attempting to describe characteristic behavior patterns for any species.

Not unexpectedly, population and group composition reflect these differences in habitat and stress. Groups living on the Gangetic plains, where trapping, harassment, and disease are important factors, are smaller, and the proportion of young members is also significantly smaller (28, 29). The long-term effects of pressures on different rhesus populations in northern and central India are now being investigated by a team of anthropologists of the National Center for Primate Biology.

A city presents a very different set of challenges to a rhesus group than does a forest. Often there are no trees to sleep in; living space must be shared with man and his domestic animals. Food is not available in the form common to other habitats, and monkeys may have to depend on their skill in stealing food from man. Often the food has been prepared by man for his own consumption, or it consists of fruits and vegetables pilfered from houses, shops, and streets. Garbage is picked through and edible portions are consumed. It is essential that the monkeys learn to differentiate between those humans who represent a real threat to their safety and those who are safe to approach. They must react quickly and learn to manipulate doors, gates, and other elements of the physical environment unique to their urban habitat. This is a tremendously different setting from that in which most rhesus live. City rhesus are more manipulative, more active, and often more aggressive than are forest rhesus. Clearly, the same species develops quite different learned habits in different environments.

ANNUAL REPRODUCTIVE CYCLE

The belief, which has been widely maintained, that there is no breeding season in monkeys and apes gave rise to the theory that the persistence throughout the year of groups, or highly organized troops, was due to continuous sexual attraction. The evidence for a breeding season has been reviewed by Lancaster and Lee (30) who found that in many species of monkeys there is a well-marked breeding season. For example, Mizuhara has presented data (31) on 545 births of Japanese macaques of Takasakiyama. There were on the average approximately 90 births per year over six consecutive years. The average length of the birth season was 125 days, but it varied from 95 to 176 days. The majority of the births occurred in June and July. Copulations were most frequent in November to March and were not observed during the birth season, and in spite of this the highly organized group continues as a social unit throughout the year.

The birth season has been studied in other groups of Japanese macaques, and in general the situation is similar. There is no doubt that both mating and birth seasons are highly restricted in the Japanese macaque. The birth season is spring and summer, but its onset and duration vary considerably. If observations were limited and combined for the whole species, as they were in early studies, the birth season would appear to be much longer than in fact it is for an individual group, and it is the events within the local group, not averages of events for the species, that bear upon the role of sexual attraction in holding primate society together.

Under very different climatic conditions, in India, rhesus macaques also have a birth season, but copulations were observed in all months of the year, although probably not with equal frequency (29). Among rhesus on a small island off Puerto Rico births occur from January to June, and copulations are restricted to July–January (32). These data confirm the point that a birth season will be more sharply defined in a local group than in a species as a whole. There is a mating season among rhesus introduced on the island, but only a peak of mating in the same species in their native India (29). It is clear that survey data drawn from many groups over a wide area must be used with caution when the aim is to interpret the behavior of a single group. Since the birth season is an adaption to local conditions, there is no reason to expect it to be the same over the entire geographical distribution of a species, and under laboratory conditions rhesus macaques breed throughout the year.

No data comparable to those for the macaques exist for other primates, and, since accurate determination of mating and birth seasons requires that reasonable numbers of animals be observed in all months of the year and that groups be observed in different localities, really adequate data exist for only the Japanese macaque. However, Lancaster and Lee were able to assemble data on 14 species of monkeys and apes. They found that probably the most common situation is a birth peak, a time of year at which births tend to be concentrated, rather than sharply limited mating and birth seasons. This is highly adaptive for widely distributed species, for it allows the majority of births to occur at the optimum time for each locality while maintaining a widely variable basic pattern. The birth season may be a more effective adaptation to extreme climatic conditions. There may be a birth peak in the chimpanzee (20), and there may be none in the mountain gorilla (19), but, since we have no more data than are necessary to clarify the reproductive pattern in a single species of macaque, we can conclude only that, while birth seasons are not present in either gorillas or chimpanzees, a peak is possible in chimpanzees, at least for those living near Lake Tanganyika.

Prior to the recent investigations there was a great deal of information on primate reproduction, and yet as late as 1960 it was still possible to maintain that there were no breeding seasons in primates and that this was the basis of primate society. Until recently the question of seasonality was raised without reference to a birth season as distinguished from a birth peak, or to a limited mating season as distinguished from matings throughout the year with a high frequency in a particular period.

FREQUENCY OF MATING

Obviously many more studies are needed, and one of the intriguing problems is the role of potency. Not only does the frequency of mating vary through the year, but also there appear to be enormous differences in potency between species that are reproducing at a normal rate. In nearly 500 hours of observation of gorillas, Schaller (19) saw only two matings, fewer than might be seen in a troop of baboons in almost any single morning. The redtail monkey (*Cercopithecus ascanius*) mates rarely (27), but the closely related vervet (*Cercopithecus aethiops*) does so frequently. To a considerable extent the observed differences are correlated with structure (33), such as size of testes, and all these species seem to be reproducing at an adequate and normal rate. There is no evidence that langurs (*Presbytis entellus*) are less successful breeders than rhesus, but the langurs copulate less frequently (34).

Now that more adequate data are becoming available, the social functions of sexual behavior should be reinvestigated. The dismissal of the theory that sexual attraction is *the* basis of primate society should open the way for a more careful study of the multiple functions of sexual behavior. The great differences among the primate species should provide data to prove or disprove new theories. In passing it might be noted that the human mating system without estrous cycles in the female and without marked seasonal variations is unique.

SYSTEMS OF MATING

Mating systems, like the presence or absence of seasonality in breeding and the frequency of copulation, are extremely variable in monkeys and apes. Eventually the relation of these variations to species adaptations will be understandable; at present it is most important to note that monkeys do not necessarily live either in harems or in promiscuous hordes as was once assumed. Restrictive mating patterns such as the stable and exclusive pair-bond formed between adult gibbons (6) and the harem system of the Hamadryas baboon (35) are comparatively rare. The most common mating pattern of monkeys and apes is promiscuity more or less influenced by dominance relationships. In species in which dominance relations are not constantly at issue, such as langurs (34), chimpanzees (20), or bonnet macaques (36), matings appear to be relatively promiscuous and are often based on the personal inclination of the estrous female. When dominance relationships are constantly at issue, as in baboons (37), Japanese macaques (38), and rhesus macaques (39, 40), sex often becomes one of the prerogatives of dominant rank. In such species dominant males tend to do a larger share of the mating than do more subordinate animals, but it is only in unusual situations that subordinate animals are barred from the mating system altogether. Mating systems probably support the general adaptation of the species to its environment. In most baboons and macaques the tendency for a few males to do much of the mating may be partly a by-product of natural selection for a hierarchy of adult males which dominates the troop so that in a dangerous terrestrial habitat external dangers will be met in an orderly way. Selection is not only for a male which can impregnate many females but it may also have favored a dominance-oriented social organization in which sexual activity has become one of the expressions of that dominance.

DOMINANCE RELATIONSHIPS

Long-term field studies of monkeys and apes in their natural habitats have emphasized that social relationships within a group are patterned and organized in very complex ways. There is no single "monkey pattern" or "ape pattern"; rather, there is great variability, both among different species and among different populations of the same species, in the organization and expression of social relationships. A difference in the relative dominance of individuals is one of the most common modes of social organization in monkey and ape societies. Dominance is not synonymous with aggression, and the way dominance is expressed varies greatly between species. In the gorilla, for example, dominance is most often expressed by extremely attenuated gestures and signals (19); a gentle nudge from the dominant male is more than enough to elicit a submissive response from a subordinate whereas in baboons, chases, fights, and biting can be daily occurrences (37). In many primates there is a tendency for the major age-sex classes to be ranked in a dominance order; for example, in baboons, macaques, and gorillas, adult males as a class are usually dominant over adult females, and females are dominant over young. This may not always be true, for in several species of macaques some females may outrank some adult males (36), although groups dominated by a female (such as the Minoo-B troop of Japanese macaques) are extremely rare (41). Dominance relationships may be quite unstructured, as in the chimpanzee (20), where dominance is expressed in interactions between individuals but where these relationships are not organized into any sort of hierarchy. A much more common situation is one in which dominance relations, among males at least, are organized into linear hierarchies that are quite stable over time, as in baboons (37), langurs (34, 42), and macaques (43, 44). Sometimes these dominance hierarchies are complicated by alliances among several males who back each other up very effectively (37) or even by an alliance between a male and a female (36). Although dominance varies widely among monkeys and apes both in its form and function, it is certainly one of the most important axes of social organization to be found in primate societies.

GENEALOGICAL RELATIONSHIPS

Recognition of individual animals and repeated studies of the same groups have opened the way to the appreciation of other long-continuing social relationships in monkeys and apes which cannot be interpreted in terms of dominance alone. Long-term studies of free-ranging animals have been made on only two species of nonhuman primates, Japanese macaques, which have been studied since 1950 by members of the Japan Monkey Centre, and Indian rhesus macaques living free on Cayo Sanitago, Puerto Rico, the island colony established by Carpenter in 1938. In these studies, when the genealogy of the animals has been known, it has been obvious that genetic relationships play a major role in determining the course and nature of social interactions (41, 45–47). It becomes clear that bonds between mother and infant may persist into adult life to form a nucleus from which many other social bonds ramify. When the genealogy of individual animals is known, members of commonly observed subgroupings, such as a cluster of four or five animals grooming or resting together, are often found to be uterine kin. Thus, members of a subgroup composed of several adult animals, both male and female, as well as juveniles and infants, may all be offspring of the same female (47). These relations continue to be very important in adult life not only in relaxed affectional relationships but also in dominance interactions. Sade saw a female rhesus monkey divert the attack of a dominant male from her adult son and saw another adult female protect her juvenile half-sisters (paternity is not determinable in most monkey societies). There is a very high frequency of grooming between related animals, and many animals never seek grooming partners outside of their own genealogies.

It should be stressed that there is no information leading us to believe that these animals are either recognizing genetic relationships or responding to any sort of abstract concept of family. Rather these social relationships are determined by the necessarily close association of mother with newborn infant, which is extended through time and generations and which ramifies into close associations among siblings. We believe that this pattern of enduring social relations between a mother and her offspring will be found in other species of primates. Because of their dramatic character, the importance of dominance and aggression has been greatly exaggerated compared to that of continuing, positive, affectional relations between related animals as expressed by their sitting or feeding together, touching, and grooming. Much of this behavior can be observed easily in the field, but the extent to which it is in fact an expression of social genealogies has been demonstrated only in the studies cited above.

Positive, affectional relations are not limited to relatives. Male Japanese macaques may take care of young by forming special protective relationships with particular infants (48), but whether these males have any special relationship to the infants as either father or brother is uncertain, and the mating system is such that paternity cannot be known either to the observer or to the monkeys. MacRoberts (49) has recorded a very high frequency of care of infants by males in the Gibraltar macaque. In addition, he has demonstrated that these positive protective relations are very beneficial to the juvenile. Two juveniles which had no such close relationship were forced to be peripheral, were at a great disadvantage in feeding, and were groomed much less than other juveniles in the group.

The status of the adult can be conferred on closely associated young (frequently an offspring when the adult is female), and for this reason the young of dominant animals are more likely to be dominant. This inheritance of rank has been discussed by Imanishi (45) for the Japanese macaque and by Koford (46) for the rhesus. Sons of very dominant females seem to have a great advantage over other males both because their mothers are able to back them up successfully in social interactions and becuase they stay with their mothers near the other dominant animals at the center of the group. They may never go through the stage of being socially and physically peripheral to the group which is typical for young males of these species. A male cannot simply "inherit" high rank; he must also win this position through his own abilities, but his chances of so doing are greatly increased if he has had these early experiences of associating with and being supported by very dominant animals.

There could hardly be a greater contrast than that between the emerging picture of an orderly society, based heavily on affectionate or cooperative social actions and structured by stable dominance relationships, and the old notion of an unruly horde of monkeys dominated by a tyrant. The 19th-century social evolutionists attributed less order to the societies of primitive man than is now known to exist in the societies of monkeys and apes living today.

COMMUNICATION

Research on the communication systems of monkeys and apes through 1962 has been most ably summarized and interpreted by Marler (50). Most of the data represent work by field observers who were primarily interested in social structure, and the signals, and their meanings, used to implement and facilitate social interactions were more or less taken for granted. Only in the last year or so have communication systems themselves been the object of careful study and analysis (see, for example, 18). Marler has emphasized both the extraordinary complexity of the communication systems of primates and the heavy dependence of these systems on composite signals (50). Most frequently it is not a single signal that passes between two animals but a signal complex composed of auditory, visual, tactile, and, more rarely, olfactory signals.

Communication in some monkey species is based on a system of intergrading signals, whereas in others much more use is made of highly discrete signals. For example, most vervet sounds (described by Struhsaker, 51) are of the discrete type, there being some 36 different sounds that are comparatively distinct both to the human ear and when analyzed by a sound spectrograph. In contrast, Rowell and Hinde have analyzed the sounds of the rhesus monkey (52) and found that of 13 harsh noises, 9 belonged to a single intergrading subsystem expressing agonistic emotions.

As more and more study is done on primates it will probably be shown that their communication systems tend to be of mixed form in that both graded and discrete signals are used depending on the relative efficiency of one or the other form in serving a specific function. In concert this use of both discrete and intergrading signals and of composites from several sensory modes produces a rich potential for the expression of very slight but significant changes in the intensity and nature of mood in the signaling animal. Marler has emphasized (50) that, except for calls warning of danger, the communication system is little applied to events outside the group. Communication systems in monkeys and apes are highly evolved in their capacity to express motivation of individuals and to facilitate social relationships. Without this ability to express mood, monkeys and apes would not be able to engage in the subtle and complicated social interactions that are a major feature of their adaptations.

SOCIAL LEARNING

Harlow and Harlow's experiments (53) show the importance of learning in the development of social life; however, monkeys and apes are so constituted that, except in the laboratory, social learning is inevitable. They adapt by their social life, and the group provides the context of affection, protection, and stability in which learning occurs. No one factor can explain the importance of social behavior, because society is a major adaptive mechanism with many functions, but one of the most important of these functions is the provision of a rich and protected social context in which young mature. Field observations, although mainly observations of the results of learning rather than of the process itself, provide necessary clues as to the nature of the integration of relevant developmental and social factors. These factors can then be estimated and defined for subsequent intensive controlled research in a laboratory or colony.

It has become clear that, although learning has great importance in the normal development of nearly all phases of primate behavior, it is not a generalized ability; animals are able to learn some things with great ease and other things only with the greatest difficulty. Learning is part of the adaptive pattern of a species and can be understood only when it is seen as the process of acquiring skills and attitudes that are of evolutionary significance to a species when living in the environment to which it is adapted.

There are important biological limitations which vary from species to species and which do not reflect differences in intelligence so much as differences in specializations. For example, Goodall (21) has observed young chimpanzees learning to fish for termites both by their observation of older chimpanzees and by practice. It takes time for the chimpanzee to become proficient with these tools, and many mistakes are made. Chimpanzees are not the only primates that like termites, and Goodall has observed baboons sitting near chimpanzees watching and waiting while the latter are getting termites. The baboons are just as eager as the chimpanzees to eat termites but are unable to learn how to fish for termites for themselves.

It is likely that there are important variables among groups of a single species that make it possible for the acquisition of new patterns of behavior or the expression of basic learned species patterns to vary from group to group and from one habitat to another. For example, the nature of the integration and operation of a social unit vary in the extent to which it depends on the personalities of individuals in the group—this is another dimension of our understanding of how social behavior may affect species survival. Particularly aggressive adult males can make the behavior of their groups relative to that of adjacent groups with less assertive males substantially different. For example, a group with very aggressive males can control a larger geographic area than is occupied by a group with much less aggressive males. The tenor of life within a group may be tenser or more relaxed depending on personalities of adults in the group.

Imprinting has traditionally been distinguished from other learning processes by the fact that in imprinting the young animal will learn to follow, to be social (54), without an external or immediate reward (55). However, among monkeys and apes, simply being with other animals is a reward, and learning is reinforced by the affectional, attentive, supportive social context of the group (56). Butler was the first to use the sight of another monkey as a reward in psychological experiments (57). The field worker sees sick and practically disabled animals making great efforts to stay with their group. Among ground-living forms, animals that have lost or broken limbs or are so sick that they collapse as soon as the group stops moving, all walk along as the troop moves. Instances of wounded rhesus macaques' moving into langur groups after the rhesus have left or been forced out of their own group have been recorded. Clearly, it is essential for the young monkey or ape to mature in a social setting in which it learns appropriate skills and relationships during early years and in which it continues to learn during adulthood. "Where the individual primate is, in temporary isolation, learning a task without reference to any other member of its species, the learning is not normal" (58).

FUTURE PRIMATE STUDIES

At present many long-term studies are in process and major films are being edited (Goodall on chimpanzee and DeVore on baboon). There will be about twice as many major accounts available in 2 years as there are now. Since it is now clear that detailed desciptive studies of undisturbed free-ranging primates can be made, and since available data show that there are substantial differences in the behavior of the different species, more species should be investigated. So far studies have concentrated for the most part on the larger ground-living forms which are easier to study. There is no study of *Cercocebus*, little on *Colobus* (59), and nothing on the numerous langurs (*Presbytis*) of southeast

Asia. New World monkeys have been investigated very little, and there are numerous genera that have not been the subjects of a major field study. Also, since local variation is important, forms such as the chimpanzee and gorilla should be studied in more and contrasting localities.

Once the general characteristics of the behaviors of several species are known, then interest can shift to topics such as detailed ecology, birth, infant behavior, peer groups, affectionate behaviors, sex, or dominance, to mention only a few. The behavior of a whole species is a large problem, and description has to be at a very general level when the goal is a first general statement. A problem-oriented study permits choice of species and elaboration of techniques. A further advantage of the problem-oriented approach is that it allows the close coordination of the field work with experimental work in the laboratory. Fortunately, no division has developed between those doing the field work and those involved in the experimental analysis of behavior. Many scientists have done both controlled experiments and field studies. The interplay between naturalistic observation and controlled experiment is the essential key to the understanding of behavior (60). The character of the natural adaptation of the species and the dimensions of the society can be determined only in the field. Many topics, such as geographic range, food, predation, group size, aggression, and the like, can be seen only under field conditions. But the mechanisms of the observed behavior can be determined only in the laboratory, and this is the more complicated task. The relation of a field study to scientific understanding is like the relation of the observation that a man walks or runs to the whole anaylsis of locomotion. The field worker lists what the animals eat, but this gives no understanding of nutrition. The kinds of interactions may be charted in the field, but their interpretation requires the laboratory. Field workers saw hours devoted to play, but it was Harlow's experiments that showed how essential this activity was to the development of behavior. As the field studies develop it is to be hoped that they will maintain a close relation to controlled experiment. It is most fortunate that the present studies are being carried on by anthropologists, psychologists, and zoologists. An understanding of behavior is most likely to come from the bringing together of the methods and interests of many sciences, and we hope that the field studies remain a part of general behavioral science and do not become independent as workers and problems become more and more numerous.

Even now, in their preliminary state, the field studies can offer some conclusions that might be pondered by students in the multiplicity of departments now dividing up the study of human behavior. Behavior is profoundly influenced by the biology of the species, and problems of perception, emotion, aggression, and many others cannot be divorced from the biology of the actors in the social system. Early learning is important, and an understanding of the preschool years is essential to an understanding of behavior. Play is tremendously important, and a species that wastes the emotions and energies of its

young by divorcing play from education has forfeited its evolutionary her-
itage—the biological motivation of learning. Social behavior is relatively simple
compared to the biological mechanisms that make the behavior possible. Ultimately a science of human behavior must include both biological and social
factors, and there is no more reason to separate the study of human behavior
into many compartments than there would be to separate the field studies from
the intellectual enrichment coming from the laboratory.

REFERENCES

1. R. M. Yerkes and A. W. Yerkes, *The Great Apes, A Study of Anthropoid Life*
   (Yale Univ. Press, New Haven, 1929).
2. H. W. Nissen, "A Field Study of the Chimpanzee," *Comp. Psychol. Monogr. No.
   8* (1931).
3. H. C. Bingham, "Gorillas in a Native Habitat," *Carnegie Inst. Wash. Publ. No.
   426* (1932).
4. C. R. Carpenter, "A Field Study of the Behavior and Social Relations of Howling
   Monkeys," *Comp. Psych. Monogr. No. 10* (1934).
5. S. Zuckerman, *The Social Life of Monkeys and Apes* (Routledge and Kegan Paul,
   London, 1932); *Functional Affinities of Man, Monkeys and Apes* (Routledge and
   Kegan Paul, London, 1933).
6. C. R. Carpenter, "A Field Study in Siam of the Behavior and Social Relations of
   the Gibbon, *Hylobates lar.,*" *Comp. Psychol. Monogr. No. 16* (1940).
7. E. A. Hooton, *Man's Poor Relations* (Doubleday, Garden City, N. Y., 1942).
8. K. R. L. Hall, *Proc. Zool. Soc. London* **14**, 265 (1965).
9. W. Köhler, *The Mentality of Apes* (Harcourt Brace, New York, 1925).
10. J. Buettner-Janusch, Ed., "The Relatives of Man," *Ann. N.Y. Acad. Sci.* **102**,
    181–514 (1962); J. Buettner-Janusch, Ed., *Evolutionary and Genetic Biology of
    Primates* (Academic Press, New York, 1963–1964).
11. S. L. Washburn, Ed., *Classification and Human Evolution,* Viking Fund Publica-
    tions in Anthropology No. 37 (Aldine, New York, 1963).
12. J. Napier and N. Barnicot, Eds., "The Primates," *Symp. Zool. Soc. London No.
    10* (1963).
13. I. DeVore, Ed. *Primate Behavior: Field Studies of Monkeys and Apes* (Holt,
    Rinehart and Winston, New York, 1965).
14. C. R. Carpenter, *Naturalistic Behavior of Nonhuman Primates* (Pennsylvania
    State Univ. Press, University Park, 1964).
15. C. H. Southwick, Ed., *Primate Social Behavior* (Van Nostrand, Princeton, 1963).
16. S. Eimerl and I. DeVore, *The Primates* (Time, Inc., New York, 1965).
17. P. Jay, in *Behavior of Nonhuman Primates,* A. M. Schrier, H. F. Harlow, F.
    Stollnitz, Eds. (Academic Press, New York, 1965), pp. 525–591.
18. S. A. Altmann, Ed., *Social Communication among Primates,* (Univ. of Chicago
    Press, Chicago, in press).

19. G. SCHALLER, *The Mountain Gorilla: Ecology and Behavior* (Univ. of Chicago Press, Chicago, 1963).
20. J. GOODALL, *Primate Behavior: Field Studies of Monkeys and Apes,* I. DEVORE, Ed. (Holt, Rinehart and Winston, New York, 1965), pp. 425–473.
21. ——, *Nature* **201**, 1264 (1964).
22. K. R. L. HALL, *Current Anthropol.* **4** (5), 479 (1963).
23. J. B. LANCASTER, "Chimpanzee tool use," paper presented at Southwestern Anthropological Association annual meeting, Los Angeles, Calif. (Apr. 1965).
24. I. DEVORE and K. R. L. HALL, in *Primate Behavior: Field Studies of Monkeys and Apes* (Holt, Rinehart and Winston, New York, 1965), pp. 20–52.
25. "Baboon Behavior," motion picture produced by I. DEVORE and S. L. WASHBURN, University Extension, Univ. of California, Berkeley (1961).
26. I. DEVORE, personal communication (1965).
27. A. J. HADDOW, *Proc. Zool. Soc. London* **122** (II), 297 (1952).
28. P. JAY and D. LINDBURG, "The Indian Primate Ecology Project (September 1964-June 1965)," unpublished manuscript.
29. C. H. SOUTHWICK, M. A. BEG, M. R. SIDDIQI, *Ecology* **42**, 538 (1961); *ibid.,* p. 698.
30. J. B. LANCASTER and R. B. LEE, in *Primate Behavior: Field Studies of Monkeys and Apes,* I. DEVORE, Ed. (Holt, Rinehart and Winston, New York, 1965), pp. 486–513.
31. H. MIZUHARA, personal communication (1965), quoted by Lancaster and Lee (*30*).
32. C. B. KOFORD, in *Primate Behavior: Field Studies of Monkeys and Apes,* I. DEVORE, Ed. (Holt, Rinehart and Winston, New York, 1965), pp. 160–174.
33. A. H. SCHULTZ, *Anat. Rec.* **72**, 387 (1938).
34. P. JAY, in *Primate Behavior: Field Studies of Monkeys and Apes,* I. DEVORE, Ed. (Holt, Rinehart and Winston, New York, 1965), pp. 197–249.
35. H. KUMMER and F. KURT, *Folia Primatologica* **1**, 4 (1963).
36. P. E. SIMONDS, in *Primate Behavior: Field Studies of Monkeys and Apes,* I. DEVORE, Ed. (Holt, Rinehart and Winston, New York, 1965), pp. 175–196.
37. K. R. L. HALL and I. DEVORE, in *Primate Behavior: Field Studies of Monkeys and Apes,* I. DEVORE Ed. (Holt, Rinehart and Winston, New York, 1965), pp. 53–110.
38. K. TOKUDA, *Primates* **3**, 1 (1961–62).
39. C. H. CONAWAY and C. B. KOFORD, *J. Mammal.* **45**, 577 (1965).
40. C. SOUTHWICK, in *Primate Behavior: Field Studies of Monkeys and Apes,* I. DEVORE, Ed. (Holt, Rinehart and Winston, New York, 1965), pp. 111–159.
41. M. YAMADA, *Primates* **4**, 43 (1963).
42. S. RIPLEY, in "Social Communication among Primates," S. ALTMANN, Ed. (Univ. of Chicago Press, Chicago, in press).
43. S. A. ALTMANN, *Ann. N. Y. Acad. Sci.* **102**, 338 (1962).
44. J. ITANI, R. TOKUDA, Y. FURUYA, K. KANO, Y. SHIN, *Primates* **4**, 1 (1963).
45. K. IMANISHI, *Current Anthropol.* **1**, 393 (1960).
46. C. B. KOFORD, *Science* **141**, 356 (1963).
47. D. S. SADE, *Am. J. Phys. Anthropol.* **23**, 1 (1965).
48. J. ITANI, *Primates* **4**, 1 (1959).

49. M. MacRoberts, "Gibraltar macaques," paper presented at Southwestern Anthropological Association annual meeting, Los Angeles, Calif. (Apr. 1965).
50. P. Marler, in *Primate Behavior: Field Studies of Monkeys and Apes*, I. DeVore, Ed. (Holt, Rinehart and Winston, New York, 1965), pp. 544–584.
51. T. T. Struhsaker, in "Social Communication among Primates," S. A. Altmann, Ed. (Univ. of Chicago Press, Chicago, in press).
52. T. E. Rowell and R. A. Hinde, *Proc. Zool. Soc. London* **138**, 279 (1962); T. E. Rowell, *Symp. Zool. Soc. London* **8**, 91 (1962).
53. H. F. Harlow and M. K. Harlow, in *Behavior of Nonhuman Primates*, A. M. Schrier, H. F. Harlow, F. Stollnitz, Eds. (Academic Press, New York, 1965), vol. 2, pp. 287–334.
54. N. E. Collias, in *Roots of Behavior*, E. L. Bliss, Ed. (Harper, New York, 1962), pp. 264–273.
55. W. Sluckin, *Imprinting and Early Learning* (Aldine, Chicago, 1965).
56. K. R. L. Hall, *Brit. J. Psychol.* **54**, 201 (1963).
57. R. A. Butler, *J. Exp. Psychol.* **48**, 19 (1954).
58. K. R. L. Hall, unpublished manuscript.
59. W. Ullrich, *Zool. Garten* **25**, 305 (1961).
60. W. A. Mason, in *Primate Behavior: Field Studies of Monkeys and Apes*, I. DeVore, Ed. (Holt, Rinehart and Winston, New York, 1965), pp. 514–543.
61. Supported by USPHS grant MH 08623. We thank Anne Brower, John Ellefson and Lewis Klein for reading the preliminary version of the manuscript and for helpful criticism.

9·The Evolution of Hunting

S. L. Washburn
and C. S. Lancaster

University of California, Berkeley

It is significant that the title of this symposium is "Man the Hunter"—for, in contrast to carnivores, human hunting by males is based on a division of labor and is a social and technical adaptation quite different from that of other mammals. Human hunting is made possible by tools, but it is far more than a technique, or even a variety of techniques. It is a way of life, and the success of this adaptation (in its total social, technical, and psychological dimensions) has dominated the course of human evolution for hundreds of thousands of years. In a very real sense our intellect, interests, emotions, and basic social life—all these are evolutionary products of the success of the hunting adaptation. When anthropologists speak of the unity of mankind, they are stating that the selection pressures of the hunting and gathering way of life were so similar and the result so successful that populations of *Homo sapiens* are still fundamentally the same everywhere. In this essay we are concerned with the general characteristics of man that we believe can be attributed to the hunting way of life.

Perhaps the importance of this way of life in producing man is best shown by the length of time hunting has dominated human history. The genus *Homo*[1]

This paper is part of a program on primate behavior, supported by the United States Public Health Service (Grant No. 8623) and aided by a Research Professorship in the Miller Institute for Basic Research in Science at the University of California at Berkeley. This chapter appears in *Man the Hunter*, edited by Irven DeVore and Richard Lee (Aldine Press). We wish to thank Dr. Phyllis C. Jay for her helpful criticism and suggestions about this paper.

has existed for some 600,000 years, and agriculture has been important only during the last few thousand years. Even 6000 years ago large parts of the world's population were nonagricultural, and the entire evolution of man from the earliest populations of *Homo erectus* to existing races took place during the period in which man was a hunter. The common factors that dominated human evolution and produced *Homo sapiens* were preagricultural. Agricultural ways of life have dominated less than 1 percent of human history, and there is no evidence of major biological changes during that period of time. The kind of minor biological changes that occurred and which are used to characterize modern races were not common to *Homo sapiens*. The origin of all common characteristics must be sought in preagricultural times. Probably all experts would agree that hunting was a part of the social adaptation of all populations of the genus *Homo*, and many would regard *Australopithecus*[2] as a still earlier hominid who was already a hunter, although possibly much less efficient than the later forms. If this is true, and if the Pleistocene period had a duration of three million years, then pre-*Homo erectus* human tool using and hunting lasted for at least four times as long as the duration of the genus *Homo* (J. Lancaster, in press). No matter how the earlier times may ultimately be interpreted, the observation of more hunting among apes than was previously suspected (Goodall 1965) and increasing evidence for hunting by *Australopithecus* strengthens the position that less than 1 percent of human history has been dominated by agriculture. It is for this reason that the consideration of hunting is so important for the understanding of human evolution.

When hunting and the way of life of successive populations of the genus *Homo* are considered, it is important to remember that there must have been both technical and biological progress during this vast period of time. Although the locomotor system appears to have changed very little in the last 500,000 years, the brain did increase in size, and the form of the face changed. But for present purposes it is particularly necessary to direct attention to the cultural changes that occurred in the last ten or fifteen thousand years before agriculture. There is no convenient term for this period of time, traditionally spoken of as the end of the Upper Paleolithic and the Mesolithic, but Binford and Binford (1966) have rightly emphasized its importance.

During most of human history water must have been a major physical and psychological barrier and the inability to cope with water is shown in the archeological record by the absence of remains of fish, shellfish, or any object that required going deeply into water or the use of boats. There is no evidence that the resources of river and sea were utilized until this late preagricultural period, and, since the consumption of shellfish in particular leaves huge middens, the negative evidence is impressive. It is likely that the basic problem

[1]The term *Homo* includes Java, Pekin, Maur, and later forms.
[2]Using the term to include both the small *A. africanus* and *A. robustus* large forms. Simpson (1966) briefly and clearly discusses the taxonomy of these forms and of the fragments called *Homo*.

in utilization of resources from sea or river was that man cannot swim naturally but to do so must learn a difficult skill. In monkeys the normal quadrupedal running motions serve to keep them afloat and moving quite rapidly. A macaque, for example, does not have to learn any new motor habit in order to swim. But the locomotor patterns of gibbons and apes will not keep them above the water surface, and even a narrow, shallow stream is a barrier for the gorilla (Schaller 1963). For early man water was a barrier and a danger, not a resource. (Obviously water was important for drinking, for richer vegetation along rivers and lakeshores, and for concentrating animal life. Here we are referring to water as a barrier prior to swimming and boats, and we stress that, judging from the behavior of contemporary apes, even a small stream may be a major barrier.)

In addition to the conquest of water, there seems to have been great technical progress in this late preagricultural period. In addition to a much wider variety of stone tools of earlier kinds, the archeological record shows bows and arrows, grinding stones, boats, houses of much more advanced types and even villages, sledges drawn by animals and used for transport, and the domestic dog. These facts have two special kinds of significance for this symposium. First, the technology of *all* the living hunters belongs to this late Mesolithic era at the earliest, and many have elements borrowed from agricultural and metal-using peoples. Second, the occasional high densities of hunters mentioned as problems and exceptions at the symposium are based on this very late and modified extension of the hunting and gathering way of life. For example, the way of life of the tribes of the Northwest Coast, with polished stone axes for woodworking, boats, and extensive reliance on products of the river and sea, should be seen as a very late adaptation. Goldschmidt's (1959:185–193) distinction between nomadic and sedentary hunting and gathering societies makes this point in a slightly different way. He shows the social elaboration that comes with the settled groups with larger populations.

The presence of the dog (Zeuner 1963) is a good index of the late preagricultural period, and domestic dogs were used by hunters in Africa, Australia, and the Americas. Among the Eskimo, dogs were used in hunting, for transportation, as food in time of famine, and as watch dogs. With dogs, sleds, boats, metal, and complex technology, Eskimos may be a better example of the extremes to which human adaptation can go than an example of primitive hunting ways. Although dogs were hardly mentioned at the symposium, they were of great importance in hunting—for locating, tracking, bringing to bay, and even killing. Lee (1965:131) reports that one Bushman with a trained pack of hunting dogs brought in 75 percent of the meat of a camp. Six other resident hunters lacked hunting packs and accounted for only 25 percent of the meat. Dogs may be important in hunting even very large animals; in the Amboseli Game Reserve in Kenya one of us saw two small dogs bring a rhinoceros to bay and dodge repeated charges.

With the acquisition of dogs, bows, and boats it is certain that hunting became much more complex in the last few thousand years before agriculture. The antiquity of traps, snares, and poisons is unknown, but it appears that for thousands of years man was able to kill large game close in with spear or axe. As Brues (1959) has shown, this limits the size of the hunters, and there are no very large or very small fossil men. Pygmoid hunters of large game are probably possible only if hunting is with bows, traps, and poison. It is remarkable that nearly all the estimated statures for fossil men fall between 5 feet 2 inches and 5 feet 10 inches. This suggests that strong selection pressures kept human stature within narrow limits for hundreds of thousands of years and that these pressures relaxed a few thousand years ago, allowing the evolution of a much wider range of statures.

The gathering and the preparing of food also seem to have become more complex during the last few thousand years before agriculture. Obviously, gathering by nonhuman primates is limited to things that can be eaten immediately. In contrast, man gathers a wide range of items that he cannot digest without soaking, boiling, grinding, or other special preparation. Seeds may have been a particularly important addition to the human diet because they are abundant and can be stored easily. Since grinding stones appear before agriculture, grinding and boiling may have been the necessary preconditions to the discovery of agriculture. One can easily imagine that people who were grinding seeds would see repeated examples of seeds sprouting or being planted by accident. Grinding and boiling were certainly known to the preagricultural peoples, and this knowledge could spread along an arctic route, setting the stage for a nearly simultaneous discovery of agricultrue in both the New World and the Old World. It was not necessary for agriculture itself to spread through the arctic but only the seed-using technology, which could then lead to the discovery of seed planting. If this analysis is at all correct, then the hunting-gathering adaptation of the Indians of California, for example, should be seen as representing the possibilities of this late preagricultural gathering, making possible much higher population densities than would have been the case in pregrinding and preboiling economy.

Whatever the fate of these speculations, we think that the main conclusion, based on the archeological record, ecological considerations, and the ethnology of the surviving hunter-gatherers, will be sustained. In the last few thousand years before agriculture, both hunting and gathering became much more complex. This final adaptation, including the use of products of river and sea and the grinding and cooking of otherwise inedible seeds and nuts, was worldwide, laid the basis for the discovery of agriculture, and was much more effective and diversified than the previously existing hunting and gathering adaptations.

Hunting by members of the genus *Homo* throughout the 600,000 years that the genus has persisted has included the killing of large numbers of big animals. This implies the efficient use of tools, as Birdsell has stressed at the symposium. The adaptive value of hunting large animals has been shown by Bourlière (1963), who demonstrated that 75 percent of the meat available to human hunters in the eastern Congo was in elephant, buffalo, and hippopotamus. It is some measure of the success of human hunting that when these large species are protected in game reserves (as in the Murchison Falls or Queen Elizabeth Parks in Uganda) they multiply rapidly and destroy the vegetation. Elephants alone can destroy trees more rapidly than they are replaced naturally, as they do in the Masai Amboseli Reserve in Kenya. Since the predators are also protected in reserves, it appears that human hunters have been killing enough large game to maintain the balance of nature for many thousands of years. It is tempting to think that man replaced the saber-toothed cat as the major predator of large game, both controlling the numbers of the game and causing the extinction of Old World saber-tooths. We think that hunting and butchering large animals put a maximum premium on cooperation among males, a behavior that is at an absolute minimum among the nonhuman primates. It is difficult to imagine the killing of creatures such as cave bears, mastodons, mammoths—or *Dinotherium* at a much earlier time—without highly coordinated, cooperative action among males. It may be that the origin of male-male associations lies in the necessities of cooperation in hunting, butchering, and war. Certainly butchering sites, such as those described by Clark Howell in Spain, imply that the organization of the community for hunting large animals goes back for many, many thousands of years. From the biological point of view, the development of such organizations would have been paralleled by selection for an ability to plan and cooperate (or reduction of rage). Because females and juveniles may be involved in hunting small creatures, the social organization of big-game hunting would also lead to an intensification of a sexual division of labor.

It is important to stress, as noted before, that human hunting is a set of ways of life. It involves divisions of labor between male and female, sharing according to custom, cooperation among males, planning, knowledge of many species and large areas, and technical skill. Goldschmidt (1966:87 and following) has stressed the uniqueness and importance of human sharing, both in the family and in the wider society, and Lee (personal communication) emphasizes orderly sharing as fundamental to human hunting society. The importance of seeing human hunting as a whole social pattern is well illustrated by the old idea, recently revived, that the way of life of our ancestors was similar to that of wolves, rather than that of apes or monkeys. But this completely misses the special nature of the human adaptation. Human females do not go out and hunt and then regurgitate to their young when they return. Human young do not stay in dens but are carried by mothers. Male wolves do not kill with tools, butcher, and share with females who have been gathering. In an evolutionary sense the whole human pattern is new, and it is the success of this particularly human way that dominated human evolution and determined the relation of biology and culture for thousands of years. Judging from the archeological record, it is probable that the major features of this human way, possibly even including the beginnings of language, had evolved by the time of *Homo erectus*.[3]

THE WORLD VIEW OF THE HUNTER

Lévi-Strauss urged that we study the world view of hunters, and, perhaps surprisingly, some of the major aspects of world view can be traced from the archeological record. We have already mentioned that boats and the entire complex of fishing, hunting sea mammals, and using shellfish was late. With this new orientation wide rivers and seas changed from barriers to pathways and sources of food, and the human attitude toward water must have changed completely. But many hundreds of thousands of years earlier, perhaps with *Australopithecus*, the relation of the hunters to the land must also have changed from an earlier relationship which may be inferred from studies of contemporary monkeys and apes. Social groups of nonhuman primates occupy exceedingly small areas, and the vast majority of animals probably spend their entire lives within less than four or five square miles. Even though they have excellent vision and can see for many miles, especially from tops of trees, they make no effort to explore more than a tiny fraction of the area they see. Even for gorillas the range is only about fifteen square miles (Schaller 1963), and it is of the same order of magnitude for Savannah baboons (DeVore and Hall 1965). When Hall tried to drive a troop of baboons beyond the end of their range, they refused to be driven and doubled back into familiar territory, although they were easy to drive within the range. The known area is a psychological reality, clear in the minds of the animals. Only a small part of even this

[3]In speculations of this kind, it is well to keep the purpose of the speculation and the limitation of the evidence in mind. Our aim is to understand human evolution. What shaped the course of human evolution was a succession of successful adaptations, both biological and cultural. These may be inferred in part from the direct evidence of the archeological record. But the record is very incomplete. For example, Lee (personal communication) has described, for the Bushmen, how large game may be butchered where it falls and only meat brought back to camp. This kind of behavior means that analysis of bones around living sites is likely to underestimate both the amount and variety of game killed. If there is any evidence that large animals were killed, it is probable that far more were killed than the record shows. Just as the number of human bones gives no indication of the number of human beings, the number of animal bones, although it provides clues to the existence of hunting, gives no direct evidence of how many animals were killed. The Pleistocene way of life can only be known by inference and speculation. Obviously, speculations are based on much surer ground when the last few thousand years are under consideration. Ethnographic information is then directly relevant and the culture bearers are of our own species. As we go farther back in time, there is less evidence, and the biological and cultural difference becomes progressively greater. Yet it was in those remote times that the human way took shape, and it is only through speculation that we may gain some insights into what the life of our ancestors may have been.

limited range is used, and exploration is confined to the canopy, lower branches, and bushes, or ground, depending on the biology of the particular species. Napier (1962) has discussed this highly differential use of a single area by several species. In marked contrast, human hunters are familiar with very large areas. In the area studied by Lee (1965) eleven waterholes and 600 square miles supported 248 Bushmen, less than the number of baboons supported by a single waterhole and a few square miles in the Amboseli Reserve in Kenya. The most minor hunting expedition covers an area larger than most nonhuman primates would cover in a lifetime. Interest in a large area is human. The small ranges of monkeys and apes restrict the opportunities for gathering, hunting, and meeting conspecifics, and limit the kind of predation and the number of diseases. In the wide area, hunters and gatherers can take advantage of seasonal foods and only man among the primates can migrate long distances seasonally. In the small area, the population must be carried throughout the year on local resources, and natural selection has been for biology and behavior that efficiently utilize these limited opportunities. But in the wide area selection is for the knowledge that enables the group to utilize seasonal and occasional food sources. Gathering over a wide and diversified area implies a greater knowledge of flora and fauna, knowledge of the annual cycle, and a different attitude toward group movements. Clearly one of the great advantages of slow maturation is that learning covers a series of years, and the meaning of events in these years become a part of the individual's knowledge. With rapid maturation and no language the chances that any member of the group will know the appropriate behavior for rare events is greatly reduced.

Moving over long distances creates problems of carrying food and water. Lee (1965:124) has pointed out that the sharing of food even in one locality implies that food is carried, and there is no use in gathering quantities of fruit or nuts unless they can be moved. If women are to gather while men hunt, the results of the labors of both sexes must be carried back to some agreed-upon location. Meat can be carried away easily, but the development of some sort of receptacles for carrying vegetable products may have been one of the most fundamental advances in human evolution. Without a way of carrying, the advantages of a large area are greatly reduced, and sharing implies that a person carries much more than one can use. However that may be, the whole human pattern of gathering and hunting to share is unique to man. In its small range a monkey gathers only what it itself needs to eat at that moment, and the whole complex of economic reciprocity that dominates so much of human life is unique to man. Wherever archeological evidence can suggest the beginnings of movement over large ranges, cooperation, and sharing, it is dating the origin of some of the most fundamental aspects of human behavior, of the human world view. We believe that hunting large animals may demand all these aspects of human behavior which separate man so sharply from the other primates. If this is so, then the human way appears to be as old as *Homo erectus*.

The price that man pays for his high mobility is well illustrated by the problems of living in the African savanna. Man is not adapted to this environment in the same sense that baboons or vervet monkeys are. Man needs much more water, and without preparation and cooking he can only eat a limited number of the foods on which the local primates thrive. Unless there have been major physiological changes, the diet of our ancestors must have been far more like that of chimpanzees than like that of a savanna-adapted species. Further, man cannot survive the diseases of the African savanna without lying down and being cared for. Even when sick, the locally adapted animals are usually able to keep moving with their troop; and the importance to their survival of a home base has been stressed elsewhere (DeVore and Washburn 1963). Also, man becomes liable to new diseases and parasites by eating meat, and it is of interest that the products of the sea, which we believe were the last class of foods added to human diet, are widely regarded as indigestible and carry diseases to which man is particularly susceptible. Although many humans die of disease and injury, those who do not, almost without exception, owe their lives to others who cared for them when they were unable to hunt or gather, and this uniquely human caring is one of the patterns that builds social bonds in the group and permits the species to occupy almost every environment in the world.

A large territory provides not only a much wider range of possible foods but also a greater variety of potentially useful materials. With tool use this variety takes on meaning, and even the earliest pebble tools show selection in size, form, and material. When wood ceases to be just something to climb on, hardness, texture, and form become important. Availability of materials is critical to the tool user, and early men must have had a very different interest in their environment from that of monkeys or apes. Thus, the presence of tools in the archeological record is not only an indication of technical progress but also an index of interest in inanimate objects and in a much larger part of the environment than is the case with nonhuman primates.

The tools of the hunters include the earliest beautiful man-made objects, the symmetrical bifaces, especially those of the Acheulian tradition. Just how they were used is still a matter of debate, but, as contemporary attempts to copy them show, their manufacture is technically difficult, taking lots of time and practice and a high degree of skill. The symmetry of these tools may indicate that they were swung with great speed and force, presumably attached to some sort of handle. A tool that is moved slowly does not have to be symmetrical, but balance becomes important when an object is swung rapidly or thrown with speed. Irregularities will lead to deviations in the course of the blow or the trajectory of flight. An axe or spear to be used with speed and power is subject to very different technical limitations from those of scrapers or digging sticks, and it may well be that it was the attempt to produce efficient high-speed weapons that first produced beautiful, symmetrical objects.

When the selective advantage of a finely worked point over an irregular one is considered, it must be remembered that a small difference might give a very large advantage. A population in which hunters hit the games 5 percent more frequently, more accurately, or at greater distance would bring back much more meat. There must have been strong selection for greater skill in manufacture and use, and it is no accident that the bones of small-brained men (*Australopithecus*) are never found with beautiful, symmetrical tools. If the brains of contemporary apes and men are compared, the areas associated with hand skills (both in cerebellum and cortex) are at least three times as large in man. Clearly, the success of tools has exerted a great influence on the evolution of the brain and has created the skills that make art possible. The evolution of the capacity to appreciate the product must evolve along with the skills of manufacture and use, and the biological capacities that the individual inherits must be developed in play and practiced in games. In this way the beautiful, symmetrical tool becomes a symbol of a level of human intellectual achievement, representing far more than just the tool itself.

In a small group like the hunting band, which is devoted to one or two major cooperative activities, the necessity for long practice in developing skills to a very high level restricts the number of useful arts and social organization is relatively simple. Where there is little division of labor all men learn the same activities, such as skill in the hunt or in war. In sports we take it for granted that one person will not achieve a very high level of performance in more than a limited set of skills. This limitation is in part biological, but it is important socially as well because great proficiency in a skill necessitates practice. In warfare a wide variety of weapons is useful only if there are enough men so that there can be division of labor and different groups can practice different skills. Handedness, a feature that separates man from ape, is a part of this biology of skill. To be ambidextrous might seem ideal, but in fact the highest level of skill is attained by concentrating both biological ability and practice primarily on one hand.

Hunting changed man's relationship to other animals and his view of what is natural. The human notion that it is normal for animals to flee and the whole concept of animals being wild, is the result of man's habit of hunting. In game reserves many different kinds of animals soon learn not to fear man, and they no longer flee. Woodburn took a Hadza into the Nairobi Park, and the Hadza was amazed and excited, because although he had hunted all his life, he had never seen such a quantity and variety of animals close at hand. His whole previous view of animals was the result of his having been their enemy, and they had reacted to him as the most destructive carnivore. In the park, the Hadza hunter saw for the first time the peace of the herbivorous world. Prior to hunting, the relationship of our ancestors to other animals must have been very much like that of the other noncarnivores. They could have moved close among the other species, fed beside them, and shared the same waterholes. But with the origin of human hunting the peaceful relationship was destroyed, and for at least half a million years man has been the enemy of even the largest mammals. In this way the whole human view of what is normal and natural in the relation of man to animals is a product of hunting, and the world of flight and fear is the result of the efficiency of the hunters.

Behind this human view that the flight of animals from man is natural lie some aspects of human psychology. Men enjoy hunting and killing, and these activities are continued as sports even when they are no longer economically necessary. If a behavior is important to the survival of a species (as hunting was for man throughout most of human history), then it must be both easily learned and pleasurable (Hamburg 1963). Part of the motivation for hunting is the immediate pleasure it gives the hunter, and the human killer can no more afford to be sorry for the game than a cat for its intended victim. Evolution builds a relation between biology, psychology, and behavior, and, therefore, the evolutionary success of hunting exerted a profound effect on human psychology. Perhaps, this is most easily shown by the extent of the efforts devoted to maintain killing as a sport. In former times royalty and nobility maintained parks where they could enjoy the sport of killing, and today the United States government spends many millions of dollars to supply game for hunters. Many people dislike the notion that man is naturally aggressive, that he naturally enjoys the destruction of other creatures. Yet we all know people who use the lightest fishing tackle to prolong the fish's futile struggle, to maximize the personal sense of mastery and skill. And until recently war was viewed in much the same way as hunting. Other human beings were simply the most dangerous game, and war has been far too important in human history for it to be other than pleasurable for the males involved. It is only recently, with the entire change in the nature and conditions of war, that this institution has been challenged, that the wisdom of war as a normal part of national policy or as an approved road to personal social glory has been questioned.

Human killing differs from killing by carnivorous mammals in that the victims are frequently of the same species as the killer. In carnivores there are submission gestures or sounds that normally stop a fatal attack (Lorenz 1966). But in man there are no effective submission gestures. It was the Roman emperor who might raise his thumb; the victim could make no sound or gesture that might restrain the victor or move the crowd to pity. The lack of biological controls over killing conspecifics is a character of human killing that separates this behavior sharply from that of other carnivorous mammals. This difference may be interpreted in a variety of ways. It may be that human hunting is so recent from an evolutionary point of view that there was not enough time for controls to evolve. Or it may be that killing other humans was a part of the adaptation from the beginning, and our sharp separation of war from hunting is due to the recent development of these institutions. Or it may be simply that in most human behavior stimulus and response are not tightly bound.

Whatever the origin of this behavior, it has had profound effects on human evolution, and almost every human society has regarded killing members of certain other human societies as desirable (Freeman 1964). Certainly this has been a major factor in man's view of the world, and every folklore contains tales of culture heroes whose fame is based on the human enemies they destroyed.

The extent to which the biological bases for killing have been incorporated into human psychology may be measured by the ease with which boys can be interested in hunting, fishing, fighting, and games of war. It is not that these behaviors are inevitable, but they are easily learned, satisfying, and have been socially rewarded in most cultures. The skills for killing and the pleasures of killing are normally developed in play, and the patterns of play prepare the children for their adult roles. At the conference Woodburn's excellent motion pictures showed Hadza boys killing small mammals, and Laughlin described how Aleuts train boys from early childhood so that they would be able to throw harpoons with accuracy and power while seated in kayaks. The whole youth of the hunter is dominated by practice and appreciation of the skills of the adult males, and the pleasure of the games motivates the practice that is necessary to develop the skills of weaponry. Even in monkeys rougher play and play fighting are largely the activities of the males, and the young females explore less and show a greater interest in infants at an early age. These basic biological differences are reinforced in man by a division of labor which makes adult sex roles differ far more in humans than they do in nonhuman primates. Again, hunting must be seen as a whole pattern of activities, a wide variety of ways of life, the psychobiological roots of which are reinforced by play and by a clear identification with adult roles. Hunting is more than a part of the economic system, and the animal bones in Choukoutien are evidence of the patterns of play and pleasure of our ancestors.

THE SOCIAL ORGANIZATION OF HUMAN HUNTING

The success of the human hunting and gathering way of life lay in its adaptability. It permitted a single species to occupy most of the earth with a minimum of biological adaptation to local conditions. The occupation of Australia and the New World was probably late, but even so there is no evidence that any other primate species occupied more than a fraction of the area of *Homo erectus*. Obviously this adaptability makes any detailed reconstruction impossible, and we are not looking for stages in the traditional evolutionary sense. However, using both the knowledge of the contemporary primates and the archeological record, certain important general conditions of our evolution may be reconstructed. For example, the extent of the distribution of the species noted above is remarkable and gives the strongest sort of indirect evidence for the adaptability of the way of life, even half a million years ago. Likewise, all evidence suggests that the local group was small. Twenty to fifty individuals is suggested by Goldschmidt (1959:187). Such a group size is common in nonhuman primates, and so we can say with some assurance that the number did not increase greatly until after agriculture. This means that the number of adult males who might cooperate in hunting or war was very limited, and this sets limits to the kinds of social organizations that were possible. Probably one of the great adaptive advantages of language was that it permits the planning of cooperation between local groups, temporary division of groups, and the transmission of information over a much wider area than that occupied by any one group.

Within the group of the nonhuman primates the mother and her young may form a subgroup that continues even after the young are fully grown (Yamada 1963; Sade 1965 and 1966). This grouping affects dominance, grooming and resting patterns, and, along with dominance, is one of the factors giving order to the social relations in the group. The group is not a horde in the 19th century sense, but it is ordered by positive affectionate habits and by the strength of personal dominance. Both these principles continue into human society, and dominance based on personal achievement must have been particularly powerful in small groups living dangerous physical lives. The mother-young group certainly continued and the bonds must have been intensified by the prolongation of infancy. But in human society economic reciprocity is added, and this created a wholly new set of interpersonal bonds.

When males hunt and females gather the results are shared and given to the young, and the habitual sharing between a male, a female, and their offspring becomes the basis for the human family. According to this view the human family is the result of the reciprocity of hunting, the addition of a male to the mother-plus-young social group of the monkeys and apes.

A clue to the adaptive advantage and evolutionary origin of our psychological tabu on incest is provided by this view of the family. Incest prohibitions are reported universally among humans and these always operate to limit sexual activity involving subadults within the nuclear family. Taking the nuclear family as the unit of account, incest prohibitions tend to keep the birth rate in line with economic productivity. If in creating what we call the family the addition of a male is important in economic terms, then the male who is added must be able to fulfill the role of a socially responsible provider. In the case of the hunter this necessitates a degree of skill in hunting and a social maturity that is attained some years after puberty. As a young man grows up this necessary delay in his assumption of the role of provider for a female and her young is paralleled by a tabu which prevents him from prematurely adding unsupported members to the family. Brother-sister mating could result in an infant while the brother was still years away from effective social maturity. Father-daughter incest could also produce a baby without adding a productive male to the family. This would be quite different from the taking of a second wife which, if permitted, occurs only when the male has shown he is already able to provide for and maintain more than one female.

To see how radically hunting changed the economic situation it is necessary to remember that in monkeys and apes an individual simply eats what it needs. After an infant is weaned, it is on its own economically and is not dependent on adults. This means that adult males never have economic responsibility for any other animal, and adult females do only when they are nursing. In such a system there is no economic gain in delaying any kind of social relationship. But when hunting makes females and young dependent on the success of male skills, there is a great gain to the family members in establishing behaviors which prevent the addition of infants, unless these can be supported.

These considerations in no way alter the importance of the incest tabu as a deterrent to role conflict in the family and as the necessary precondition to all other rules of exogamy. A set of behaviors is more likely to persist and be widespread if it serves many uses, and the rule of parsimony is completely wrong when applied to the explanation of social situations. However, these considerations do alter the emphasis and the conditons of the discussion of incest. In the first place a mother-son sexual avoidance may be present in some species of monkeys (Sade 1966), and this extremely strong tabu among humans requires a different explanation from the one we have offered for brother-sister and father-daughter incest prohibitions. In this case the role conflict argument may be paramount. Second, the central consideration is that incest produces pregnancies, and the most fundamental adaptive value of the tabu is the provision of situations in which infants are more likely to survive. In the reviews of the incest tabu by Aberle and associates (1963) and Mair (1965) the biological advantages of the tabu in controlling the production of infants are not adequately considered, and we find the treatment by Service (1962) closest to our own. Slater (1959) misunderstood the demographic factors, and incest is most likely in small groups in which the majority of males die young but a few live on into middle age.

That family organization may be attributed to the hunting way of life is supported by ethnography. Since the same economic and social problems as those under hunting continue under agriculture, the institution continued. The data on the behavior of contemporary monkeys and apes also show why this institution was not necessary in a society in which each individual gets its own food.[4] Obviously, the origin of the custom cannot be dated, and we cannot

---

[4]The advantage of considering both the social group and the facilitating biology is shown by considering the "family" in the gibbon. The social group consists of an adult male, an adult female, and their young. But this group is maintained by extreme territorial behavior in which no adult male tolerates another, by aggressive females with large canine teeth, and by very low sex drive in the males. The male-female group is the whole society. (Carpenter 1940, reprinted in 1964; Ellefson, thesis in preparation.) The gibbon group is based on a different biology from that of the

prove *Homo erectus* had a family organized in the human way. But it can be shown that the conditions that make the family adaptive existed at the time of *Homo erectus*. The evidence of hunting is clear in the archeological record. A further suggestion that the human kind of family is old comes from physiology; the loss of estrus is essential to the human family organization, and it is unlikely that this physiology, which is universal in contemporary mankind, evolved recently.

If the local group is looked upon as a source of male-female pairs (an experienced hunter-provider and a female who gathers and who cares for the young), then it is apparent that a small group cannot produce pairs regularly, since chance determines whether a particular child is a male or female. If the number maturing in a given year or two is small, then there may be too many males or females (either males with no mates or females with no providers). (The problem of excess females may not seem serious today or in agricultural societies, but among hunters it was recognized and was regarded as so severe that female infanticide was often practiced.) How grave the problem of imbalance can become is shown by the following hypothetical example. In a society of approximately 40 individuals there might be 9 couples. With infants born at the rate of about one in 3 years, this would give 3 infants per year, but only approximately one of these 3 would survive to become fully adult. The net production in the example would be one child per year in a population of 40. And because the sex of the child is randomly determined, the odds that all the children would be male for a three year period are 1 in 8. Likewise the odds for all surviving children being female for a three year period are 1 in 8. In this example the chances of all surviving children being of one sex are 1 in 4, and smaller departures from a 50/50 sex ratio would be very common.

In monkeys, because the economic unit is the individual (not a pair), a surplus of females causes no problem. Surplus males may increase fighting in the group or males may migrate to other groups.

For humans the problem of imbalance in sex ratios may be met by exogamy, which permits mates to be obtained from a much wider social field. The orderly pairing of hunter males with females requires a much larger group than can be supported locally by hunting and gathering, and this problem is solved by reciprocal relations among several local groups. It takes something on the order of 100 pairs to produce enough children so that the sex ratio is near enough to fifty-fifty for social life to proceed smoothly, and this requires a population of approximately 500 people. With smaller numbers there will be constant random fluctuations in the sex ratio large enough to cause social problems. This argument shows the importance of a sizable linguistic community, one large enough to cover an area in which many people may find

human family and has none of its reciprocal economic functions. Although the kind of social life seen in chimpanzees lacks a family organization, to change it into that of a man would require far less evolution than would be required in the case of the gibbon.

suitable mates and make alliances of many kinds. It does not mean either that the large community or that exogamy does not have many other functions, as outlined by Mair (1965). As indicated earlier, the more factors that favor a custom, the more likely it is to be geographically widespread and long lasting. What the argument does stress is that the finding of mates and the production of babies under the particular conditions of human hunting and gathering favor both incest tabus and exogamy for basic demographic reasons.

Assumptions behind the argument are that social customs are adaptive, as Tax (1937) has argued, and that nothing is more crucial for evolutionary success than the orderly production of the number of infants that can be supported. This argument also presumes that, at least under extreme conditions, these necessities and reasons are obvious to the people involved, as infanticide attests. The impossibility of finding suitable mates must have been a common experience for hunters trying to exist in very small groups, and the initial advantages of exogamy, kinship, and alliance with other such groups may at first have amounted to no more than, as Whiting said at the conference, a mother suggesting to her son that he might find a suitable mate in the group where her brother was located.

If customs are adaptive and if humans are necessarily opportunistic, it might be expected that social rules would be particularly labile under the conditions of small hunting and gathering societies. At the conference Murdock pointed out the high frequency of bilateral kinship systems among hunters, and the experts on Australia all seemed to believe that the Australian systems had been described in much too static terms. Under hunting conditions systems that allow for exceptions and local adaptation make sense and surely political dominance and status must have been largely achieved.

CONCLUSION

While stressing the success of the hunting and gathering way of life with its great diversity of local forms and while emphasizing the way it influenced human evolution, we must also take into account its limitations. There is no indication that this way of life could support large communities of more than a few million people in the whole world. To call the hunters "affluent" is to give a very special definition to the word. During much of the year many monkeys can obtain enough food in only three or four hours of gathering each day, and under normal conditions baboons have plenty of time to build the Taj Mahal. The restriction on population, however, is the lean season or the atypical year, and, as Sahlins recognized, building by the hunters and the accumulation of gains was limited by motivation and technical knowledge, not by time. Where monkeys are fed, population rises, and Koford (1966) estimates the rate of increase on an island at 16 percent per year.

After agriculture human populations increased dramatically in spite of disease, war, and slowly changing customs. Even with fully human (*Homo sapiens*) biology, language, technical sophistication, cooperation, art, the support of kinship, the control of custom and political power, and the solace of religion—in spite of this whole web of culture and biology—the local group in the Mesolithic was no larger than that of baboons. Regardless of statements made at the conference on the case with which hunters obtain food some of the time, it is still true that food was the primary factor in limiting early human populations, as is shown by the events subsequent to agriculture.

The agricultural revolution, continuing into the industrial and scientific revolutions, is now freeing man from the conditions and restraints of 99 percent of his history, but the biology of our species was created in that long gathering and hunting period. To assert the biological unity of mankind is to affirm the importance of the hunting way of life. It is to claim that, however much conditions and customs may have varied locally, the main selection pressures that forged the species were the same. The biology, psychology, and customs that separate us from the apes—all these we owe to the hunters of time past. And, although the record is imcomplete and speculation looms larger than fact, for those who would understand the origin and nature of human behavior there is no choice but to try to understand "Man the Hunter."

REFERENCES

ABERLE, D. F., *et al.* 1963, The incest taboo and the mating patterns of animals. *American anthropologist,* **65**:253–264.

BINFORD, L. R., and S. R. BINFORD, 1966, The predatory revolution: a consideration of the evidence for a new subsistence level. *American Anthropologist,* **68**:508–512.

BOURLIÈRE, F., 1963, Observations on the ecology of some large African mammals. In: *African Ecology and Human Evolution.* Eds. F. C. Howell and F. Bourlière, Viking Fund Publications in Anthropology, Number 36. pp. 43–53.

BRUES, A., 1959, The spearman and the archer. *American Anthropologist,* **61**:457–469.

CARPENTER, C. R., 1940, A field study in Siam of the behavior and social relations of the gibbon, *Hylobates lar. Comparative Psychology Monographs,* **16**:1–212.

———, 1964, *Naturalistic behavior of nonhuman primates.* (Pennsylvania State University Press, University Park.)

DeVORE, I., and K. R. L. HALL, 1965, Baboon ecology. *In Primate Behavior: Field studies of monkeys and apes.* Ed. I. DeVore. (New York, Holt, Rinehart and Winston, Inc.) pp. 20–52.

———, and S. L. WASHBURN, 1963, Baboon ecology and human evolution. In: *African Ecology and Human Evolution.* Eds. F. C. Howell and F. Bourlière, Viking Fund Publications in Anthropology, Number 36. pp. 335–367.

ELLEFSON, J. O., in prep. Doctoral dissertation (University of California, Berkeley).

FREEMAN, D., 1964, Human aggression in anthropological perspective. In: *The Natural History of Aggression*. Eds. J. D. Carthy and F.J. Ebling. (Academic Press, Inc., New York.) pp. 109–119.

GOLDSCHMIDT, W., 1959, *Man's Way*. (Holt, Rinehart and Winston, New York.)

———, 1966, *Comparative Functionalism*. (University of California Press, Berkeley.)

GOODALL, J., 1965, Chimpanzees of the Gombe Stream Reserve. In: *Primate Behavior: Field studies of monkeys and apes*. Ed. I. DeVore. 425–473. (Holt, Rinehart and Winston, Inc., New York.)

HAMBURG, D. A., 1963, Emotions in the perspective of human evolution. In: *Expression of the Emotions in Man*. Ed. P.H. Knapp. (International Universities Press, Inc., New York.) pp. 300–317.

KOFORD, C. B., 1966, Population changes in rhesus monkeys: Cayo Santiago, 1960–1964. *Tulane Studies in Zoology* **13**:1–7.

LANCASTER, J. B., ms., The evolution of tool-using behavior: primate field studies, fossil apes and the archeological record.

LEE, R. B., 1965, Subsistence ecology of Kung Bushmen. Doctoral Dissertation (University of California, Berkeley).

LORENZ, K., 1966, *On agression*. (Harcourt, Brace, & World Inc., New York.)

MAIR, L., 1965, *An introduction to social anthropology*. (Clarendon Press, Oxford.)

NAPIER, J. R., 1962, Monkeys and their habitats. *New Scientist* **15**:88–92.

SADE, D. S., 1965, Some aspects of parent-offspring and sibling relations in a group of rhesus monkeys, with a discussion of grooming. *American Journal of Physical Anthropology* **23**:1–18.

———, 1966, Ontogeny of social relations in a group of free ranging rhesus monkeys (*Macaca mulatta* Zimmerman) Doctoral Dissertation (University of California, Berkeley).

SCHALLER, G., 1963, *The mountain gorilla: ecology and behavior*. (University of Chicago Press, Chicago.)

SERVICE, E. R., 1962, *Primate Social organization; an evolutionary perspective*. (Random House, New York.)

SIMPSON, G. G., 1966, The biological nature of man. *Science,* **152**:472–478.

SLATER, M. K., 1959, Ecological factors in the origin of incest. *American Anthropologist,* **61**:1042–1059.

TAX, S., 1937, Some problems of social organization. In: *Social anthropology of North American tribes*. Ed. F. Eggan. 3–34 (University of Chicago Press, Chicago.)

YAMADA, M., 1963, A study of blood-relationship in the natural society of the Japanese macaque. *Primates* **4**:43–66.

ZEUNER, F. E., 1963, *A history of domesticated animals*. (Harper & Row, Publisher, New York.)

10 · The Common Denominator of Cultures

George Peter Murdock
University of Pittsburgh

Most of anthropological theory has revolved about the interpretation of the similarities and differences between the various cultures of mankind. Cultural differences, perhaps because they are more immediately obvious, have received especially close attention. They have been variously explained in terms of distinct stages of postulated evolutionary series, of allegedly disparate racial endowments, of diverse geographic or economic conditions, of nonrepetitive historical accidents, of endlessly varying social contexts, of unique configurations of like or unlike elements, of divergent personality characteristics created by differential childhood training, and so on. Cross-cultural similarities have received theoretical consideration, in the main, only when they have been confined to a limited number of particular cultures, in other words, when they could be regarded as exceptions in a universe of cultural diversity. Such instances of similarity have been explained in terms of the transplantation of culture through migration, of cultural diffusion through contact and borrowing, of parallel development from similar cultural backgrounds, of convergent development from unlike backgrounds, of the independent burgeoning of hereditary potentialities, or of the allegedly determining influence of like geographical factors. In comparison, universal similarities in culture, the respects in which all known cultures resemble each other, have received relatively little theoretical treatment. It is this subject—the common denominator of cultures—with which the present paper will be exclusively concerned.[1]

Reprinted from *The Science of Man in the World Crisis* edited by Ralph Linton, New York, Columbia University Press, p. 123–142, 1945. By permission of the author and the publisher.
[1] The views of the author have been significantly influenced by John Dollard, Clellan S. Ford, Clark Hull, Albert G. Keller, Ralph Linton, Bronislaw Malinowski, John Whiting, Earl Zinn,

Early reports of peoples lacking language or fire, morals or religion, marriage or government, have been proved erroneous in every instance. Nevertheless, even today it is not generally recognized how numerous and diverse are the elements common to all known cultures. The following is a partial list of items, arranged in alphabetical order to emphasize their variety, which occur, so far as the author's knowledge goes, in every culture known to history or ethnography: age-grading, athletic sports, bodily adornment, calendar, cleanliness training, community organization, cooking, coöperative labor, cosmology, courtship, dancing, decorative art, divination, division of labor, dream interpretation, education, eschatology, ethics, ethnobotany, etiquette, faith healing, family, feasting, fire making, folklore, food taboos, funeral rites, games, gestures, gift giving, government, greetings, hair styles, hospitality, housing, hygiene, incest taboos, inheritance rules, joking, kin-groups, kinship nomenclature, language, law, luck superstitions, magic, marriage, mealtimes, medicine, modesty concerning natural functions, mourning, music, mythology, numerals, obstetrics, penal sanctions, personal names, population policy, postnatal care, pregnancy usages, property rights, propitiation of supernatural beings, puberty customs, religious ritual, residence rules, sexual restrictions, soul concepts, status differentiation, surgery, tool making, trade, visiting, weaning, and weather control.

Cross-cultural similarities appear even more far-reaching when individual items in such a list are subjected to further analysis. For example, not only does every culture have a language, but all languages are resolvable into identical kinds of components, such as phonemes or conventional sound units, words or meaningful combinations of phonemes, grammar or standard rules for combining words into sentences. Similarly funeral rites always include expressions of grief, a means of disposing of the corpse, rituals designed to protect the participants from supernatural harm, and the like. When thus analyzed in detail, the resemblances between all cultures are found to be exceedingly numerous.

Rarely if ever, however, do these universal similarities represent identities in specific cultural content. The actual components of any culture are elements of behavior—motor, verbal, or implicit—which are habitual, in the appropriate context, either to all the members of a social group or to those who occupy particular statuses within it. Each such component, whether called a folkway or a cultural trait or item, can be described with precision in terms of the responses of the behaving individuals and of the stimulus situations in which the responses are evoked. Eating rice with chopsticks, tipping the hat to a woman,

and others of his present and past colleagues of the departments of Anthropology and Sociology and the Institute of Human Relations at Yale University. So great is the personal interdependence in scientific endeavor that he is incapable of isolating those portions of the present contribution which are independently his own from those which he has acquired from others, much less of distributing adequately the credit for the latter. Since he is writing from his post in the naval service he is unable even to cite supporting bibliographical references.

scalping a slain enemy, and attributing colic to the evil eye are random examples. Any such specifically defined unit of customary behavior may be found in a particular society or in a number of societies which have had sufficient contact to permit acculturative modifications in behavior. It is highly doubtful, however, whether any specific element of behavior has ever attained genuinely universal distribution.

The true universals of culture, then, are not identities in habit, in definable behavior. They are similarities in classification, not in content. They represent categories of historically and behaviorally diverse elements which nevertheless have so much in common that competent observers feel compelled to classify them together. There can be no question, for example, that the actual behavior exhibited in acquiring a spouse, teaching a child, or treating a sick person differs enormously from society to society. Few would hesitate, however, to group such divergent acts under the unifying categories of marriage, education, and medicine. All of the genuinely widespread or universal resemblances between cultures resolve themselves upon analysis into a series of such generally recognized categories. What cultures are found to have in common is a uniform system of classification, not a fund of identical elements. Despite immense diversity in behavioristic detail, all cultures are constructed according to a single fundamental plan—the "universal culture pattern" as Wissler has so aptly termed it.

The essential unanimity with which the universal culture pattern is accepted by competent authorities, irrespective of theoretical divergences on other issues, suggests that it is not a mere artifact of classificatory ingenuity but rests upon some substantial foundation. This basis cannot be sought in history, or geography, or race, or any other factor limited in time or space, since the universal pattern links all known cultures, simple and complex, ancient and modern. It can only be sought, therefore, in the fundamental biological and psychological nature of man and in the universal conditions of human existence.

The fact that all cultures conform in structure to a single basic plan was already recognized by anthropologists of the nineteenth century. Morgan, Spencer, and Tylor not only established the broad outlines of the universal culture pattern but also filled in many of the details. No adequate understanding of the phenomenon was available, however, until a reasonably satisfactory integration of sociological and psychological theory with anthropological science was at last achieved during the third and fourth decades of the twentieth century.

Most attempts to explain the universal culture pattern have started with the "psychic unity of mankind"—with the assumption, now firmly grounded in social science, that all peoples now living or of whom we possess substantial historical records, irrespective of differences in geography and physique, are essentially alike in their basic psychological equipment and mechanism, and that the cultural differences between them reflect only the differential responses of essentially similar organisms to unlike stimuli or conditions. In its broader aspects this position is probably not open to serious challenge. However, the great majority of theorists have sought the unifying factor in a single facet of man's fundamentally similar psychology, namely, in the common impulse factors in behavior. All cultures are said to resemble one another because men everywhere are driven to action by an identical set of inborn impulses which direct their behavior along parallel lines.

Until a few decades ago these common impulses were widely regarded as instincts. The success and prestige of the biological sciences since Darwin's day led many, if not most, social scientists to equate human behavior with that of the lower animals and to explain social institutions as the expression of a series of universal instincts. Marriage was equated with animal mating, house-building with nesting behavior, government with the rule of the herd by the strongest male. The marked parallels between the social behavior of ants, bees, wasps, and termites and the cultural behavior of man appeared especially convincing. However, the progress of science began to show increasingly the importance of learning and habit, even among the lower animals, and anthropological research, in particular, demonstrated beyond possibility of rebuttal that human behavior shows infinite variation from society to society and perpetual change in any one society as it exists through time, instead of the identity and persistency demanded by an instinct theory. It became abundantly clear that the invariable association of a particular series of responses with a specific stimulus, which always characterizes an instinct, is not only not the rule in man's social behavior but is acutally so rare as to be practically undiscoverable. Culture is in no respect instinctive; it is exclusively learned. Since the publication of Bernard's *Instinct* in 1924, it has been impossible to accept any theory of instincts as an explanation of the universal culture pattern, or indeed as a solution of any cultural problem.

As instinct theories lost scientific respectability, strenuous efforts at salvage were made. Admitting the importance of the habit-forming mechanism and recognizing that different forms of behavior may be associated, through learning, with an identical stimulus, many authorities clung to the impulse factor in instinct and compiled various lists of "drives," "wishes," "needs," "dispositions," or "prepotent reflexes" which were asserted to underlie cultural behavior in much the same way as instincts had previously been invoked. The principal distinction lay in the divorce of impulses from invariable behavioral expressions and in the recognition that different and even diverse forms of behavior may be evoked by the same impulse in consequence of learning under differential conditions. It was maintained nevertheless that the impulses, being fundamentally physiological in nature, could be allayed only by behavior which relieved the conditions which gave rise to them, so that various responses to the same impulse, however else they might differ, would resemble each other in this vital respect. Responses to the hunger drive, for example, must have the ingesting of food in common.

Many attempts have been made to interpret the universal culture pattern along these lines, explaining cross-cultural similarities in the basic plan, structure, or organization of cultures in terms of a series of fundamental drives or impulses. Among the best known are the division of all social institutions, by Sumner and Keller, into those of self-maintenance, self-perpetuation, self-grati-fication, and religion on the basis of the four "socializing forces" of hunger, love, vanity, and fear, and the somewhat more complex functional analysis of institutions, by Malinowski, in terms of the satisfaction of certain basic "needs." Comparable but on the whole less satisfactory efforts are legion.

It is not the purpose of this paper to discredit such interpretations. On the contrary, the author believes them to be suggestive and, within limits, sound. Modern psychology and physiology have established the existence of a number of basic impulses—those of ingestion (hunger, thirst, inhalation), of excretion (urination, defecation, exhalation, sexual emission, lactation), and of avoidance (pain, heat, cold). To these must certainly be added anger or aggression, in-duced by frustration of the expression of other drives, and anxiety or fear, in-duced apparently by situations resembling those in which pain or deprivation have been experienced. There can be little question but that these impulses or drives represent a common factor in the experience of all human beings, that they are aroused from time to time in all individuals of all societies, that the kinds of behavior that will allay them are universally limited by the funda-mental biological and psychological nature of man, and that they consequently operate to channelize cultural as well as individual behavior. They certainly serve as a partial explanation of the universal culture pattern. There are, however, substantial grounds for believing that they do not provide a complete explanation.

In the first place, the impulses or drives that have been scientifically estab-lished do not account for all parts of the universal pattern in an equally satis-factory manner. It seems reasonably safe to attribute the food quest to the hunger drive, shelter to heat and cold avoidance, war to aggression, and mar-riage to the sex impulse. To what recognized impulses, however, can we assign such equally universal cultural phenomena as the arts and crafts, family organi-zation, and religion? Defenders of the interpretation in question are prone to invent hypothetical impulses to meet such cases, postulating, for example, an instinct of workmanship, a parental drive, or a religious thrill. Such inventions, however, find no shred of support in physiological or psychological science. On the contrary, a fully satisfactory alternative explanation of the underlying moti-vations is available in the psychological theory of acquired or derived drives.

It is common knowledge that only a small proportion of men's actions in any society spring directly from any of the demonstrable basic drives. In most human behavior the motivation is exceedingly complex and derivative. Even in the case of eating, the widespread prevalence of food preferences and taboos reveals the importance of acquired appetites as contrasted with the inborn drive of hunger. We eat what we like, at hours to which we are habituated, in surroundings which we enjoy. Daily in our habitual eating behavior we satisfy appetitive cravings, but rarely in adult life are we driven by actual hunger pangs. In obeying the dictates of an acquired appetite we incidentally satisfy, of course, the hunger drive, and thereby reinforce the appetite, but the actual incentive is the derived and not the basic impulse.

What is true of eating is even more characteristic of other forms of behavior. Many of our sexual responses, for example, are also appetitive in character; acquired drives impel us to seek the company of persons of opposite sex on the basis of age, appearance and garb, social congeniality, and other factors irrelevant to physical sex, and to engage in conversation, dancing, and divers other activities short of copulation. In still other aspects of social behavior—for example, in religious ritual and the fine arts—the factor of basic-drive reduction shrinks to relative insignificance by comparison with derivative motivations, and may even become impossible to identify. In the case of those elements of the universal culture pattern which cannot readily be attributed, at least in part, to some recognized basic drive, it seems more scientific to ascribe them to derived or acquired drives, which naturally vary from society to society, than to invent hypothetical new drives for which no factual evidence can be advanced.

A second substantial reason for rejecting the impulse factor in behavior as the sole explanation of the universal culture pattern is the fact that most social institutions or culture complexes actually give satisfaction to several basic impulses as well as to a variety of derived drives. To attribute marriage to sex alone, for example, is greatly to oversimplify a complex social phenomenon. As Lippert was the first to point out clearly, the economic factor in marriage is at least as important as the sex factor. The latter can really account only for copulation; it is the conjunction of the former that produces an enduring marital association. The relation of the hunger drive to marriage is seen, for example, in the division of labor by sex, which characterizes marital unions in all societies and, in most of them, demonstrably increases, diversifies, and stabilizes the food supply available to each spouse. Even our own society, which emphasizes the sex factor in marriage to an exceptional degree, has enshrined the hunger factor in a proverb about the most direct way to a man's heart. Marriage gives expression to still another basic impulse in various forms of relief from anxiety; for example, escape from the social disapproval commonly encountered by celibates, economic security gained through union with a wealthy spouse or a good provider, and the personal solace achievable in an intimate relationship.

Similarly, war is motivated not alone by aggression but often in large measure by fear, by the desire for feminine approbation (derivative in part from the sex impulse), and by greed for gain (in which the hunger drive may be significantly involved). Religious behavior is often rooted in anxiety—in fear of the unknown and unpredictable, in dread of what the future may bring, or in a sense of personal inadequacy. In addition, it frequently has a strong erotic component, as psychiatrists have pointed out; or it expresses aggression as in sorcery or religious intolerance; or it reflects the need for food or material comforts, as in magic or prayer. Analysis of almost any other large segment of cultural behavior would reveal a similar conjunction of diverse motives. This interlacing of basic drives, which is, of course, rendered infinitely more complex by the intervention of acquired motivations, makes it exceedingly difficult to segregate cultural phenomena according to their impulse components.

It must be conceded, therefore, that the analysis of collective behavior from the point of view of underlying motives, although suggestive, does not yield a fully satisfactory explanation of the universal culture pattern. Its principal defect seems to lie in the fact that it does not take into account the complete psychological mechanism involved in habitual behavior. Derived as it is from earlier instinct theory, it considers exclusively the impulse factor in behavior and ignores all else. When other aspects of the mechanism of habit formation and perpetuation are taken into account, a more adequate interpretation of the universal culture pattern emerges.

Fundamentally, all behavior is designed to mediate between two types of situations in which organisms find themselves, namely, those in which impulses are aroused and those in which they are satisfied. An organism encountering a situation of the first type is stimulated to activity; encountering a situation of the second type, it experiences a reduction in drive, and its activity ceases or is replaced by behavior in response to other stimulation. Once initiated by a drive, behavior in response thereto continues until satisfaction has been achieved, or a stronger drive intervenes to impel behavior in another direction, or unsuccessul responses have brought exhaustion or fatigue. In the last case, the drive-impelled behavior will recommence after an interval, and continue to appear until satisfaction is achieved or, if success is essential to life, until the organism dies.

Living organisms have evolved two distinctive means of adapting their behavior so as to transform situations evoking drives into those bringing about their reduction. The first, shared by all forms of life, is instinct, a precise organization of behavior developed through natural selection and transmitted through heredity. An instinct enables an organism to respond automatically to a drive-arousing situation by specific forms of behavior which have been established by the evolutionary process because they normally result in drive reduction. In cases where this does not happen, however, the individual organism is helpless; it is incapable of producing alternative forms of behavior. This defect is corrected by the second mechanism, that of habit formation, which is well developed in all the higher forms of life, including man. Through this mechanism, an individual can meet a drive-evoking situation for which the species has evolved no suitable instinctive response, by varying his behavior and by acquiring as a habit any new response which happens to lead to reduction of the drive. It is this second psychological mechanism upon which all cultural behavior depends.

Now it is significant that, in the process of establishing and maintaining habits, the crucial factor is not the source of the behavior in impulse or stimulus but its effect in drive reduction. It is the latter which fixes, reinforces, or perpetuates the responses that have occured. Whenever a drive is reduced, the probability of the recurrence of the same behavior in a similiar situation is increased. Mere repetition of the stimulation, in the absence of drive reduction, does not strengthen the ensuing behavior. On the contrary, it leads to its extinction and to the appearance of random responses of other kinds, that is, to trial-and-error behavior.

Whenever behavior results in the allaying of a drive, even though by sheerest accident, its effect is to connect that behavior not only with the impulse which produced it but with all the stimuli concurrently impinging upon the organism. With repetition, not only of the behavior but of its drive-reducing effect, certain of the concurrent stimuli, singly or in combination, gain the power to evoke the now habitual responses even though the original impulse is not present. Such stimuli which have gained the force of drives are essentially what is meant by "acquired drives." They are the product of learning as much as are the responses they evoke. It is in this way, for example, that the appetite for food can be aroused, in the absence of perceptible hunger, by the sight, the odor, or even the verbal description of a juicy steak.

The fact that the crucial factor in habitual behavior is its effect rather than its origin suggests that an explanation of widespread cultural similarities might more profitably be sought in an examination of cultural forms from the point of view of their relation to drive reduction or reward than in an analysis of their impulse components. The interplay of different motives in the same behavior and the problem of differentiating acquired from basic drives offer no obstacles to this type of interpretation. If a particular kind of behavior regularly results in drive reduction, any or every motive which may evoke it will be reinforced, and complex and derivative motivations are to be expected.

Since cultural behavior is always habitual in character, and since habits are maintained only so long as they bring rewards, every established element of culture is necessarily accompanied and supported by impulse satisfaction. The insistence of the "functionalists" in anthropology on this point has the full backing of psychological science. When traditional forms of behavior cease to gratify impulses, random responses supervene and cultural change is in the making. The present paper is not concerned, however, with cultural change. It takes cognizance only of cultural forms which are firmly entrenched and of widespread occurrence, and which consequently are regularly bulwarked by rewards.

Cultural behavior may be related to rewards in various ways. In some instances it leads directly and almost exclusively to the reduction of a basic drive. Thus the food quest leads directly to hunger satisfaction, the use of fire and clothing in northern latitudes to cold avoidance, and various sex practices to sexual gratification. The behavior must conform to conditions set by human physiology and psychology for the reduction of the drive in question, and the variant customs of different societies have in common the fact that they all meet these conditions. They can be regarded as alternative solutions to identical problems posed by original human nature. If this were the only relation of cultural behavior to rewards, analysis in terms of underlying impulse factors would provide an adequate explanation of the universal culture pattern.

Many cultural habits, however, instead of gratifying basic drives directly, serve only to facilitate their eventual satisfaction. Cultures contain an immense number of so-called "instrumental responses" which of themselves reduce no basic drives but merely pave the way for other acts which have rewarding results. Instrumental acts acquire in time, of course, the support of learned or derived drives, but they are seldom innately rewarding in themselves. Making a spear or a pot, for instance, gratifies no basic impulse, although at some future time the result may serve to lessen the interval or the expended effort between the onset of the hunger drive and its reduction. The reciprocal habits embodied in social and economic organization represent another outstanding example of instrumental behavior. Through interpersonal relationships and organization, individuals are enabled to use other individuals as instruments to facilitate eventual impulse gratification in much the same way as technology enables them to use artifacts.

Instrumental responses do not become established because they themselves bring gratification but because of a particular characteristic of the learning mechanism. Any response which reduces the elapsed time or the expended effort intervening between drive and reward is reinforced and strengthened, and thus tends to be repeated under similar conditions until it becomes fixed as a habit. Such responses become as readily associated with attendant external stimuli as with whatever drives are operative, and in this way they tend to become supported by derivative rather than primary motivations. Since acquired drives can differ widely from society to society, it is unsafe to attribute cross-cultural similarities in instrumental responses to identical basic impulses. Resemblances are more likely to be due to the particular characteristics of the instrument, whether artifact or social arrangement, or to similarities in the conditions under which reward occurs.

A like situation prevails with respect to a third and very large category of cultural habits, namely, those in which behavior is followed by rewards that bear no relation, or only an incidental one, to the impulses prompting the behavior. A gambling spell may be followed by a lucky fall of the dice, or rainmaking magic by a providential thunderstorm, and thus become entrenched as a habit. Neither action, however, either produced the rewarding situation or facilitated it in instrumental fashion. Such cultural responses can survive frequent nonsuccess because of the psychological fact that a habit is commonly strengthened by a single successful exercise more than it is weakened by several failures.

Another example is seen in instances where behavior motivated by one drive results in the gratification of other drives not actually involved in particular response. A superstitious fear of blood may motivate a tribe to isolate its women after childbirth, but this action may incidentally achieve the fortunate results of assuring postparturient mothers of a needed rest period and of preventing the spread of puerperal fever or other infections, and these may be at least as rewarding as the effect in relieving anxiety. Similarly, even though marriage may often be prompted in large measure by the sex drive, the matrimonial relationship brings other rewards—food, physical comforts, and security—without which, as we have seen, the institution would be difficult to explain.

All cultures, moreover, exhibit numerous adaptive responses which are not directly supported by primary impulse satisfactions. Some authors have attributed these to "social needs," which are defined as depending not upon drives but upon requirements which must be met if groups of individuals and the cultures they bear are to survive in competition with other societies bearing other cultures. One example is the so-called need of education. A culture cannot persist unless it is transmitted from generation to generation, and a society cannot survive without culture, which embodies in the form of collective habits the successful experience of past generations in meeting the problems of living. Hence every society is said to be characterized by the need of educating its young. Unlike reproduction, which is assured in large measure by the sex impulse, education is supported by no primary drive. The immense effort which must be expended by parents and teachers over so many years to inculcate in the young the full cultural equipment of adults is not in itself rewarding but must be bulwarked with auxiliary rewards.

Similarly every society is said to have a "need" for government—for a political organization sufficiently developed to provide for effective common action against potential enemies, to maintain internal order against dangerous interferences with the routine of social living, and to furnish necessary social services not achievable in other ways. Public service is not self-rewarding. Men cannot be depended upon to devote themselves to the common weal through altruism alone. Every society consequently surrounds the holders of political positions with prerogatives and dignities.

The concept of social needs, though useful as a first approximation, is a loose and not wholly satisfactory solution of the scientific problem presented by the universality of certain social institutions or culture complexes which are not directly maintained by specific primary impulse gratifications. It seems preferable to state rather that they have their origin in the ordinary processes of cultural change and their support in the gratification of complex and derivative impulses. Under the pressure of frustration and nonsuccess, behavior is altered. Certain responses, either random in their origin or borrowed from contiguous societies which appear to have achieved greater success, are tried out. If they chance to be followed by rewards of any sort, or even by a lesser degree of discomfort than attends alternative responses, they tend to be repeated and to become established as habits. The situations under which they arise acquire increasing power to evoke them. Learned or derivative impulses develop in support of them, and primary impulses which chance to be satisfied incidentally are pressed into their service, until they are amply fortified with auxiliary rewards.

In the case of education, acquired drives such as pride, prestige, identification, and parental love spring to the support of instruction. The primary drives of pain and anxiety are mobilized in the form of social sanctions for nonconformity. The children themselves, as they become socialized and acquire skills, reciprocate with materially rewarding behavior in ever increasing measure, and in many societies become actual economic assets at an early age. In divers ways an adjustment is evolved whereby the effort expended in education is balanced by a complex system of commensurate rewards.

In the case of government, through a similar process of adaptive cultural change, chiefs are induced to assume war leadership, maintain public order, and perform other social services by according them deference, the right to exact tribute, the privilege of polygyny, or other rewards. Feudal lords receive rents and services, municipal officials enrich themselves by graft, legislators secure jobs for their relatives or special favors for themselves and their business associates, and so on. Actually, of course, the power and pelf of political office are usually sufficiently great to attract a plethora of applicants, and the social problem is more commonly that of keeping exploitation within moderate limits—by revolution or "voting the rascals out"—rather than that of finding somebody who will assume the responsibilities. Only the naïve expect good government at no cost.

The process by which adaptive behavior that is not obviously expressive of basic drives or rewarded by their gratification becomes established in human cultures has been likened by some authors to the process of organic evolution in biology. Human societies enter into competition, it is alleged, as do subcultural organisms, and as they succeed or fail in the competition for life their customs are perpetuated or eliminated. The chances of success are enhanced to the extent that the customs are adaptive, irrespective of whether or not they are rationally devised. Within the same society, moreover, alternative customs—old and new, native and borrowed—compete with one another, as it were, and over time the fitter tend to survive. There is thus operative in cultures, it is asserted, a selective process analogous to natural selection on the biological plane by which adaptations in culture are brought into being and perpetuated.

This theory has been received with scant respect by American anthropologists, who have dismissed it as an unwarranted analogy from biology. In the opinion of the present writer the dismissal was not wholly warranted. Despite certain deficiencies, the theory represented a distinct advance over the crude invention-diffusion hypothesis inherited by the critics via Boas from the French sociologist, Tarde. Its real defect is not its derivation from biological science, for a scientist may legitimately seek his hypotheses anywhere, and it in no way confused the cultural and the organic. Nor is it necessarily invalidated by the epistemological criticism of circular reasoning, namely, that adaptation and survival are defined in terms of each other. Its principal fault appears to be that it attempts to explain too much.

It is difficult to escape the conclusion that cultural change depends upon conflict and survival in certain extreme instances. Thus Carthaginian culture certainly disappeared and Roman culture spread as a consequence of the extirpation of the Carthaginians in the Punic Wars. Since the Discoveries Period, moreover, native cultures have been exterminated with their bearers in various parts of America and Oceania, and replaced by European civilization. It is also probable that cultures have occasionally disappeared from the stage of history in consequence of maladaptive practices pursued until the entire society became extinct, much as numerous animal species have failed to survive because they were unable to produce adaptive mutations when needed.

On the other hand, the obliteration of a culture through the elimination of the entire society that bears it is by no means the rule in human history. If defeat in war or depopulation from maladaptive practices leaves any survivors, cultural change comes about through another and far less drastic mechanism. Prompted by discomfort and frustration, the survivors try out innovations in behavior, invented or borrowed, and through successful trial and error arrive at new cultural adjustments. They may end up, to be sure, with a culture much like that of their more successful neighbors. However, this result has not been produced by a pseudo-biological process of selective elimination and replacement of culture bearers, but through the ordinary psychological process of learning, undergone on a mass scale. All normal cultural change proceeds in precisely the same manner. The usual adaptive mechanism in human history, then, is neither that of biological evolution nor yet one that it unique to man. Instead of a new phenomenon in nature, that of social or cultural evolution, there is simply the age-old phenomenon of habit formation, operating under the distinctive conditions of human society and culture.

The essentially psychological character of the processes and products of culture change suggests that we look into the principles of learning for an interpretation of the universal culture pattern. One factor, that of basic drive or impulse, has already been isolated and found helpful, though not sufficient in itself to provide a complete explanation. A second factor is that of stimulus or cue. Any recurrent element or pattern of elements in the situations in which particular responses occur and are rewarded may acquire the power to evoke those responses, even in the absence of the original impulse. Any prominent stimuli that are of worldwide occurrence might thus be expected to be associated with cultural responses in numerous societies. Among the stimuli of this type are night and day, the heavenly bodies, widespread meteorological and geographical phenomena, certain animals and plants, and the features of human anatomy and physiology. As a matter of fact, nearly all peoples have cultural beliefs about, and cultural responses to, such phenomena as the sun and moon, darkness, rain, thunder, the ocean, mountains, streams, blood, hair, the heart, the genitals, sneezing, breathing, menstruation, childbirth, sickness, and death. Although these cultural forms need have nothing in common save their stimuli, the principle of limited possibilities and the psychological factor of generalization, not to mention cultural diffusion, often result in striking similarities among different populations. In any event, widely occurring natural stimuli provide a useful auxiliary basis for classifying and interpreting cultural universals.

A third important factor in learning is that of prior habit. Since pre-existing habits greatly affect behavior in a learning situation, experimenters in animal learning always use naïve subjects, that is, those as free as possible from unknown prior habits that might predetermine their behavior. It is perhaps for this reason that the psychologists themselves have been so uniformly unsuccessful in their attempts to interpret cultural behavior, for no adult human being in any society ever enters naïve into a situation of cultural learning; on the contrary, men carry into every learning situation a battery of cultural habits in comparison with which the prior conditioning of the most maze-wise experimental rat appears infinitesimal.

From the point of view of the universal culture pattern, prior habit becomes important especially in connection with the psychological factor of generalization, by which is meant the tendency of any learned response to be repeated under similar conditions of drive and stimulus. In consequence of generalization, a response adapted to one situation will tend to reappear in another in proportion to the elements of similarity between the two. Cultures provide innumerable examples. Supernatural beings are regularly anthropomorphized and dealt with in ways that have proved successful in human relations—by supplication (prayer), gift (sacrifice), aggression (exorcism), flattery (laudation), self-abasement (asceticism), or etiquette (ritual). Political organization commonly follows the model of the family, with which it has an authoritarian element in common. Departed spirits are often assimilated to the breath, which also leaves the body in death. Menstrual and lunar phenomena are frequently equated because of their similar periodicity. Numerous indeed are the cross-cultural similarities which result from generalization.

A final important factor in learning is that of limitation in the range of potential responses. In any learning situation the number of possible responses an organism can make is always limited. No animal can respond with an act for which it is not physically adapted. A man cannot jump or fly to the top of a tree to gather its fruits; his responses are limited to such acts as climbing, cutting down the tree, or employing a pole or missile. Prior habits or their lack sharply limit the range of possible behavior. Familiar situations tend to evoke familiar responses and inhibit novel ones, and complex responses, like speaking a new language or making an important invention, are impossible until a whole series of prerequisite habits has been acquired. Limitations are also set by the structure of the situation in which behavior occurs. Under identical conditions of drive, reward, and prior conditioning, an experimental rat will behave differently in two mazes of different shape, and a human being in two differing social situations. The limiting conditions of geographical environment have often been pointed out; a Samoan cannot build an igloo or an Eskimo prepare kava.

The most important of limitations on the possibilities of response are probably those set by the nature of man himself and of the world in which he lives, as these are known to science. Technological activities must conform to the physical and chemical properties of the materials with which men work. There are relatively few ways, for example, in which fire can be generated or a pot constructed. Customs in hunting and animal husbandry must conform not only to the physical but also to the biological and behavioral characteristics of the animals concerned. Human physiology and psychology set limits to the ways in which disease can be cured or a child brought into the world. Habit and custom must be observed in social relations. Successful responses—and all established cultural responses are successful, that is, normally rewarded—must cope with all the conditions under which they take place. These conditions introduce into culture the principle of limited possibilities, which is of extreme importance in determining the universal culture pattern.

Where the limitations on potential responses are slight, the variation in detail between unrelated cultures may be immense, even though traits be fundamentally related through a common drive, stimulus, or other universal factor. Thus, though every society has a language with a vocabulary, the words for any universal phenomenon, such as water, walk, or woman, may be and are formed by an almost infinite variety of phonetic combinations among the different peoples of the earth. Folktales, taboos, and ceremonials reveal a similar variety in detail. In nearly all such cases, specific similarities are reasonably attributable to a historical connection.

In other instances the limitations are greater and the possible responses can be exhausted in a short list. Every society affiliates a child with a group of relatives through a rule of descent. Only three alternatives are known, namely, patrilineal, matrilineal, or bilateral descent, and every culture incorporates one of these rules or some combination thereof, such as optional, alternating, or double descent. Again all societies have to deal with the corpses of the dead, and face therein a limitation in practicable possibilities. Among these the most prominent are abandonment of the place of death, feeding the corpse to carnivorous animals or birds, inhumation, rock burial, water disposition, tree or scaffold burial, cremation, mummification, and embalming. In such cases it is to be expected that different and even historically unconnected peoples will frequently chance upon the identical solution to the same problem.

The extreme situation is encountered in those instances where the number of practicable or satisfying responses is limited to one. When this happens, cultural uniformities are not of pattern or structure only but of content as well. Disparities in actual behavior become minimal. Perhaps the most striking example is seen in family organization.

Complex family forms, such as polygynous and extended families, are variable, but all known societies have the same fundamental form, the nuclear family of father, mother, and children.[2] This may stand alone, as in our own society; it may be complicated in particular cases by the inclusion of other relatives; or it may exist as a distinguishable unit within a more complex social grouping. Extended families, for example, normally consist of a number of nuclear families united by a common line of descent, and polygynous families typically include several nuclear families in which the same man plays the role of father in each. In contrast to many lower animals, the father is always a member of the human family—presumably because education is one of the family's universal functions and only a man is capable of training a male child in masculine cultural skills.

In all societies the nuclear family is established by marriage, and the relationship between its adult members is characterized by a division of labor according to sex. Sexual intercourse is always permitted between father and mother, but invariably prohibited as incestuous between father and daughter, mother and son, brother and sister. Seeming exceptions, such as dynastic incest, pertain only to small groups of peculiar status, never to an entire society. The nuclear family is always an economic unit, and it is universally charged with the functions of child rearing, socialization, and early education. The family may gather to itself other functions in particular societies, but throughout history and ethnography it is invariably the focus of the sexual, economic, reproductive, and educational relationships indicated above. This coincidence of

[2] The propositions with respect to the family stated herewith are inductions from a careful analysis of 220 societies made in a study of the relationship between sex behavior and social structure, the completion of which was interrupted by the outbreak of war. In no case is a statement of fact made to which there is a single exception either in the sample of 220 or in any other society known to the author from his general anthropological reading.

behavior is truly remarkable in view of the diversity of responses in other departments of culture.

The explanation is not far to seek. The sex drive accounts for co-habitation, and indirectly for reproduction. Its satisfaction tends to give at least some permanence to sexual association, during which the advantages inherent in a division of labor have an opportunity to manifest themselves. Primary sex differences channelize economic pursuits, and economic rewards fortify the sexual association. Children make their appearance in this context, and are bound to the mother through lactation. Their care and training are more naturally assigned to the mother and her sexual and economic partner than to anyone else. In so far as derivative motivations are required to support the parents in these tasks, they will be supplied in the manner previously outlined.

At no point in this development are the initial responses so difficult as to lie outside the range of probable occurrence in any society. Factors of drive, stimulus, and circumstances sharply limit alternative possibilities. Finally, the particular constellation of relationships provides individuals with such powerful rewards and solves at once so many problems of vital importance to society that, once made, the responses are certain to be fixed and perpetuated. Man has never discovered an adequate substitute for the family, and all Utopian attemps at its abolition have spectacularly failed.

The only universal characteristics of the family that have proved difficult to explain are its associated incest taboos. Freudian psychology offers the most hopeful lead, but the problem is too complex for the consideration here. It is of interest to note, however, that Freud chose this particular cultural universal, the family, as the keystone of his entire theoretical system. Reversing the usual scientific practice of making psychology an underlying discipline in relation to the social sciences, Freud founded his psychology on a cultural fact, though he used the terminology of instinct. Whereas behaviorists look primarily to the inherited mechanism of learning for the interpretation of behavior, Freudians look to the conditions of learning, and in particular to the structure of family relationships under which the earliest human learning occurs in all societies. Both approaches are presumably sound, and the psychology of the future will doubtless result from their amalgamation.[3]

---

[3]The author, whose acquaintance with Freudian psychology stems from experience in analysis as well as from books and discussion, predicts that behaviorism will prevail in the synthesis because of its far more rigorous scientific methodology. It must, however, take full account of the conditions of human learning, not only as these have been illuminated in Freud's momentous contributions but also as they are established by anthropological science with its unique cross-cultural orientation. The peculiar Freudian mechanisms—repression, regression, identification, and projection—have already been reasonably well translated into behavioristic terms. The therapeutic technique and clinical value of psychoanalysis will, of course, survive. Freud's attempts at cultural interpretation, however, deserve the oblivion they have already achieved.

11·Emotions in the Perspective of Human Evolution

David A. Hamburg, M.D.
Stanford University

"The most general principle of all in biology is evolution" (Simpson *et al.*, 1957). In spite of this fundamental fact, and the demonstrated power of an evolutionary view in relation to a wide variety of biological problems, students of human behavior have so far paid little attention to the evolution of living organisms or of man himself. Anthropology alone among the behavioral sciences has taken evolution seriously and made it a major focus of research. This neglect applies as much to the emotional aspects of behavior as to any other, and is remarkable in this context since Darwin was so strongly interested in emotions and pointed the way for future investigators. It is therefore quite appropriate that this Symposium, through its title and some of its papers, should again establish a link between human emotions and evolutionary processes.

In recent years, there have been very important advances in research on the evolution of living organisms. The most basic of these has been the modern synthesis of evolution, a powerful theory which has led to a variety of significant new observations and experiments, and has been able to integrate effectively an extraordinary variety of data from all fields of biology. Moreover, the heretofore sketchy record of human evolution has been substantially filled in, although it is by no means complete. The evidence bearing on human evolution is much more abundant and penetrating than it was even ten years ago, and the implications of this evidence are now being carefully worked out.

Within the past few years, biologists in various fields have shown increasing appreciation of behavior in relation to natural selection and, in keeping with the development of population genetics, have drawn attention not only to individual behavior but to the organization and function of groups.

At this point, I believe it will be helpful to sketch very briefly a few central concepts of the modern evolutionary synthesis and indicate their linkage to behavior. In order to do this, I have chosen excerpts from recent publications of three distinguished biologists: a geneticist, a paleontologist, and a zoologist.

Dobzhansky (1956) delineates the concept of natural selection as follows:

Modern versions of the theory of natural selection are in a way simpler than the classical. *In any one generation, the carriers of different genotypes make, on the average, unequal contributions to the hereditary endowment of succeeding* generations. The fit genotypes, and, by extension, the fit phenotypes, are those which transmit efficiently their genes to future generations. The less fit genotypes transmit their genes less effectively; the unfit ones leave little or no surviving, reproductively competent progeny. . . . Countless *genotypes with different reaction patterns* are formed in every species by *mutation* and *sexual reproduction*. *Natural selection perpetuates the genotypes which react to promote survival and reproduction in the environments which the species encounters more or less regularly in the territory which it inhabits* [my italics].

George Gaylord Simpson (1958) presents a penetrating statement on reproductive success and its relation to behavior:

Reproductive success may be comparatively simple in asexual organisms . . . in biparental populations the matter becomes highly intricate. (1) Male and female must occur in proximity or must find each other. (2) In many, especially the more complex, animals they must be sexually acceptable to each other and must mate. (3) Fertilization must occur. (4) The gametes must be genetically compatible. (5) Normal embryological development must occur. (6) Offspring must survive to breeding age and become successful reproducers in their turn. Relatively greater or less success may occur at any one of these stages and at substages within them, and selection depends on the total outcome. . . .

A central problem of evolutionary theory has always been the explanation of adaptation, and the synthetic theory maintains . . . that *adaptation is a result of natural selection*. But it also demonstrates that *natural selection always favors reproductive success of a population*, and nothing else. It might be suitable to redefine adaptation as such reproductive success, but some confusion might arise from the fact that *reproductive success of the population involves all phases of individual life cycles and will incomparably more often than not be favored by individual adaptation to the environment*. Such adaptation will therefore almost always be favored by natural selection. Nevertheless the possibility remains that selection, as here defined, could favor population reproduction at the expense of individual adaptation. . . .

An aspect of the synthetic theory especially pertinent here is that it again brings in behavior as a central element. It not only points the way to *evolutionary, historical explantions of existing behavior patterns* but also involves *behavior as one of the factors that produce or guide evolution. Some phases of selection, as in zygote and embryo, are not directly behavioral, but aspects of breeding, care of young, and subsequent survival are pre-eminently so and are obviously crucial elements in selection* [my italics].

Scott (1958) emphasizes social behavior in adaptation:

ʻThe evolution of any species, and particularly of a highly *social* species, cannot be understood without studying its behavior and social organization. *Evolution is one of the fundamental theories of biology. Its basis is adaptation, and one of the important kinds of adaptation is behavior* [my italics].

Where does emotion come into this? Interestingly, basic reference works on evolution rarely mention emotion, and similar works on emotion rarely mention evolution.

Why are emotional phenomena so universal in man and so important in behavior if they have not served some adaptative functions in evolution? I believe that emotional processes have served motivational purposes in getting crucial jobs done. What crucial jobs? Finding food and water, avoiding predators, achieving fertile copulation, caring for the young, training the young to cope effectively with the specific requirements of a given environment. In the case of man, we may go further and emphasize, as Julian Huxley (1943) has done, his increasing independence of and control over the environment, his growing ability to exploit a wide range of environmental opportunities.

Selection favors those populations whose members, on the whole, are organized effectively to accomplish these tasks. This is where emotion comes in. Let us consider for a moment the sexually aroused mature adult. We say readily enough he is quite emotional. By this, we usually mean that he feels strongly a particular kind of inner experience. From an observer's view, we can also say that in this state the likelihood of his achieving fertile copulation is greater than when he is not in this state. From an evolutionary viewpoint, we can further say that he now *wants* to do what the species needs to have done, whether he is aware of it or not. His emotion reflects a state of heightened motivation for a behavior pattern that is critical in species survival.[1]

Thus, the emotion has several components: a subjective component, an action component, and a physiological component appropriate to the action. Emotion as usually considered emphasizes the subjective component—but this is in fact the subjective aspect of a motivational pattern. On the whole, these are motivational patterns that have had selective advantage over a very long time span. There is substantial genetic variability in every aspect of structure and behavior. Selection has operated on this variability, preserving those motivational-emotional patterns that have been effective in getting the tasks of survival done.

I want to add an important qualification here. I am *not* saying that emotional responses occur *only* in connection with behavior that facilitates reproductive success of *contemporary* human populations. For one thing, contribution of an individual to reproductive success of his species may be difficult to tease out in the very large and complex human societies of recent times. Some nonreproducers may contribute much to the reproductive sucess of the *species*; e.g., the many bachelors who have made contributions in disease prevention. Moreover, as every clinician knows, the human is quite capable of learning motivational-emotional patterns that are maladaptive by any reasonable standard.

Any mechanism—structure, function, or behavior—that is adaptive *on the average* for populations over *long time spans* has many exceptions, may be "fooled" by extraordinary environmental circumstances, and may even become largely maladaptive when there are radical changes in environmental conditions. When we consider the profound changes in human environmental conditions within *very recent* evolutionary times, it becomes entirely conceivable that some of the mechanisms which evolved over the millions of years of mammalian, primate, and human evolution may now be less useful than they once were. Since cultural change has moved much more rapidly than genetic change, the *emotional response tendencies* that have been built into us through their suitability for a long succession of past environments may be less suitable for the very different *present* environment. In this sense, there may be some respects in which modern man is obsolete; and this seems to me an important area for research in human biology.

In the remainder of this paper, I would like to illustrate this evolutionary concept by returning to the theme mentioned by MacLean early in this Symposium, i.e., the emotional experiences associated with interpersonal bonds—the feelings and actions referred to by terms such as attachment, affection, respect, and love. I believe this to be an important area for such illustration because these experiences were crucial in human evolution, are seriously neglected in behavioral and biological sciences, and have recently been clarified to a significant extent by research in several fields. The principal points I want to make are as follows: primates are group-living forms; the primate group is a powerful adaptive mechanism; emotional processes that facilitate interindividual bonds (participation in group living) have selective advantage; the formation of such bonds is pleasurable for primates; they are easy to learn and hard to forget; their disruption is unpleasant and precipitates profound psychophysiological changes that tend to restore close relations with others of the same species.

---

[1] I am here deliberately ignoring other aspects of such behavior which may become exceedingly complex from the viewpoint of individual psychology in modern society. What I am here emphasizing is long-run functions in evolution.

Since behavior, unlike physical structure, does not leave fossils, the behavior of early man must be reconstructed inferentially from a variety of sources. Some inferences regarding behavior can be drawn from the fossil record; as the richness of that record increases, which is in fact currently happening, such inferences will become increasingly dependable. Some inferences regarding behavior of early man, in its most general features, can be drawn from the study of living forms—the more complex nonhuman primates and the most primitive humans. In doing so, we must be cautious because: (a) the living nonhuman primates are not our direct ancestors—rather, the contemporary old-world primates and *Homo sapiens* have come from some common ancestor; (b) all the living humans are *Homo sapiens*, they have had some contact with European culture, and many of them have been driven into marginal subsistence areas by more technologically developed peoples. Nevertheless, they have something to teach us.

Sahlins (1959) has recently published a provocative analysis of the most rudimentary of documented human social systems, based on an extensive survey of available data. I have selected a few excerpts from his paper that are relevant to my main theme.

We include in our comparison the following primitive societies: Australian Aborigines, Tasmanians, Semang, Andamanese, Philippine and Congo pygmies, Bushmen, Eskimo, Great Basin Shoshoni, Naskapi, Ona and Yahgan. It is assumed that these societies parallel early cultural society in general features. This is simply an assumption of order and regularity. The technologies and low productivity of modern hunters and gatherers resemble the archaeologically revealed productive systems of early cultures. Granting that a cultural social system is functionally related to its productive system, it follows that early human society resembles rudimentary, modern human society. This reasoning is supported by the large degree of social similarity among the present hunters and gatherers themselves, despite the fact that some of them are as historically distant from each other, as separated in contact and connection, as the paleolithic is separated from modern times. Further, simply because many food gatherers have been driven into marginal areas, they are not thereby disqualified from consideration. There still remain strong social resemblances between marginal peoples, such as Bushmen, Ona, and Eskimo, and those found in isolated, but otherwise not ecologically marginal areas, such as many Australian groups and the Andaman Islanders. . . .

Hunters and gatherers live in relatively open groups between which relations are usually friendly. . . . It is the kinship ethic of mutual aid that permits populations of hunters and gatherers to shift about according to the distribution of resources. Kinship is thus selectively advantageous in a zoological sense; it permits primitives to adjust to more variable habitats than subhuman primates. . . .

Given the division of labor by sex and the formation of domestic units through marriage, it follows that sharing food and other items, rather than being non-existent, as among monkeys and apes, is a *sine qua non* of the human condition. Food sharing is an outstanding functional criterion of man. In the domestic economy of the family there is constant reciprocity and pooling of resources. And, at the same time that kinship is exended throughout the band of families, so are the principles of the domestic economy. Among all hunters and gatherers there is a constant give and take of vital goods through hospitality and gift exchange. Everywhere, generosity is a great social virtue. Also general is the custom of pooling large game among the entire band, either as a matter of course, or in times of scarcity. Where kinship is extended beyond the local group by interband marriage, so are reciprocity and mutual aid. Goods may pass over great distances by a series of kinship transactions. Trade is thus established. Hunters and gatherers are able to take mutual advantage of the exploitation of distant environments, a phenomenon without parallel in the primate order.

Goldschmidt (1959) has quite recently published a stimulating work of synthesis on the evolution of human societies, drawing from diverse sources chiefly in the field of cultural anthropology. I wish to quote a few passages pertinent to the present discussion.

There is no reason to suppose that the earliest man had anything but a nomadic hunting and food-gathering system. In every major land area a few of these still exist. . . . The common and recurrent elements in their social system offer us the closest approximation to the earliest form of human social life that can be reconstructed on the basis of ethnographic data. . . .

The general characteristics of nomadic hunting and food-gathering societies are these: they are formed into bands of from twenty to fifty persons who camp together, share a territory which they protect from enemy invasion, and interact with other coequal bands inhabiting contiguous but separate territories. . . . The band is subdivided into families or hearth groups, a marital couple . . . and their immature and unmarried children. The individual family (or sometimes groups of closely related families) may split off into separate units under dire economic circumstances, but the band usually remains together throughout the year . . . most characteristically the band is the core of social unity and action. . . .

Values remain personal and direct. Where a population is close to subsistence, as is usually the case, the knowledge necessary for finding food, skill in hunting, and the requisite energy and industry to do so are likely to loom large.

[On the basis of his exhaustive review of the ethnographic evidence, Goldschmidt draws this important conclusion:] . . . man is by nature committed to social existence, and is therefore inevitably involved in the dilemma between serving his own interests and recognizing those of the group to which he belongs. Insofar as this dilemma can be resolved, it is resolved by the fact that man's self-interest can best be served through his commitment to his fellows. . . .*Need for positive affect* means that each person craves response from his human environment. It may be viewed as a hunger, not unlike that for food, but more generalized. Under varying conditions it may be expressed as a *desire for contact*, for *recognition* and *acceptance*, for *approval*, for *esteem*, or for *mastery*. . . . As we examine human behavior, we find that persons not only universally live in social systems, which is to say they are drawn together, but also *universally act in such ways as to attain the approval of their fellow men* [my italics].

Margaret Mead (1958) has recently contributed an important paper on cultural determinants of behavior. She says:

. . . each cultural system which survives has to meet the same set of minimum requirements for maintenance and for survival. Each human language—highly diversified though languages appear to be—must be one which every normal member of the group can learn to speak; each culturally patterned dietary must provide for human growth; each family and community system must provide for the care of human children during their long dependency and for their education, must regulate the patterns of mating and of competition, and must pattern the behavior of members of the social group. As each variant of culture must meet the same basic requirements, cultural systems have a regularity which makes it possible for human beings, of whatever level of culture, to recognize and borrow from the cultural behavior of members of other cultural systems.

. . . only those cultural behaviors which are shared by every group of human beings are irreversible gains . . . these irreversible patterns would include language; the family (including a sexual and an age-graded division of labor); tool using; selective exploitation of the environment to provide food, shelter, and protection; the idea of a group organization which unites a group of families and determines their relationship to other like groups; some idea of the elaboration of ornamentation . . . and some system of relating man to the perceived universe.

Thus, the past few years have seen substantial progress in the integration of a great variety of observations on technologically primitive human populations. The available evidence strongly indicates that, throughout the long course of his evolution, man has been a group-living form—probably characterized by intense and persistent attachments between individuals within an organized, cohesive small society. Moreover, it is very likely that the human group, throughout the history of the species, has been a powerful problem-solving tool, coping with all sorts of harsh and taxing environmental contingencies. It has been an adaptive mechanism *par excellence.*

Another field of research that has a significant bearing on human evolution is the observation of behavior of the more complex nonhuman primates under natural conditions. The past few years have seen a burst of activity in this direction, with six species being carefully, systematically, and extensively observed under free-ranging conditions. These species are: baboon, gorilla, howler monkey, Indian langur, Japanese macaque, and rhesus macaque (the usual laboratory monkey). Most of the studies have not yet been reported in detail, but some important features are emerging.

The one fact that I wish to emphasize here is that all of these species are pre-eminently group-living forms. They do not come together in some minimal fashion that simply permits reproduction. They are not loosely associated herds. Rather they are intensely and persistently bound up with each other, living usually in cohesive troops, organized in a fairly complex way. Bourlière (1962) has recently made an extensive review of available field observations on social organization of primates including the most primitive ones. While field observations are very limited for many species, the evidence to date suggests that practically all living primate species are intensely and persistently group-living forms. Only a few of the most primitive Prosimians species may turn out to be exceptions. So far as the more highly developed primates are concerned, it seems clear enough that strong interanimal bonds are highly characteristic of them.

Washburn, from his extensive baboon observations, points out that the troop is a survival mechanism. The competence of the troop as a whole far exceeds that of any individual. For example, Washburn and DeVore (1962) put considerable emphasis on protection of the entire group by the powerful adult male baboon. DeVore (1962) says:

> Once a monkey group begins living on the ground, the much greater danger from predators would alone be sufficient to account for a more strictly organized social system, one which, e.g., placed a premium upon male specialization in group defense. . . . While observing free-ranging baboons, Washburn found that the adult males were continually solicitous of the welfare of the young baboons, especially, e.g., when a troop was moving (a situation of more than usual danger) . . . the females with infants, not necessarily those in estrus, stayed nearest the protective, dominant males.

Altmann's observations of rhesus macaque and Carpenter's of howler monkeys also indicate the role of the adult males in policing the group internally as well as protecting it from outside danger.

All of this recent work—both the field observations of nonhuman primates and the synthesis of observations on preagricultural human groups—suggests that group living has conferred a powerful selective advantage upon more highly developed primates. This includes: (1) protection against predation; (2) obtaining food and water supply; (3) dealing with climatic problems; (4) coping with injury and illness; (5) facilitating reproduction, especially in care and training of the young. Indeed, it is likely that a wide range of adaptive functions has been facilitated by the evolution of primate social organization. The selective advantage of such organization must lie not only in the impressive extension of sensorimotor equipment which the group provides over that available to any individual, but also in the greatly increased possibilities for generating, storing, and mobilizing alternative coping strategies for dealing with a wide variety of environmental contingencies. The latter point seems to be particularly important in the case of early man.

Schultz (1950) has pointed out a high incidence of injury and illness among living primates in the wild. In this connection, one of Washburn and DeVore's baboon observations is especially pertinent:

> When the troop moves out on the daily round, *all* members must move with it, or be deserted. We have seen sick and wounded animals making great efforts to keep up with the troop, and finally falling behind. At least three of these were killed, and the only protection for a baboon is to stay with the troop, no matter how injured or sick. In

wild primates injuries are common . . . and animals which are so sick that they can be spotted by a relatively distant human observer are frequent. For a wild primate, a fatal sickness is one which separates it from the troop.

This observation suggests one of the many ways in which selection pressure may have operated in favor of those individuals having strong motivation for group membership. In a situation such as the one described, those individuals having powerful attachment to others in the troop would be more likely to stay with the troop, in spite of the difficulty, and so be more likely to survive and pass their genes along to the next generation.

The adaptive function of primate groups should alert us to look for processes in the individual that facilitate the development of interindividual bonds. In seeking such processes, we may find useful guidance in the principle that *individuals seek and find gratifying those situations that have been highly advantageous in survival of the species.* That is, tasks that must be done (for species survival) tend to be quite pleasurable; they are easy to learn and hard to extinguish. Their blockage or deprivation leads to tension, anger, substitutive activity, and (if prolonged) depression. Such blockage is often accompanied by emergency-type physiological responses that support actions necessary to correct the situation. In the postinfancy human, a remarkable variety of coping behavior may be mobilized by such blockage or deprivation, determined in substantial part by cultural patterning.

In view of the extreme dependence on learning in the human species, such bonds would most likely be greatly strengthened through learning. Selection may operate on *differential readiness for learning responsiveness and attachment to others of the same species.*

Harlow's work (1958) gives us one important lead as to how the development of such motivational systems may be analyzed experimentally. He found that infant monkeys form attachment for an object that provides contact comfort. This attachment is very persistent—exceptionally difficult to extinguish. More recently, Harlow has shown that in the infant rhesus macaque, the clinging response even takes precedence over the postural righting reflex. When this fact is related to observations of macaques and baboons in the wild, its significance is clarified. When the troop moves, the mother moves, and the infant can only stay with the mother by clinging securely to her. There is no alternative: cling or perish. The mother's hands are not free to hold the baby; she must use them for locomotion. Those infants born with weak clinging responses do not get a chance to pass their genes along to the next generation.

This situation provides a nice illustration of the evolutionary concept of emotion I am trying to delineate. The monkey infant must cling to survive; apparently the infant likes to cling and forms attachment to an object that provides the opportunity for clinging; he wants to do what in fact he has had to do over the course of many generations.

many species, and the formation of human mutuality is seen as attained via many evolved mechanisms which are mutually reinforcing and which assure social interaction (see evolutionary analysis in last section).

For the present thesis, then, personality is defined as a Gestalt array of species traits, usually related to interpersonal behavior, which varies uniquely for each individual because the genotype is unique, the individual experience is unique, and the interaction between genotype and experience is unique. The fresh aspect of this definition is that it brings the species concept to the fore and thereby provides a structure in which all hominids may be compared on the basis of their unique variation on the basic hominid theme.

This emphasis on evolved behavior is not meant to deny that familial and cultural institutions do indeed differentially influence behavior and personality. We will, rather, emphasize that such institutions only support or shape man's behavior and do not creat it, as it were, out of the blue.

DEVELOPMENTAL THEORIES—A BRIEF OVERVIEW

In considering current psychological theories concerned with development of personality, psychoanalysis contains the only systematic treatment of how relationships develop between humans. Among the other developmental theories, Piaget's cognitive theory has essentially an epistemological goal; one may read Piaget's brilliant observations of mental development in his own children (for example, Piaget 1952) without the realization a) that these children have unique personalities, or b) that Piaget or anyone else was emotionally involved with them. Not unexpectedly, Piaget's attempts to deal from his cognitive point of view with affective aspects of behavior, such as guilt, have resulted in a rather pallid treatment of the subject (Waddington 1960).

Gesell, too, had only passing interests in the development of affective attachments, and his main concern was the maturation of perception and motor behavior, an area in which his work is incomparable. For their part, learning theorists have interested themselves in the mechanisms of how knowledge is acquired, and the development of attachments has been a second order concern forced onto the field by the high interest in psychoanalysis. As a point of fact, there has been a more marked influence of learning theory on psychoanalysis than vice versa, and the notion of "stamping-in" by way of reinforcement has taken over psychoanalytic developmental theory (Anna Freud 1963).

Within psychoanalysis there are problems at various levels. Bowlby (1958) has observed that "psychoanalysts are at one in recognizing the child's first object relations as the foundation stone of his personality, yet there is no agreement on the nature and dynamics of this relationship." Infancy, for example, has been a convenient period to which some psychoanalysts have attributed various complex experiences supposedly causal to later behavior. Such mistakes were largely due to ignorance about infants, and from Klein (1957) and Sullivan (1965), to name but two, one gets the impression that these fathomless little creatures have a capacity for registering nuance of experience that no human beyond infancy shares. It has also become a matter of professionalism to defend the oral, anal, phallic trichotomy (for example, Shur 1960; Spitz 1960) in the face of overwhelming evidence that babies and children simply do not learn to relate by way of erotic zones (Orlansky 1949; Bowlby 1958).[1]

Despite the resistance to radical revisions, emphasis on libido theory has become muted within psychoanalysis, and two major developmental psychoanalysts, Erikson and Spitz, have managed only clumsily to retain libido theory in their work (Erikson 1950; Spitz 1965). Conversely, although in the same vein, the notion of "mastery" now has a place in the mainstream of psychoanalysis, but its relation to libido theory is complex if not confusing (for example, Hartmann 1950).

It will become apparent that the present author considers these problems as soluble, but only with substantial revision in theoretical outlook. The direction of change has been heralded in Bowlby's 1958 article, "The nature of the child's tie to his mother," in which an ethological (evolutionary) view of the formation of attachments was proposed. It is considered here that revivification of psychological developmental theory can best be accomplished within a broader evolutionary framework than that proposed by Bowlby, and much of what follows is written with that end in mind.

Individual Differences

We acknowledge today two major sources of individual differences in personality—biological structure and familial-cultural milieu. The emphasis in the social sciences has been overwhelmingly on the environmental sources of variance; cultural anthropology and neo-Freudianism have joined in demonstrating to the world that people are differentially shaped by different total milieus.

This may be termed the "modern" view to distinguish it from older views, which were definitely slanted in a biological direction. Hippocrates, for example, wrote of what today would be called biochemical or hormonal predispositions to temperament: predominance of blood, black bile, yellow bile, or

---

[1]When faced with objective evidence that, for example, anal training and the anal triad of traits (parsimony, obstinacy, orderliness) are not significantly related (Orlansky 1949), psychoanalysts counter that the outcome of anal training depends on the child's subjective experience. If this logic is carried far enough it can be seen as an argument for genotypic differences; however, most analysts do not carry their thinking this far, despite the fact that Freud (1918) did.

phlegm yielded, respectively, sanguine, melancholic, choleric, and phlegmatic temperaments (Allport 1937).

Many forms of typology have since been proposed, culminating in the recent systems of Jung (extroversion-introversion), Kretschmer (cyclothymic-schizothymic), and Sheldon (endomorphy-mesomorphy-ectormorphy). Each of these typologies is "dynamic" in that there is an apposition of opposing behavioral tendencies so that they generate a spectrum of possible combinations. It is perhaps because of the simplicity of these dynamic systems that they have been more influential than the complex factoring approaches, from Franz Joseph Gall's in 1835 to those of Spearman and R. Cattell, or than the complex taxonomic systems from Fourier's in 1851 to Murray's (MacKinnon 1944).

Summarizing the typological approach MacKinnon writes:

> All typologies are based upon the assumption that personality is characterized by a more or less enduring structure. Typologists may disagree as to the nature of this underlying structure; some conceive of it in psychological terms, others conceptualize it physiologically, and yet others think of it in terms of neural structure. It is not by chance that most typologists have been biologically oriented. Typologists may emphasize different traits and characteristics as most fundamentally differentiating the basic types of personality but on one point they agree, namely, that there are intrinsic traits of personality (1944, pp. 24–25).

Psychoanalysis has also produced a typology, but it is unique in that it simultaneously divides mental structure into dynamically related layers or segments[2] and at the same time offers a theory of how character types *develop*. Psychoanalysis, in fact, appears to be the first truly developmental psychological system.

In the early days of psychoanalysis, when libido theory was predominant, libidinal fixations about the mouth, anus, phallus (or clitoris) were considered the basic ingredients of a typology, and libidinal fixation at any stage theoretically gave the developing human characterological uniqueness in his subsequent relationships; but oral, anal, phallic, and genital characters are spoken of with decreasing frequency, even as shorthand descriptions, since their usefulness has been in serious question for many years (Orlansky 1949). Similarly, in the early days of cultural anthropology, the influence of the psychoanalytic typology led to descriptions of oral, anal, and phallic cultures (Gorer 1941). Although the tendency lingers on, Mead, for example, long a devotee of psychoanalytic characterology (for example, Mead 1949), has changed her thinking in the direction of "ego psychology" (Mead 1955). Psychoanalysis is clearly in flux and, as a matter of fact, needs help to direct it into more viable ways.

---

[2]The topological system, conscious *vs.* unconscious, or the structural system involving the dynamic balance of ego, id, and superego (Fenichel 1945).

What's wrong with typologies? The philosophical basis in much of early science was typological, going back to the *eidos* of Plato. This implies that the "typical" aspects of the phenomenon can be described, and that all variation is due to imperfect replicas of the type, all variants being, in the terms of Plato's allegory, "shadows on a cave wall." Such typological thinking is still prevalent in most branches of physics and chemistry and to a considerable extent in functional biology, where the emphasis is on the performance of a single individual. The typological concept has been completely displaced in evolutionary biology by the population concept. The basis of this concept is the fact that in sexually reproducing species no two individuals are genetically alike, and that every population is therefore to be characterized only by statistical parameters such as means, variances, and frequencies. . . .Genetic variability is universal, a fact which is significant not only for the student of morphology but also for the student of behavior. It is not only wrong to speak of *the* monkey but even of *the* rhesus monkey. The variability of behavior is evident in the study not only of such a genetically plastic species as man but even of forms with very rigid, stereotyped behaviors such as the hunting wasps. . . .The time has come to stress the existence of genetic differences in behavior, in view of the enormous amount of material the students of various forms of learning have accumulated on nongenetic variation in behavior (Mayr 1958, p. 351).

The point is that all diploid populations (those with two sets of chromosomes, one set paternal and one set maternal) show a wide range of genetic variation and that no two genotypes are precisely alike (save in identical multiple births). This gives a population greater viability as well as increasing the possibilities for ultimate speciation. The exceedingly slim chances in man, for example, of the same mother and father producing two identical offspring can be seen from the fact that each may produce 2^{23} (8,388,608) kinds of gametes. As if this were not sufficient variation, if one additionally assumed only two percent of the genes were heterozygous, a single cross-over between each pair of strands would raise the figure to 8,388,608 followed by 23 zeros, a very conservative figure at that (Stern 1960).

It is not surprising, then, that the search for a stable typology of personality, if indeed personality has biological roots, is a doomed project before it starts. Let us consider, for example, the genetics which most probably underlie correlations between body build and personality such as those found by Sheldon (1942). This is best illustrated by animal experimentation where the proper matings and controls are possible, but as far as we know the logic holds for all living forms.

Stockard (1931), in his work with temperament and behavior in dog breeds, was able to genetically dissociate behavioral traits from body build by crossing experiments, and dissociation always occurred in the F_2 and backcross generations, as one would expect from Mendelian models. For example, he was able to take the lethargic and low-slung Basset hound and, by way of the proper matings, produce Basset-like dogs with high-strung behavioral characteristics. It can therefore be deduced that the lethargic low-slung Basset hound was simultaneously bred for lethargy and body build since the two are genetically independent.

In all probability there is an analogous history to the correlations found between human temperament and body build. In the history of human groups there may well have been selective packaging of genes so that today certain body builds go with certain temperaments more often than by chance; but we must assume that such correlations can be broken, and that all combinations of temperament and body build are possible. Sheldon's own data bear this out, in fact, in that he finds no pure "types." In light of modern biological thinking, then, it is safest to assume the potential for continuous variation of behavior rather than a natural "piling-up" into discontinuous categories or types.

The relationship between human personality and genetic variability is clearly illustrated by the following two studies comparing identical and fraternal twins. In the first investigation, a group of twins was studied on a weekly basis over their first four months of life and in the second, a group was studied on a monthly basis over the first year (Freedman 1965; Freedman and Keller 1963). Usually, twin studies are open to the criticism that mutual imitation or special parental treatment has caused the greater concordance in identicals, but these criticisms were effectively ruled out in these studies. Parents were unaware of zygosity and their treatment of the twins was carefully watched and assessed; also, since mutual imitation does not start until after one year of age, it could be ruled out as affecting behavior in the first year.

In the group seen weekly through four months, the focus was on the development of social attachments, with specific emphasis on eyes-closed smiling (first month and after), the time at which the infant's eyes start to fix on the adult face, the subsequent onset of social smiling and its frequency and ease of elicitation, the intensity and extent of cooing, and the timing and ease of eliciting laughter. It was found that fraternal pairs were substantially different on these measures and that identical pairs were substantially alike. Identicals often differed in the onset of these behaviors (so that what A was doing one week, B was doing the next), but the over-all patterns were far more alike than in the fraternals, where both timing *and* patterning were substantially unlike.

The same general findings characterized the second study as well. In a particularly well-controlled aspect, monthly motion pictures were taken over the first year in which each twin of a pair was filmed separately in the same situations. At the end of the study the films of one twin were rated on a behavior scale by a group of four professionals who had worked with infants, and the films of the other were rated by a second comparable group. In this way a possible "halo" effect was avoided, and again intrapair differences among fraternal twins were significantly larger. Two of the items which proved significantly more concordant in identicals were intensity of *social orientation* and degree of *fear of strangers*, both of them items which would be admitted to any list of personality traits.

Given these results, there seems no reasonable alternate to the explanation that heredity plays a role in the development of the social behaviors investigated. It also follows that the behavioral phenotypes will vary from generation to generation as the genes follow general Mendelian laws, no matter if the behavior is monogenetically or polygenetically instituted; for it is not at all likely that pertinent environmental conditions will co-vary so as to continuously compensate for genetic rearrangements.[3] Inasmuch as biological determinism is often incorrectly equated with fixity, it is worth stressing that the tie between personality and genetics is evidence for the continuous variation of personality and evidence against typological systems.[4]

CULTURE AND INBREEDING

Cultural anthropology has changed popular thought as few sciences have done in the past. We know, as did no earlier age, that the typicality shown by various nations and tribes is due largely to a lifetime of learning and social interaction within given milieus. One can see on the film the Balinese boy, Karba, growing from a universal infancy into a withholding, muted, graceful, suspicious child, typical of the Balinese (Bateson and Mead 1942).

But was it a universal infancy? This is a reference to the very real possibility that the Balinese gene pool is unique in the world as a result of its specialized genetical history, and that Balinese are somewhat differently constituted than, say, a similarly isolated New Guinean tribe. This somewhat touchy subject has received little attention in the past due to the spectre of racism, but, hopefully, that period is passing.

Let us first consider the genetics of the situation. In the evolutionary sense all people are related since at some remote stage in their history they had common ancestors, and the Adam and Eve story is allegorically correct.

Thus Harrison (1964) writes:

So far as some particular population is concerned, its past size, if all individuals were unrelated, would have been far greater than it actually could have been, since every individual has two parents, four grandparents, eight great-grandparents, and 2 ancestors *n* generations ago. Assuming that on average there have been four generations

---

[3]As noted in the introduction, a phenotype is always the result of a complex interaction between genotype and environment. Studies of twins reared apart, such as that of Newman, Freeman, and Holzinger (1937), have been somewhat misleading in this respect. When separate rearing leads to different performance in identicals, as was found in this study, the explanation is that G times E interaction has been different, and it is of course not proof that the behavior in question is independent of heredity. See the discussion of continuity *vs.* noncontinuity later in this chapter for further discussion of this point.

[4]Science has been described at the making of discontinuities from continuities and continuities from discontinuities. At this stage in personality theory it seems advantageous to promulgate the latter.

per hundred years, an individual would have 2^{40} or approximately a million million ancestors a thousand years ago, if there had been no consanguinity. It seems probable that the total population of the world in the tenth century did not exceed 200 million and it was very much smaller in yet earlier times! (p. 158)

This reasoning that renders all men relatives also makes it clear that in the history of any closed cultural group there has been considerable inbreeding. This, together with the "founder" principle, that is, the dependency of the gene pool on the founding generation, leads to the irrefutable conclusion that the gene pool is to some extent unique for each such population. In light of our previous discussion, it should be clear that this may as readily produce distinct behavioral phenotypes significant for personality as it does significant physical variations. In addition, there is the fact that different cultures may emphasize different mating tracks so that, as in the development of domestic breeds, unique cultural selective processes may lead to uniquely organized genotypes (Ginsburg and Laughlin 1966).

There are few data in this area, but it is now well known that African babies in several sections of Africa are born with greater skeletal maturity and more developed motor abilities than comparable groups of European infants (Geber 1956). They retain this relative precocity until the third year, when the tests become highly verbal, and when gross motor items are no longer used (for example, how well a child plays ball, leaps, jumps rope, and so forth). The Caucasian children subsequently do better with verbal abstractions. The same pattern is seen in Negro-White comparisons in the United States (Bayley, 1965; Lesser *et al.* 1965). The usual interpretation of the switchover at age three is that there is less chance for Negro children to apply verbal abstraction in their milieus (for example, Geber 1956). On the other hand, there is little choice but to acknowledge the genetic aspects of the racial differences found in the first years.

There is no other carefully controlled work along these lines, but there are many possibilities. In Hawaii, for example, clear-cut differences have been observed between Japanese and Polynesian babies in their reactions to the first inoculations at three months. Polynesian babies rarely cry and, if they do, they recover quickly. Japanese babies usually have an intense reaction, remain fearful for a considerable period, and in some cases continue to cry on subsequent visits to the doctor (Marshall 1965). While this reaction may be indirectly due to differential tension between the mothers, it would be possible to study such group variations with the proper controls.[5]

To my knowledge no ethnologists are currently working with gene-pool hypotheses, although ideas which flow from population genetics hold far more promise for extending our knowledge of man than the worn hypotheses concerned with libidinal fixations.

As a final word on this point, it should be emphasized that all humans share basic traits and that there is continuous variation within all groups that gives them considerable overlap with all other human groups (Dobzhansky 1964). We have chosen to emphasize potential genetic factors which make relatively inbred groups unique because this is once again a fresh approach.

SEXUAL DIMORPHISM

Boy-girl differences are reported from time to time on many different behavioral continua (Ausubel 1958; Mussen 1963), and for the most part these differences are explained in terms of cultural and familial influences. Bandura and Walters (1963), for example, explain the repeated findings that boys are more aggressive than girls as follows: "This finding is not surprising for children brought up in a society in which aggression is much more tolerated in boys and in which the socially approved physically aggressive models, e.g., sports and film idols, are males" (p. 378).

It is a frequent finding that females are more passive and dependent than comparable groups of males (Ausubel 1957). Kagan and Moss (1960), on finding that females are more *consistently* passive and dependent than males from birth through adolescence, interpret their data as follows: "It was suggested that environmental disapproval and punishment of dependent behavior in young males led to inhibition of and conflict over dependency in the growing boy. The social acceptance of passive and dependent behavior in females would be expected to result in greater stability for this class of responses for women than for men" (p. 466).

Ausubel writes of children between eighteen and forty-two months as follows: "Girls apparently manifest less negativism at this age than do boys for two reasons: first, because they see themselves as more accepted and intrinsically valued by parents and have a more available like-sexed person with whom to identify, they can acquire more derived status. Second, they are able to obtain more subsidiary primary status than boys can by participating in female household tasks" (Ausubel 1958, p. 293).

Margaret Mead noted that a difference between boys and girls which holds in all cultures is the greater investigativeness and intrusiveness of boys as evidenced, for example, in their tendency to wander farther from home. At the time (1949), she gave this finding a psychoanalytic interpretation, relating such behavior to the acquisition of the "phallic mode." It was not clear, however, whether Mead viewed the phallic mode as universally learned or as primarily the result of maturation.

---

[5]In a recent factor-analytic study of personality in twins, Loehlin (1965) found that the same factors which had a high hereditary loading also had a high environmental loading. There is the clear implication in these data that cultural institutions have developed in support of man's biological nature.

To summarize these examples, young males were found to be more negativistic, more aggressive, more investigative, and less passive and dependent than females, and in each case, with the possible exception of Mead, it was assumed that social pressures caused these sexual differences.[6] Interestingly enough, these very traits typify male-female differences among many primate species, and we must suppose, following the above, that human culture or, in the case of Mead, human libidinal development has patterned itself on biological differences at the sub-human level. Once again, an evolutionary perspective will help us evaluate these data.

First, what is the function of sex? The evolutionary answer is that it provides a population with tremendous variability unobtainable in asexual reproduction (see the previous discussion of individual differences), and such variability usually makes possible the continuing survival of at least some members of population under conditions which are lethal to most.

Once introduced into the course of evolution, sexual differences themselves became exploited, so to speak, via secondary sex characteristics. Etkin's discussion of differences in aggressive potential is to the point:

A secondary sex characteristic, which may be designated as aggressive potential, is the difference between male and female with regard to capacity for fighting. This type is common among vertebrates. Most prominent among these dimorphisms are differences in size and strength. One of the extreme examples is seen in the seals and related marine carnivores. Elephant-seal males are as much as two and a half, and fur-seal males ten times as large as their females. Though this is extreme, a difference of 50 per cent or so is not at all rare among mammals. In a majority of mammals, the male tends to be bigger and heavier than the female. Only exceptionally, as in the European rabbit, is the female the larger.

Aggressive potential in favor of the male often takes the form of weapons. Horns and antlers are in many instances differentiated between sexes. We are familiar with them in many species of deer. Teeth as weapons are also frequent secondary sex characteristics of mammalian males. We see this in the enlarged canine teeth in male baboons and, in extreme form, in the single large tooth of the narwal. In birds, examples of dimorphism in weapons are fewer, but the spurs of the rooster provide a good one. (1963, p. 110).

There are many other considerations in sexual dimorphism, such as the display coloration in males of many species usually associated with territorial defense and mating. Less dimorphic animals tend to share more tasks, including nest-building, care of young, hunting, and the like.

While it has long been recognized that there are male forming and female forming hormones in vertebrate embryos (Willier *et al.* 1955), we are only now learning something about the behavioral correlates of embryonic hormonal ac-

[6]In a subsequent publication Kagan and Moss (1962) discuss the possible constitutional bases for the boy-girl differences found in their studies. It is slowly becoming clear to many workers that "social role" and "constitutional type" are facets of the same self-actualizing process, that is, the cultural and the biological are in fact inseparable.

tivity. Young and co-workers (1965), for example, injected pregnant rhesus monkeys with testosterone propionate, and thereby made male pseudo-hermaphrodites of the female fetuses, that is, at birth these were virilized genetically female monkeys. Tests of early development revealed typical male rhesus behavior with regard to social encounters; facial threats, invitations to play, and rough and tumble play were distinctly male-like. Similar injections after birth did not have comparable effects, although in rats analogous behavioral effects occurred with testosterone injections up through five days after birth. In both these studies it appeared that testosterone propionate affected the developing central nervous system in some complex way to produce the male phenotype, and recent evidence with human male pseudo-hermaphrodites indicates that human sexual differentiation occurs in the same way (Landau 1966).

Despite these data, there has been in recent years considerable propaganda claiming sexual neutrality in humans at birth, largely due to publications by Money and Hampson on sexual reassignment of constitutionally anomalous individuals; the clear implication has been that in humans the sexual role is predominantly a learned affair. This extreme position has become somewhat more balanced (for example, Money 1965), and a recent critique of the Money and Hampson view by Diamond (1965) makes a good case for returning to a more classical biological view of sexuality—not very surprising in light of the foregoing.

With regard to the "Oedipus complex," it seems likely that the upsurge of rivalrous feelings which human four- and five-year-olds experience is due primarily to hormonal shifts acting on the central nervous system. Male-male competition in particular seems predicated upon the evolution of dominance rivalry so widely seen among group-living species, and hominid infantilization seems to account for the precocious appearance of this need to win and to be "top dog." Little experimental work has been done to date in tracing the longitudinal course of androgen-estrogen balance, but it is clear that we can no longer persist in the notion that behavioral consequences of hormonal differentiation of the sexes occurs for the first time at puberty (for example, Ausubel 1958).

In summary, there can be little doubt that human dimorphism follows the general mammalian trend and that it shares similar functions. Thus when we find little boys less passive, more negativistic, more aggressive, more rivalrous, or more investigative than little girls, we probably have our mammalian-primate ancestry to thank and not some proposed libidinal stage nor some make-shift social force. This is not to deny, of course, that cultural institutions do indeed support and differentially shape such biological trends.

An evolutionary analysis[7] of human dimorphism has never been seriously

----

[7]What we mean by evolutionary analysis will be further discussed later in the chapter. To give a brief example—it is of substantial evolutionary interest that human females mature more quickly than males in such diverse areas as bone age, teeth eruption, language development, and later in sexual readiness (Ausubel 1958). It seems that this is an evolved trend with a major adaptive

undertaken, but would probably go a long way in making sense of the numerous but scattered findings on male-female differences.

"Critical Periods" in the Development of Attachments

Varying rates of growth in ontogenetic maturation are well known. So are the embryological findings that normal growth is interfered with depending on *when* an experimental transplant or teratogenic agent is introduced (Willier *et al.* 1956). Furthermore, there are numerous findings that in postnatal life interference with normal sensory input can cause tissue degeneration and/or the dropping-out of normal responsivity. Here, again, timing is important (Riesen 1961).

These findings have been of interest to developmental psychologists as models for viewing behavior, and hence the notion that the absence of certain experiences during some hypothetically critical time will yield a behavioral defect. In the sphere of social behavior Spitz (1945; 1965), Bowlby (1952), and Goldfarb (1955) have all stressed the importance of infants forming attachments sometime in the first year if subsequent behavior is not to be abnormal (described later). Experimental work with isolated monkeys, dogs, and other lower animals has supported this contention by demonstrating that early social deprivation, if sufficiently prolonged, can cause social animals to become permanently maimed in their social interactions (Mason, 1965; Freedman, 1961).

The postulate that there is a critical period for the formation of human attachments was first elaborated by Spitz (1945) when he presented evidence from a South American orphanage in which progressive deterioration occurred in infants after their mothers left when the infants were three months of age. "The infants remained in the Foundling Home, where they were adequately cared for in every bodily respect. Food, hygiene, medical care and medication, etc. were as good as, or even superior to, that of any other institutions we have observed."

At the end of the second year about 40 per cent of these children had died, and the remainder had developmental quotients at the level of severe defectives. This information was first published in 1945, and as of his most recent publication Spitz (1965) still insists this wasting away, called marasmus, was due entirely to lack of "mothering." The fact is that the "Foundling Home" was located in a severe protein deficiency belt and that marasmus was and is a major public health problem there, even among home-reared babies

sexual readiness (Ausubel 1958). It seems that this is an evolved trend with a major adaptive function of extending the female reproductive years relative to the male; a "sensible" arrangement considering her limited and his relatively unlimited reproductive posibilities. There are undoubtedly other functional aspects to the relatively precocious maturation of females, and it will be apparent in the discussion later in the chapter that any designated evolutionary trend is inextricably involved with numerous other trends.

(Scrimshaw and Behar 1961); it is therefore small wonder that no temperate-zone worker has ever found such lethal results from lack of mothering.

Facts such as these, as well as Spitz's poor reporting (Pinneau 1955), have cast doubt on the entire notion of the first year as critical peiod in the formation of attachments, but there is nevertheless ample evidence that Spitz's pioneering work was in the right direction. Bowlby's famous monograph of 1952, *Maternal Care and Mental Health*, has withstood the test of criticism and time; in a recent re-evaluation Ainsworth (1962:153–154) gave the following excellent summary of the results of affective deprivation:

(1) Recovery from a single, brief, depriving separation experience seems fairly prompt and complete with respect to overt behavior under ordinary conditions; there is evidence, however, of vulnerability to future threats of separation—that is, there is at least one "hidden" impairment that prevents the reversibility from being described as complete.

(2) Relief from deprivation after even fairly prolonged deprivation experiences in early infancy can result in rapid and dramatic improvement in overt behaviour and in generalized intellectual functioning; vocalization, however, may be retarded, even though the relief occurs before twelve months of age, and effects on other specific aspects of intellectual and personality functioning cannot be ruled out until these aspects have been explored in research.

(3) Prolonged and severe deprivation beginning early in the first year of life and continuing for as long as three years usually leads to severely adverse effects on both intellectual and personality functioning that do resist reversal.

(4) Prolonged and severe deprivation beginning in the second year of life leads to some grave effects on personality that do resist reversal, although the effects on general intelligence seem to be fairly completely reversible; specific impairment of intellectual functions has not yet been studied.

(5) The effects of age at the onset and relief of the deprivation experience are undoubtedly important factors in influencing reversibility, but these are not understood in enough detail to set precise limits for a "sensitive phase" of development of special processes.

(6) In general, in the first year of life, the younger the infant when deprivation is relieved (and hence the less prolonged the deprivation experience), the more normal is the subsequent development; yet after the first year of life has passed, the older the child at the onset of deprivation the more readily and completely reversible seem to be the effects of a deprivation of a given duration.

(7) Certain impairments seem to be less readily and less completely reversible than others—impairments in language, in abstraction and in the capacity for strong and lasting interpersonal attachments.

(8) Especially if undertaken when the child is still very young, intensive therapeutic efforts may result in marked improvement of some very severe effects that resist reversal through ordinary relief from deprivation.

(9) Subsequent experiences of insufficiency, distortion or discontinuity in interpersonal interaction may be important in reinforcing impairments that otherwise might have been reversed more or less completely.

While these findings are remarkable straightforward,[8] it is difficult to pinpoint the rising fear of strangers in infants (see the evolutionary analysis later in this chapter) as a natural end to the period in which primary attachments are formed, as Gray (1958) has proposed; but it is also a safe guess, on the basis of the data reviewed by Ainsworth, that for most infants attachments by seven months are essential. In evolutionary terms, it is highly adaptive that attachments between human infant and caretaker form by this age so that subsequent development of autonomy, in the newly motile child, may take place relatively unfettered by recurring dependency.[9] Erikson's (1950) surmise that a basic sense of trust or mistrust is established in the first year is a complementary way of dealing with the same set of events.

Erickson (1950) has further proposed that the major theme of the second and third years is the development of autonomy. Few observers would deny that the demand for and insistence on autonomy forms a major aspect of the lives of two- and three-year-olds, nor is there much difficulty in surmising the evolutionary importance at this age of such self-propelling investigation of the environment.[10]

In considering the relation of developing autonomy to attachments formed in the first year, Harlow's (1959) observations of monkeys who had not re-

[8]Casler (1961) has chosen to emphasize the shortcomings of research in this area and, like the man seeking lost keys only where the light is good, suggests perceptual deprivation rather than affective deprivation is the basis for these findings. Actually, no such sharp distinction is possible, for cognition, perception, and affective behavior all work in concert and represent our own somewhat artifical abstractions. In addition, as Ainsworth (1962) points out, in the early months of life perceptual deprivation is equivalent to social deprivation since it is primarily the caretaker who provides the infant with perceptual stimulation.

[9]The evolutionary point, so to speak, is to form the attachment and get on with the next stage. Also, it is apparent that precise decisions about a critical period for attachment in humans is not possible in contrast, say, to imprinting in precocial ground-nesting birds. Evolutionally speaking, the latter must be on their feet soon after hatching or they would be open to severe predation. The situation is the same in precocial mammals, such as the wild forms of sheep, goats and cattle, all naturally preyed-upon animals, and attachments are made within hours after birth, after which the flight response to strangers develops (Freedman 1961). In animals not under direct predator pressure, such as man, the time period in which primary attachments occur is always longer and more variable. Additionally, we have in man the factor of extensive infantilization, that is, the prolongation of dependency over the longest period of time of any mammal. Thus attachments have a long time to form and, as will be discussed later in the chapter, there are numerous alternate (or complementary) mechanisms through which this may be accomplished.

[10]That parental thwarting of autonomy will result in shame, as Erikson holds, has much less to recommend it. The feeling of shame is a common Japanese emotion, for example, yet autonomy in boys is greatly encouraged and considered desirable in that culture (Haring 1956).

ceived "contact comfort" as infants is to the point. These sensually deprived Rhesus infants explored very little, preferring to lie in one spot, and in effect suffered from impaired autonomy. The young orphaned children described and filmed by Appel and Aubry (1951) behaved with striking similarity; they were fearful, they explored very little, and they had to be helped to find out what the world was like. Ainsworth reports other such data, and it seems that this is one way in which events of the first year may affect ensuing development. We can assume further that the manner in which years two and three are negotiated affects the relatively unique developments of the four-year-old period, and so on, and logically each period must to some extent be "critical" for the next.

As for individual differences in relation to critical periods, experimental work with animals provides a helpful paradigm. Ginsburg (1965) has demonstrated that the handling of some strains of mice during a preweaning period will exaggerate adult aggressiveness whereas handling another strain will result in unusually pacific animals. In addition, the amount of handling also makes a difference in later aggression depending on the strain of mice used. Since each strain is essentially a single sample of the species' possibilities, it is clear that tremendous variability exists in responsivity to early stress. Breeds of dogs yield similar information (Freedman 1958) and there is no reason to suspect the same is not true of humans. Experiences critical for one child may well have entirely different effects in another, and variability rather than uniformity of response is to be expected within the broad framework of the species pattern, providing the experiences or deprivations are not completely antagonistic to the nature of the species. With regard to this last point, Murphy (1964) has pointed out that individual differences are maximal in the relatively healthy, and the extreme deprivation discussed by Ainsworth amounts to a species-wide debilitation where individual differences become submerged by the shocking nature of the general symptomatology.

CONTINUITY VS. NONCONTINUITY IN PERSONALITY

One of the earliest reports in this area is that of Neilon (1948) who contacted in late adolescence the individuals Mary Shirley had studied over their first two years of life (Shirley 1933). General personality descriptions were made of these young men and women which were in turn blindly matched to Mary Shirley's descriptions of them as two-year-olds. Matching was well above chance, and the conclusion was drawn that there is considerable continuity in personality structure.

On the other hand, studies which have tried to be more specific by using trait checklists or rating scales (Bayley 1964; Moss and Kagan 1962; Thomas *et al.* 1963) or those which have tried to predict behavior (Fries and Woolf 1953; Escalona and Heider 1959; Benjamin 1959) have been much less suc-

cessful. Macfarlane (1964), for example, is more impressed by the changes than
by the continuities in the thirty-five years her growth study has been active, and
it is her view that the most interesting aspects of personality are those which
are essentially not predictable, for example, how someone may deal with an
emergency. This is borne out by the work of D. MacKinnon (1948) and his
O.S.S. colleagues during World War II, in which on the basis of extensive personality assessment they unsuccessfully tried to predict what people would do
in various emergency situations.

In this same regard, in the study reported by Murphy (1964) in which
over sixty children were studied from infancy through prepuberty, "over half
the children changed markedly in one or another aspect of functioning. . . .
Children showing most continuity had greater developmental balance and less
vulnerability in infancy, and were growing up in environments which were relatively homogeneous, stable, free from traumatizing vicissitudes, and congenial
to the child's natural style of development" (p. 113). Murphy was impressed
with the individual styles of coping which, whether continuous or discontinuous
over the years, tend to be unique for each person.

The attempt to assess continuities by way of preset categories of rating
scales has been only minimally successful, for the "meaty" individualized aspects of personality descriptions have been lost. Recent reports by Kagan and
Moss (1962) and Schaeffer and Bayley (1963) on separate longitudinal studies
of about thirty years' duration are to the point. Schaeffer and Bayley reported
the most stable dimensions over the years were "active, extroverted vs. inactive,
introverted" behaviors, while Kagan and Moss found consistency from the
preschool years to adulthood in the aggressive behavior of males and in the
passivity and dependence of females. The latter finding is borne out by Honzik
and Macfarlane (1964) who found greater consistency in females over the years
on the independence-dependence dimension, and also by the Schaeffer and
Bayley (1963) study in which relative stability among females in an active-
passive dimension was found. While these findings are interesting, particularly
from the point of view of evolved sexual dimorphism discussed earlier in this
chapter, they are rather sparse representatives of what we usually think of as
personality.

Is there a contradiction in the very attempt to use prearranged categories
in trying to assess personality? The author believes so and offers here an evolutionary definition of personality by way of explanation. It derives in part from
the longitudinal study of twins discussed earlier in this chapter (Freedman
1965), some of whom have now been followed from birth through five years.

In the course of this study there was no difficulty in describing in subtle
detail the personality of fraternal individuals, but it was not possible to describe
identicals with the same richness.[1] This went beyond our own inadequacy, for
even within their own families, instead of becoming a "someone," indenticals
often become merged as "the twins" (see Leonard 1961). It became clear that

what we were calling personality amounted to an *individual's unique variation on the basic hominid theme*, and the fact that identical twins co-varied over so many traits confused and tongue-tied the investigators.[11] It became equally clear that just as all evolved physical structures are standard for a species, yet variable from individual to individual, the same holds true for behavior.

To put it in a different way, personality is a Gestalt of species traits, varying uniquely for each genotype. Individuals are unique because the genotype is unique, the individual's experience has been unique, and the interaction between genotype and experience has been unique. The fact that Mr. A does most things in his own way is what makes him recognizable as someone and, at the same time, since he retains basic hominid traits, we can compare him with everyone else we have known.[12]

In the same vein, the Gestalt of behavior which we are calling personality may retain the same or similar total quality, although individual traits are or are not apparent from time to time. For this reason we may find individual items on a rating scale showing little reliability over long periods of time, as Bayley (1964) found; yet, as Neilon has shown, the personality retains its unique flavor. These are not surprising findings since it is obvious that various processes continue to mature up to, through, and past the burgeoning of adolescence, and that personality traits frequently become repatterned in order to maintain "centeredness" in the face of maturational and environmental changes (Goldstein 1939).

From the evolutionary point of view, these maturational events can be looked at as *phylogenetically worked-out adaptations to each point in ontogeny*. For example, toddlerhood, adolescence, and parenthood necessarily involve considerably different sets of evolved adaptations (as discussed later in the chapter).

In our view, then, the two major nonartifactual reasons for discontinuity are 1) the fact that flexibility of behavior is a built-in characteristic of hominids; 2) different stages in ontogeny are characterized by (phylogenetically) evolved behavior adaptive to that stage.

As for illustrations of constitutional times environmental interactions

---

[11]We are so used to meeting and knowing another in a one to one relationship, and to assessing the uniqueness of that encounter, that the act of relating identically to two individuals is accomplished only clumsily. It may also be that we are so constructed as to *require* uniqueness of those to whom we relate. . . . The solution for the researcher is simple: Each of an identical pair should be assessed by a separate investigator.

[12]There is, in addition to this description from "without," that aspect of personality which can only be described from "within": "The ego only persists by becoming ever more itself, in the measure in which it makes everything else itself. So man becomes a person in and through personalization" (de Chardin, *The Phenomenon of Man*, New York, Harper and Row, Publishers, 1961, p. 172). This activating and self-making ego, however, works within the constraints of one's genetic and biological parameters.

over time,[13] the best examples come from various animal studies with inbred groups. To take but one study, Freedman (1958) reared puppies of four dog breeds in either a very permissive fashion or under a strict regimen of training and found:

(1) Each breed (genotype) reacted to the same mode of rearing in a unique way.

(2) The breed times environment interactions varied kaleidoscopically, depending on the test or task imposed.

(3) The same behavior in one breed might be due *primarily* to constitution and in another primarily to conditions of rearing (termed a "phenocopy" by geneticists).

(4) In the follow-up period, which lasted over a year, three breeds showed a straight-line continuity in their social reactions to humans modeled on behavior learned during early rearing.

(5) In one breed the permissively reared animals changed markedly over time, whereas the disciplined group continued to show the same fawning behavior developed in puppyhood.

(6) Some breeds were more deeply affected by the early modes of rearing than others.

It should be made clear that this study is presented as an illustration of a few well-worked-out genetic times environmental permutations, and in actual fact the number of G times E interactions must have been far more numerous. In addition, if other breeds or other methods of rearing had been used, the interactions would have probably been considerably different. In work with humans, of course, such G times E interactions cannot be dealt with in an accurate or repeatable way, but there is every reason to believe that this study offers a reasonable, general paradigm for analogous interactions which must occur in hominid growth.

---

[13]Since all conditioned reactions require some unconditioned behavior at the outset, logically speaking, there is no behavior that does not at some level of analysis involve an heredity times environment interaction. Thus, if identical twins are raised in different linguistic environments, to take an extreme example, their speaking different languages is not independent of some genetically based ability to acquire language. However, the question of the *extent* to which a behavioral trait is inherited *vs.* the extent to which it is acquired is basically an unsolved problem. This is usually dealt with by calculating a "heritability" score based on within-pair differences of identical *vs.* same-sexed fraternal twins. Unfortunately, this method is more often than not misleading. For example, high concordance in bleaching of hair has been found in identical pairs and not in fraternal pairs, which gives hair-bleaching a substantial heritability score (Nichols 1966). The answer to this seeming absurdity must lie in an analysis of what probably went into the finding: Presumably women of certain hair colors bleach with greatest frequency, and it makes sense to assume that the genetic component enters at the level of hair color. More often such an analysis is not possible, and we are simply left with an "un-understandable" score of heritability.

An Evolutionary View of Early Attachments

In 1958 Bowlby wrote, "Psychoanalysts are at one in recognizing the child's first object relations as the foundation stone of his personality: yet there is no agreement on the nature and dynamics of this relationship."

He then went on to make the first fresh analysis of the nature of the child's emotional tie to the mother since Freud's "Three Contributions to the Theory of Sex" (1918). Bowlby described sucking, clinging, following, crying, smiling, and possibly cooing and babbling as evolved[14] responses (in the Darwinian sense), all in the service of assuring an attachment between infant and adult in their earliest manifestations. Each, to be sure, was seen as serving a variety of other purposes as well as it became transmuted, to varying degrees, through the life span.

Bowlby's major critique was that "psychoanalytic theory has become fixated on orality," and it was his avowed purpose to free psychoanalysis "for broader development." Unfortunately, psychoanalysts have tended to reject this attempted revision as coming from outside psychoanalysis and in effect have accused Bowlby of playing quite another game (A. Freud 1960; Shur 1960; Spitz 1960).

The following is intended as an extension of Bowlby's insights, and the ways he proposes that a child achieves attachments will be considered in a somewhat extended evolutionary context.

As a first step it will be appropriate to consider the characteristics of modern evolutionary thinking. For one thing, evolutionary thought is often seen as circular. Something is said to have adaptive value for a species, and the proof offered for this contention is that the species has survived. For example, imprinting or the rapid formation of primary attachments is an adaptation of ground-nesting precocial birds to intense predator pressure, and the proof is said to be that these birds have survived predator pressure.

The point is, however, that evolutionary thinking depends on a nexus of relationships in which each datum, although weak by itself, grows in strength when considered in the context of other evidence. Evolutionary theory is primarily oriented towards the understanding of an event with regard to its adaptive function rather than, say, the biochemical process underlying it. The latter form of research is sometimes called the "atomistic approach" (Wad-

[14]In this paper we are using the term *evolved* and have avoided the ambiguous dichotomy of innate *vs.* acquired. Evolution has been termed opportunistic (Simpson 1964), so that in a species in which learning can become well developed any major genetic innovation in behavior will be completely interdependent with learning. Imprinting, for example, obviously involves both innate and acquired elements. Rather than becoming lost in a make-believe partitioning of these elements, it is preferable to speak of imprinting as "evolved behavior." This latter term has the further advantage over "innate" of having clear phylogenetic reference without any implications regarding neurophysiological processes.

dington 1966), and ideally the two approaches are coupled in mutually supporting theory and discovery.

In this regard, it is assumed that all the genes within an organism act in concert and that, for example, the XX chromosomally constituted female and the XY male are not dimorphic as *direct* action of the different chromosomes and genes involved; rather the XX or XY takes the entire genome in the direction of maleness or femaleness by way of complex interactions, which have in turn come about phylogenetically by a series of "mechanistic" processes. In other words, evolution has yielded organization, and it is up to the scientist to discover the mechanisms involved, always having in mind total functioning.

The same holistic logic holds for the analysis of behavior, that is any item of behavior takes on meaning only when examined in light of the total species' adaptation (Von Uexkull 1957). *Thus, an item of infant behavior, for example the smile or cry, must be considered in terms of total hominid adaptation, including the total life span.*

From this point of view, the equation of development with ontogeny is erroneous and can lead to false conclusions; it is no more logical to start with the baby in a description of the life span than with any other stage of life, for species survival and the evolution of adaptations involve all phases of the life span. This is in distinction to psychological systems which assume a strict causal chain between earlier and later events.

Formation of the Family

Before considering infant behavior a few words about biological aspects of the family system are in order. We know that the infant will generally be born into a family since the family system is universal in man (Malinowski 1956). Why men and women form families in every culture has never been adequately analyzed, but clearly there have evolved a number of assurances that men and women will mate, and further that they will tend to stay together.

Consider, for example, that the mature human female is the only mammal with breasts which are prominent when not lactating, and it becomes apparent that the upright hominid posture made possible the evolution of the distended breast as a sexual releaser. Needless to say, there are many other aspects of female structure and behavior which attract males, yet what current psychological theory concerns itself with the obvious function of female beauty as an evolved sexual attractant? In the same vein, the ability to fall in love is rarely thought of as an evolved species characteristic but it, too, seems to be another hominid universal; and it characteristically occurs with greatest intensity at the most adaptive time, just after puberty. Continual sexual readiness and receptivity among hominids seems also to bind the partners together by way of the resulting emotional reinforcement, although we know that fairly permanent pairing may occur in the Anatidae, who have only seasonal sexual activity, through various nonsexual behavior mechanisms (Lorenz 1966).

Note that this approach is distinct from so-called cultural evolution, that is, the view that culture provides for the evolution of behavior independently of biological determinants (White 1949). The major weakness of this latter view is that it considers culture as something "layered on," instead of a process that responds to and reflects man's evolved nature.

We will now go on to a consideration of the formation of attachments in the baby.

Crying, Holding, and Caretaking

The very first behavior exhibited by the newborn is the cry, a common mammalian occurrence. Detailed analyses of the behavior around human crying are only now being made (Wolff 1966) but crying seems to share the common mammalian function of exciting the parent to caretaking activities. In dogs, for example, a puppy removed from the nest immediately starts to cry and continues until exhausted. The bitch will usually become extremely excited, seek the source of the cry until the puppy is found, and then fetch him back. What we have here, clearly, are two complementary evolved mechanisms, and neither has to be learned.[15]

In the human, similarly, it can be demonstrated that within hours after birth most crying infants will quiet when held and carried. Consider how this cessation of crying coordinates beautifully with the intense anxiety felt by the parent until the infant is quieted. Aside from caretaking and feeding, body contact is the inevitable result of crying, and the human baby does as well as the macaque in getting next to the parent without the ability to cling. There seems little doubt that such contact is normally a mutually reinforcing experience, and affectionate or appeasing tactual contacts of one form or another remain an important means of relating throughout the life span.[16]

---

[15]It is a general mammalian and avian characteristic that the very young, when left alone or when lost, yelp, cry, or chirp. When these noises are heard by the parent, various forms of retrieval behavior occur. While such vocalization exposes the young to predation, they would die in any event without parental aid; so that, like many evolutionary mechanisms, a compromise is reached between two opposing possibilities. Few mechanisms do not to some extent compromise the chances of survival, and this occurs with such frequency that compromise can be termed a general rule of evolution. Bright coloration and complex song in male songbirds aid territoriality, conspecific dispersal, as well as mating, but marks the male's whereabouts and leaves him vulnerable to predation. Similarly, the fact that black-headed gulls remove the glistening eggshells soon after hatching probably serves to lower visibility of nest sites to predators, but while the parents are gone with the shells predators may attack the defenseless chicks (Tinbergen 1965).

[16]This does not imply, as does psychoanalytic logic, that if a type of behavior occurs earlier in time it is necessarily causal to related behavior appearing later in time. Within evolutionary logic, for example, attachments between adults of a social species are as "primary" as are attachments between infant and adult.

Smiling

Smiling is also quite clearly an evolved mechanism (Ambrose 1960; Freedman 1964). It is universally present in man and it has the same or similar interpersonal function everywhere, that of a positive greeting or of appeasement. Smiling is first seen in reflexive form in newborns, including prematures, when they are dozing with eyes closed, usually after a feeding. Even at these early ages, however, smiles can also be elicited by a voice or by rocking the infant and, since it occurs in infants whose gestational age is as low as seven months, there seems little doubt that smiling can also occur in utero. Visually elicited smiles occur somewhat later than sound elicited ones, though they are occasionally seen within the first week of life. These are called social smiles since they occur most readily when the eyes of infant and adult meet. In the auditory mode the preference for a voice over other sounds also marks such smiles as "social" (Wolff 1963).

The major function of smiling, then, from a very early age is responsivity to another. As Bowlby pointed out, it provides an important means of attachment between adult and infant, and in later life it lends ease and promotes attachment in a wide variety of social encounters. It is also widely displayed between adults as a gesture of appeasement in that it is a major means of either overcoming or precluding dissension and angry feeling.

It is pure surmise, of course, as to whether the smiling response appeared phylogenetically as an adult-adult mechanism or as an adult-infant mechanism. It is most akin to the "frightened grin" in other primates, a gesture which occurs quite frequently by a subordinate animal when passing close to a dominant one (Hall and DeVore 1965). Human smiling may well have originated with such a gesture in an evolutionary "turning to the opposite."

Regarding individual differences in smiling, some newborns never, or rarely, exhibit so-called reflexive smiling while others may become the pets of the nursery because of their constant display. From a five-year longitudinal study, we have found consistency in the use of smiling as a social technique dating back to the reflexive eyes-closed smiles. For example, a frequent eyes-closed smiler in the first months tends to be a frequent social smiler at five years.

The importance of the auditory and visual receptors in the young human infant seems directly related to its general motoric immaturity. Thus the eyes begin to search for form and movement in the environment soon after birth (Frantz 1963; Greenman 1963), and by two weeks of age over 50 percent of all infants will follow a moving person (Bayley 1961).

At about two months the infant's searching for the adult face can be very impressive. If held at the shoulder an infant may hold its unsteady head back to get a view of the holder's face, craning its neck like an inquisitive goose. One is left with the ineluctable feeling that searching out the enface position is itself an evolved mechanism. Supporting this contention are the large numbers of experimental studies which find the face a preferred stimulus for most infants including newborns and the fact that the adult feels "looked-at" for the first time just preceding the onset of social smiling.

The human orientation towards the face of another is undoubtedly bound up with many aspects of evolutionary adaptation, including the upright stance, relative hairlessness, and rich musculature of the face; thus, there are the myriads of obvious and subtle nonverbal communications in which hominids engage. The culture-boundness *vs.* culture-independence of many of these expressions are under current investigation (Eibl-Eibesfeldt 1965).

Cooing, Laughter, and Play

A few weeks after enface smiling starts, the infant begins to coo at the beholding adult, who in turn feels the irresistible urge to respond, and as a result much time may be spent in such happy "conversation." Feedings and sleep have by then decreased and normally more and more time is spent in direct social interactions.

A somewhat more robust order of interaction is initiated by laughter, usually at four months, when the baby and caretaker begin to engage in mutual play. The joy the adult feels in this engagement is probably no less an evolved mechanism than is the laughter of the baby, and doubtless such mutually reinforcing emotion ends up as attachment.

The factor of time spent together is also a solidifier of attachment (St. Exupery 1943), and this is served, of course, by all the above mechanisms.

Fear of Strangers

As the infant becomes embedded in the lives of those about him, another common phenomenon emerges, the fear of strangers. As early as three months of age in some infants, a definite preference for a parent or caretaker may be seen. This may be manifested at first by preferential smiling and cooing and following with the eyes. The infant may then cry when confronted by a stranger, especially if the place is also novel, as in a doctor's office.

The possible phylogenetic origins of this response have been discussed by Freedman (1961, 1965), who pointed out that many mammals and birds show similar fear responses to strangers and strange places after they have formed their initial attachments. In carnivores the fear response starts as they begin to travel farther and farther from the nest (about five weeks of age in dogs). In preyed-upon herd animals the young are on their feet within minutes after birth, attachment is quickly formed to the mother, and the fear response can be seen soon thereafter. Closely related is the advent of fear of heights which follows soon after the beginnings of motility in animals and humans, and without prior experience of falling (Gibson and Walk 1960). With motility, all animals become exposed to many new dangers as their investigative drives take them from the nest, and self-protective counter drives are necessary to assure survival.

While motility and fear of strangers are related mechanisms in lower mammals, when a human infant develops its fear of strangers, usually between six and nine months, it simply does not have the motor ability to escape a predator. It therefore seems a reasonable hypothesis that in human infants the fear of strangers serves mainly to prevent dilution of primary relationships and, in addition, serves to intensify the bonds between the infant and those already close to him.[17] In this regard the experimental work of Kovach and Hess (1963) with chicks indicates the reaction of fright makes primary bonds even stronger, so that this function is already served in lower forms.

To summarize, social attachment is an adaptive, evolved characteristic of hominids, and the formation of human mutuality is attained through many evolved mechanisms which are mutually reinforcing and which assure social interactions. Some examples are the desire for physical proximity, the appearance of mutual watching, mutual smiling, cooing, mutual laughter and play; protection of the young when they cry or become fearful may also be viewed as means by which attachment is increased as may the very act of time spent together. By the time imitation[18] and the first use of words start[19] late in the first year, social bonds are normally very strong and the child is an integral part of the lives of those about him.

What is the relationship between style of attachment and personality? Let us go back to Bowlby's (1958) statement that there is agreement ". . .in recognizing the child's first object relations as the foundation stone of his personality." We are in a position now to question the implicit logic of this statement, that is, that early attachments "cause" personality. The point is that early attachments *are* personality and that we are persons, or personalities, from the very start. To speak of these early attachments as causing personality is to

---

[17]There have been a number of alternative explanations of the fear of strangers, and Mieli (1957) has postulated that the fear is caused by an inability to assimilate the perceptual input. One trouble with such cognitive interpretations, however, is that they never ask the prior question: Why this particular response and not another?

Spitz (1950) has made a cognitive-psychoanalytic interpretation by attributing the fear reaction to the infant's insight that other people are "not mother," so that the fear reaction for Spitz is a sort of anticipatory separation anxiety. A simple experiment by Jacobson (1966) has served to eliminate this overly-sophisticated interpretation, for she found that babies are simply more fearful of an adult stranger than of a child stranger who is dressed the same and rehearsed to behave just like the adult. There seems little doubt that it is the stranger qua stranger that is feared, and that size adds to the fright.

[18]Imitation is clearly a magnificent means for the acquisition of all forms of behavior, and it becomes an effective force towards the end of the first year. As in sucking, craning the neck to see the face, reaching, turning over, sitting and standing, the drive to emulate is extremely strong. Only in the human is it carried to such persistent extremes, and it is a comment on psychoanalytic theory that it should be concerned with "anal" play in the second year, while imitation, which is flowering, has been largely undiscussed. What better way to work into eventual autonomy than to practice directly an experienced partner's methods of coping with the world?

commit the logical fallacy of the *tabula rasa* mind, that is, where there was nothing, something eventually appears. While it is true one is always becoming, one is also always *being*, and the style in which these early interactions occur is itself personality. Each infant negotiates these behaviors in a unique way, that is, in his very own variation on the basic species theme.

Regarding this latter point, as we have seen, the process of forming attachments involves the constant actualization[20] of phylogenetically derived capacities, and a theoretical model which neglects this fact is bound to develop illogicalities to account for the appearance of these behaviors. As acknowledged by Bowlby, the tendency has been to consider infantile experience the source of later behavior, and as a consequence there has been a considerable increase in interest and in actual work with infants in the hope of getting at causes. If the author reads these trends correctly, the next step will involve attributing the origins of infant behavior to uterine life, and then to the genome and DNA. In point of fact this is a regression to "homunculus" theory; since selection can and did occur in terms of developments at all ontogenetic points, the entire life span is a product of evolutionary adaptation and a psychologist interested in causes of behavior must simultaneously consider phylogeny and ontogeny, difficult as it may seem.

While this has been a far from complete analysis of how attachments and personality form, our main purpose was to illustrate the logic of the evolutionary approach and the fact that hypotheses derived from evolutionary thinking are open to experimental work. In terms of its scope, power, and intellectual appeal evolutionary theory has no equal and is simply waiting for interested psychologists to put it to work. In the words of Herman Muller (1959), "One hundred years without Darwinism are enough."

REFERENCES

Ainsworth, M. S., 1962, The effects of maternal deprivation: A review of findings and controversy in the context of research strategy. *Public Health Papers*, 14. (World Health Organization, Geneva).

Allport, G. 1937, *Personality: a Psychological Interpretation*. (Holt, Rinehart and Winston, Inc., New York).

Ambrose, J. A. 1960, The smiling and related responses in early human infancy: an experimental and theoretical study of their course and significance. Ph.D. dissertation, University of London.

[19]The evolutionary aspect of language acquisition is receiving much current attention.

[20]By *actualization* we have in mind Goldstein's (1939) meaning: There is only one drive which is invariant and characteristic of all living organisms, the drive to actualize their inborn capacities. All other so-called drives are variable and subsidiary to this one.

APPELL, G., and J. Aubry, 1951, Maternal deprivation in young children. Film: 16 mm; 22 min; sound. Distributors: New York University Film Library; Tavistock Child Development Research Unit, London (United Nations, Geneva).

AUSUBEL, D. P., 1958, *Theory and Problems of Child Development.* (Grune and Stratton, Inc., New York).

BANDURA, A., and R. H. WALTERS, 1963, Aggression. In H. W. Stevenson, J. Kagan, and C. Spiker (Eds.), *Child Psychology.* (The University of Chicago Press, Chicago).

BATESON, G., and M. MEAD, 1942, Karba's First Years. Sound film. New York University Film Library, New York.

BAYLEY, N., 1964, Consistency of maternal and child behaviors in the Berkeley growth study. *Vita Humana, 7*:73–95.

————, 1961, Personal communication.

BEACH, F. A., Evolutionary aspects of psychoendocrinology. In A. Roe and G. G. Simpson, *Behaviour and Evolution.* (Yale University Press, New Haven).

BENJAMIN, J. D., 1959, Prediction and psychopathologic theory. In L. Jessner and E. Pavenstadt (Eds.), *Dynamic Psychopathology in Childhood.* (Grune and Stratton, New York).

BOWLBY, J., 1952, *Maternal Care and Mental Health.* Monograph Series No. 2 (World Health Organization, Geneva).

————, 1958, The nature of the child's tie to his mother. *Int. J. Psychoanal., 30*:350–373.

————, 1960, Symposium on psychoanalysis and the development of object relations. *Int. J. Psycho-Anal., 41*:313.

CASLER, L., 1961, Maternal deprivation: a critical review of the literature. *Monog. Soc. Res. Child Develop., 26*:2.

CASSIRER, E., 1944, *An Essay on Man.* (Yale University Press, New York).

DIAMOND, M., 1965, A critical evaluation of the ontogeny of human sexual behavior. *Quart. Rev. Biol., 40*:2.

DOBZHANSKY, T., 1964, *Heredity and the Nature of Man.* (Harcourt, Brace & World, Inc., New York).

EIBL-EIBESFELDT, I., 1965, personal communication.

ERIKSON, E. H., 1950, *Childhood and Society.* (W. W. Norton & Co., Inc., New York).

ESCALONA, S., and G. M. HEIDER, *Prediction and Outcome.* (Basic Books, Inc., New York).

ETKIN, W., 1964, Types of social organization in birds and mammals. In W. Etkin (Ed.), *Social Behavior and Organization Among Vertebrates.* (The University of Chicago Press, Chicago).

FENICHEL, O., 1945, *Psychoanalytic Theory of Neuroses.* (W. W. Norton & Co., Inc., New York).

FREEDMAN, D. G., 1958, Constitutional and environmental interactions in rearing of four breeds of dogs. *Science, 127*:585–586.

————, 1961, The infant's fear of strangers and the flight response. *J. Child Psychol. Psychiat.,* 242–248.

————, 1965, An ethological approach to the genetical study of human behaviour. In S. Vandenberg (Ed.), *Methods and Goals in Human Behavior Genetics.* (Academic Press, Inc., New York).

————, (1966), in preparation.

————, J. A. KING, and O. ELLIOT, 1961, Critical period in the social development of dogs. *Science,* **133**:1016–1017.

FREUD, A., 1963, The concept of developmental lines. In *Psychoanalytic Study of the Child.* 18:245–265 (International Universities Press, Inc, New York).

FREUD, S., 1918, Three contributions to the theory of sex. *Nerv. Ment. Dis. Monogr.,* 7.

FRIES, M., and D. WOOLF, 1953, Some hypotheses on the role of the congenital activity type in development. *Psychoanal. Stud. Child,* **8**:48.

GEBER, M., 1956, Problèmes posé par le développment du jeune enfant Africain en fonction de son milieu social. *Le Travail Humain.,* **6**:17–29.

GIBSON, E. R., and R. D. WALK, 1960, The visual cliff. *Sci. American* 202.

GINSBURG, B. E., 1966, Genetic parameters in behavior research. J. Hirsch (Ed.), *Genetics and behavior. (McGraw-Hill, Inc., New York).*

————, and W. S. LAUGHLIN, 1966, The multiple bases of human adaptability and achievement: a species point of view. *Eugen. Quart.*

GOLDFARB, W., 1955, Emotional and intellectual consequences of psychologic deprivation in infancy: a reevaluation. In P. Hoch and J. Zubin (Eds.), *Psychopathology of Childhood.* (Grune & Stratton, Inc., New York).

GOLDSTEIN, K., 1939, *The Organism.* (American Book Company, New York).

GORER, G., 1955, Theoretical approach: 1941. In M. Mead and M. Wolfenstein (Eds.), *Childhood in Contemporary Cultures.* (The University of Chicago Press, Chicago).

GRAY, P. H., 1958, Theory and evidence of imprinting in human infants. *J. Psychol.,* **46**:155–166.

GREENMAN, G. W., 1963, Visual behavior of newborn infants. In A. J. Solnit and S. A. Provence, *Modern Perspectives in Child Devlopment.* (International Universities Press, Inc., New York).

HALL, K. R. L, and I. DeVORE, 1965, Baboon social behavior. In I. DeVore (Ed.), *Primate Behavior.* (Holt, Rinehart and Winston, Inc., New York).

HARING, D. G., 1956, Comment on Japanese personal character: pre-war. In D. G. Haring (Ed.), *Personal Character and Cultural Milieu.* (Syracuse University Press, New York).

HARLOW, H. F., and R. R. ZIMMERMANN, 1959, Affectional responses in the infant monkey. *Science,* **130**:421–432.

HARRISON, G. A., 1964, Human genetics. In *Human Biology—an introduction to human evolution, variation and growth.* (Oxford University Press, New York).

HARTMANN, H., 1950, Psychoanalysis and developmental psychology. *Psychoanal. Stud. Child,* 5–12.

HEBB, D. O., 1953, Heredity and environment in mammalian behavior. *Brit. J. Animal Behav.,* 1, **2**:43–47.

HONZIK, M. P., 1964, Personality consistency and change: Some comments on papers by Bayley, Macfarlane, Moss, Kagan, & Murphy. *Vita Humana,* 7:67–72.

JACOBSON, Joan, 1966, unpublished data (University of Chicago).

KAGAN, J., and H. A. MOSS, 1960, Stability of passive and dependent behavior from childhood through adulthood. *Child Develpm.,* **31**;577–591.

————, and ————, 1962, *Birth to Maturity: A Study in Psychological Development.* (John Wiley & Sons, Inc., New York).

KLEIN, Melanie, 1957, *Envy and Gratitude, A Study of Unconscious Sources. (Basic Books, Inc., New York).*

KOVACH, J. K., and E. H. HESS, 1963, Imprinting: effects of painful stimulation upon the following response. *J. comp. physiol. Psychol.*, **56**:461–464.

LANDAU, R. L., work in progress. (University of Chicago).

LEONARD, M. R. 1961, Problems in identification and ego development in twins. In *Psychoanalytic Study of the Child*, **16**:300–318.

LESSER, G. S., FIFER, G., and D. H. CLARK, 1965, Mental abilities of children from different social-class and cultural groups. *Monogr. Soc. Res. Child Develpm.*, 102, 30, 4.

LOEHLIN, J. C., 1965, A hereditary-environment analysis of personality inventory data. In S. G. Vandenberg (ed.), *Methods and Goals in Human Behavior Genetics.* (Academic Press, New York).

LORENZ, K., 1957, Companionship in bird life. In C. H. SCHILLER (ed.), *Instinctive Behaviour.* (Methuen & Co., Ltd., London).

————, 1966, *On Agression.* (Harcourt, Brace & World, Inc., New York).

MACFARLANE, J. W., 1964, Perspectives on personality consistency and change from the guidance study. *Vita Humana*, **7**:115–126.

MACKINNON, D. W., 1944, The structure of personality. In J. McV. HUNT (ed.), *Personality and the Behavior Disorders*, Vol. 1 (The Ronald Press Company, New York).

————, (ed.), 1948, *Selection of Personnel for the Office of Strategic Services; Assessment of Men.* (Holt, Rinehart and Winston, Inc., New York).

MALINOWSKI, B., and R. BRIFFAULT, 1956, *Marriage: Past and Present.* Porter Sargent, Boston.

MARSHALL, D., 1965, personal communication (Honolulu).

MASON, W. A., 1965, The effects of social restriction on the behavior of Rhesus monkeys: I. Free social behavior. In T. E. McGILL (ed.), *Readings in Animal Behavior.* (Holt, Rinehart and Winston, Inc., New York).

MAYR, E., 1958, Behavior and systematics. In A. Roe and G. G. Simpson (eds.), *Behavior and Evolution.* (Yale University Press, New Haven).

MEAD, M., 1959, *Male and Female.* (William Morrow & Company, Inc., New York.

————, 1955, Theoretical setting. In M. MEAD and M. WOLFENSTEIN (eds.), *Childhood in Contemporary Cultures.* (The University of Chicago Press, Chicago).

MEILI, R., 1957, *Anfänge der charakterentwicklung.* (Verlag Hans Huber, Bern).

MONEY, J., 1965, Psychosexual differentiation. In J. MONEY (ed.), *Sex Research: New Developments.* (Holt, Rinehart and Winston, Inc., New York).

MULLER, H. J., 1959, One hundred years without Darwinism are enough. *Sch. Sci. Math.*, **59**:304–316.

MURPHY, G., 1947, *Personality.* (Harper & Row, Publishers, New York).

MURPHY, L. B., 1964, Factors in continuity and change in the development of adaptational style in children. *Vita Humana*, **7**:96–114.

MUSSEN, P. H., J. J. CONGER, and J. KAGAN, 1963, *Child Development and Personality*, 2d ed. (Harper & Row, Publishers, New York).

NEILON, P., 1948, Shirley's babies after fifteen years. *J. Genet. Psychol.*, **73**:175–186.

NEWMAN, H. H., F. N. FREEMAN, and K. J. HOLZINGER, 1937, *Twins: a Study of Heredity and Environment.* (University of Chicago Press, Chicago).

NICHOLS, R., 1966, Unpublished paper, 2d. Conf. on Hum. Behavior Genetics (Louisville).

ORLANSKY, H., 1949, Infant care and personality. *Psychol. Bull.*, **46**:1–48.

PEPPER, S. C., 1961, *World Hypotheses.* (University of California Press, Berkeley).

PIAGET, J., 1952, *Origins of Intelligence in Children.* (International Universities Press, Inc., New York).

PINNEAU, S. R., 1955, The infantile disorders of hospitalism and anaclitic depression. *Psychol. Bull.*, **52**:429.

RIESEN, A. H., 1961, Stimulation as a requirement for growth and function in behavioral development. In *Functions of Varied Experience.* (The Dorsey Press, Inc., Homeward).

ST. EXUPERY, A. DE, 1943, The Little Prince (Harcourt, Brace & World, Inc., New York).

SCHUR, M., 1960, Discussion of Dr. John Bowlby's paper. In *Psychoanalytic Study of the Child.* 15, 63 (International Universities Press, Inc., New York).

SCOTT, J. P., 1962, Critical periods in behavioral development. *Science*, **138**:949–958.

SCHAEFFER, E. S., and N. BAYLEY, 1963, Maternal behavior, child behavior, and their intercorrelations from infancy through adolescence. *Monogr. SRCD*, **28**:1–27.

SCRIMSHAW, N. S., and M. BEHAR, Protein malnutrition in young children. *Science*, **133**:2039–2047.

SHELDON, W. H., and S. S. STEVENS, 1942, *The Varieties of Temperament.* (Harper & Row, Publishers, New York).

SIMPSON, G. G., 1964, *The Meaning of Evolution.* (Yale University Press, New Haven).

SPITZ, R. A., 1945, Hospitalism. In *Psychoanalytic Study of the Child.* **1**:53. (International Universities Press, Inc., New York).

———, 1946, Hospitalism: a follow-up report. In *Psychoanalytic Study of the Child.* 2, 113 (International Universities Press, Inc., New York).

———, 1960, Discussion of Dr. Bowlby's paper. In *Psychoanalytic Study of the Child.* 15, 85 (International Universities Press, New York).

———, 1965, *The First Year of Life.* (International Universities Press, Inc., New York).

STERN, C., 1960, *Principles of Human Genetics*, 2d ed. (W. H. Freeman and Company, San Francisco).

STOCKARD, C. R. *The Physical Basis of Personality.* (W. W. NORTON and Co., 1931.

SULLIVAN, H. S., 1965, *Collected Works.* (W. W. NORTON & Company, Inc., New York).

THOMAS, A., S. CHESS, H. G. BIRCH, M. E. HERTZIG, S. KORN, 1963, *Behavioral Individuality in Early Childhood.* (New York University Press, New York).

TINBERGEN, N., 1965, The Shell menace. In T. E. MCGILL (ed.), *Readings in Animal Behavior.* (Holt, Rinehart and Winston, Inc., New York).

WADDINGTON, C. H., 1960, *The Ethical Animal.* Atheneum Publishers, New York).

———, 1966, *The Nature of Life.* (Harper & Row, Publishers).

WALTERS, R. H., and R. D. PARKE, 1965, The role of the distance receptors in the development of social responsiveness. In L. P. Lipsitt and C. C. Spiker (Eds.) *Advances in Child Development and Behavior*. (Academic Press, Inc., New York).

WHITE, L. A., 1949, Energy and the evolution of culture. In *The Science of Culture*, 363–393.

WILLIER, B. H., P. A., WEISS, and V. HAMBURGER, (Eds.), 1955, *Analysis of Development*. (W. B. Saunders Company, Philadelphia).

WOLFF, P. H., 1963, Observations on the early development of smiling. In B. M. Foss (Ed.), *Determinants of Infant Behavior, II*. (Methuen & Co., Ltd., London).

———, 1967, Natural history of crying. B. M. Foss (Ed.), *Determinants of Infant Behavior, IV*. (Methuen & Co., Ltd., London).

VON UEXKÜLL, J., 1957, A stroll through the world of animals and men. In C. H. Schiller (Ed.), *Instinctive Behavior*. (International Universities Press, Inc., New York).

YARROW, L. J., 1961, Maternal deprivation: toward an empirical and conceptual reevaluation. *Psychol. Bull.*, 58, 6:459–490.

YOUNG, W. C., 1965, The organization of sexual behavior by hormonal action during the prenatal and larval periods in vertebrates. In F. Beach (Ed.), *Sex Behavior*. John Wiley & Sons, Inc., New York).

———, R. W. GOY, and C. H. PHOENIX, Hormones and sexual behavior. In J. Money (Ed.), *Sex Research: New Developments*. (Holt, Rinehart and Winston, Inc., New York).